Suffer the Children:
The Story of Thalidomide

Suffer the Children:
The Story of Thalidomide
was written by
Phillip Knightley
Harold Evans
Elaine Potter
Marjorie Wallace

Suffer the Children: The Story of Thalidomide

The Insight Team of *The Sunday Times* of London

THE VIKING PRESS

NEW YORK

Copyright © Times Newspapers Ltd., 1979
All rights reserved

First published in 1979 by The Viking Press
625 Madison Avenue, New York, N.Y. 10022

LIBRARY OF CONGRESS CATALOGING IN PUBLICATION DATA
Main entry under title:
Suffer the children.
Bibliography: p. 289
Includes index.
1. Great Britain. Attorney-General.
2. The Sunday Times, London.
3. Distillers Co. (Biochemicals) Ltd.
4. Liberty of the press—Great Britain.
5. Thalidomide—Side effects.
6. Abnormalities, Human.
I. The Sunday Times, London.
KD379.5.G7s9   344′.41′042   78-12594
ISBN 0-670-68114-8

Printed in the United States of America
Set in CRT Baskerville

Foreword by Harold Evans

This book is by the Insight team of *The Sunday Times* of London. Its collective authorship requires more than normal explanation. Something like a score of non-fiction investigative narratives have been produced by *Sunday Times* writers working in groups of two or three (most recently *The Yom Kippur War*, *Hoax*, and *Destination Disaster*). The practice is for each writer to specialize in some area of the work but for everyone writing to be subject to revision by the collaborating authors. There is normally also a team leader or editor. This book follows that system, but it has a further complication. *The Sunday Times* itself was involved in the thalidomide saga, so the authors find themselves collectively responsible for writing, in part, about their own activities. This is a nuisance, since any hint of self-regard in the thalidomide story would be an impertinence. As David Mason, the father of a thalidomide child, said: "Nobody is getting any glory out of this; at the end of the day, my daughter Louise still has no legs."

It is not possible to tell the story or explain the authorship of this work without saying what various individuals did at certain stages. We have tried to tell this as simply as we can in the book itself, but in this foreword, before the anonymous general author takes over, it is necessary for me to be more personal.

My own role can be briefly indicated: it was concerned principally with introducing and closing the book and describing *The Sunday Times'* thalidomide campaign. The main burden of the preparation of the book has been borne by Phillip Knightley, who among us stayed longest with the thalidomide story, beginning in 1967, and acted as team leader for the book. It would never have been completed but for his integrity, good temper, and organizational skills. Bruce Page, who is no longer with the paper, was mainly responsible for the pharmacological detective work, but all of us would say that the thalidomide story could not have been un-

v

ravelled without the intellectual originality and dedication he brought to the subject when he was managing editor of Special Projects. The equally crucial role of James Evans, our legal adviser at the time, is more easily described in the main narrative. The fourth person who must be mentioned is Elaine Potter, who began work with Bruce Page in 1972 and pursued her inquiries—mainly on the legal scene—with a remarkable combination of passion and scholarship. Mr. Justice Melford Stevenson told me, on a later occasion, how during one of our court hearings, he was vividly aware of the presence in the well of the court of Elaine Potter grimacing at every legal point made against us. Finally, there is Marjorie Wallace, who brought to the narrative a sensitive understanding of the plight of the children and their parents.

For this book the authors are additionally grateful to Robert Jones, our scientific adviser since 1973, who is responsible for the Appendix; Oliver Gillie, our medical correspondent; Antony Whitaker, legal manager to Times Newspapers; Antony Terry, our correspondent first in Bonn and then Paris; Rosemary Wittman, for work in New York; Rosemary Righter; Sarah Jane Phillips, of André Deutsch, for editing in Britain; and Elisabeth Sifton, our editor at The Viking Press in New York, who raised our sights.

Contents

Suffer the Children:
The Story of Thalidomide

Introduction

The thalidomide babies whose births shocked the world have grown up. They were born almost twenty years ago with a terrible range of deformities, because the thalidomide sedative pill their mothers took during pregnancy was not a wonder drug but a cruel perverter of the growing body in the womb. The thalidomide teen-agers are coping with life as best anyone can when they lack arms or legs or suffer from other serious deficiencies. In Britain nineteen-year-old David Bickers, who has no legs and only rudimentary digits where his arms should be, studies mathematics and electronics and produces his own talking magazine for the blind. Terry Wiles, who is barely two feet tall and has no arms or legs and only one eye, writes and types his own short stories. Gary Skyner, who has short flippers where his arms should be, works as a telephone switchboard operator in his local hospital. Marion Ryan is one of one hundred thalidomide teen-agers who has learned to drive a car and passed the test. There are many remarkable, inspiring stories.

Something like eight thousand thalidomide children are alive in the United States, Germany, Japan, Britain, Ireland, Sweden, Australia, Canada, Brazil, Italy, and Spain; altogether the pill known internationally as thalidomide claimed victims in forty-six countries where it was prescribed by doctors and sold across the counter under a variety of trade names on licence from the original German inventors, Chemie Grünenthal. Mothers who took the pill in the first trimester of pregnancy, when limb buds of the foetus form, produced children with a wide but distinctive range of deformities. Some have no arms, just flippers from the shoulder; some no legs, just toes from their hips; some have limbless trunks, with just a head and body. Some appear to be physically normal but were injured internally. Most of these children have a normal range of intelligence, but a few are vegetables. Some are deaf or blind or suffer from autism, epilepsy, and other manifestations of severe

1

brain damage. They are all victims not merely of a drug accident but of the dangerous myth invented in Germany and exported to a credulous world: that thalidomide was better than all other tranquillizers because it was non-toxic, had no side effects, and was completely safe for pregnant women. None of these statements, announced by the drug companies and accepted by the doctors, was true.

Some lessons were learned—imperfectly—from the tragedy. Some governments—but not all—took steps to screen drugs more thoroughly before they reached their populations, and also to monitor the longer-term effects of approved drugs. But the causes of the thalidomide tragedy itself have remained unexplored, and the victims themselves, the hapless instigators of benevolent change, suffered a second time around. There is a dismaying symmetry in the thalidomide story: the universal poisoning was succeeded by universal neglect of the poisoned.

Everywhere there was horror and shame when the deformed births made the headlines in 1961; everywhere there was a flurry of pity and concern for the families; yet everywhere they have had to endure years of hardship and neglect. Governments and social institutions not only failed to keep the drug off the market but in some cases did not act quickly even when its effects were realized. Official indolence in Japan meant that several hundred thalidomide babies were born long after the world had learned of the danger: for more than a year after thalidomide had been withdrawn from sale or prescription in other countries, the Japanese authorities allowed mothers in Japan to go on taking it without prescription. In Sweden, the drug was withdrawn, but the authorities did not warn mothers against using thalidomide pills already released—at least five babies were born needlessly crippled—and the drug was kept on sale in Argentina by the Swedish manufacturer for three months after it had been withdrawn in Sweden. Thalidomide stayed on the market in Canada for three months after it had been withdrawn in Britain and Germany, but this sorry record was surpassed in Italy. Thalidomide was sold under ten different trade names there, and some pills were still on sale ten months after the withdrawal of the drug in Germany. Tolerance might explain these as unhappy oversights. But it is hard to know how to characterize the near-universal abandonment of families after their afflictions. In every country (except Germany, where the official prosecutor took over), they were left to fight their own legal battles for compensation against the drug companies. (In Japan, the government shared the eighteen-million-dollar compensation payment with the Dai-Nippon Pharmaceutical Company, but only in 1974, after twelve years of inertia.)

The victims in the United States had a happier legal experience than most, but most mothers and fathers were faced with not only the physical and moral agonies of rearing a damaged child but the wrenching anxiety of real or incipient poverty. They were matched as supposed equals in a long legal struggle with great corporations that had massive resources. In Britain, where thalidomide was prescribed on the National Health Service and yet where the minister of health, Enoch Powell, washed his hands of all direct responsibility, the neglect of the families was a national scandal but a secret one, so that a social and legal tragedy was allowed to flower for a decade and more on the debris of the original disaster. How that happened in this most advanced and civilized of countries is one of the main themes of this book.

These are not the common perceptions of the thalidomide story. The received view, understandably persistent after years of misinformation, is that there was something amounting to an act of God. The drug was tested to the best standards of the time, but a mistake was made that no one could have foreseen, one of those terrible prices humanity must pay on the road to progress. It was really a matter, was it not, of reaching a sensible compromise between two unlucky parties, the drug companies on the one hand and the families on the other? Though it did take a long time, the law showed its adaptability in the end to a unique catastrophe, and a satisfactory solution emerged—so that there was a happy ending and society, too, benefited by learning from the lessons of what went wrong.

This agreeably cosy view is sustained by the knowledge that what appears to be tolerable financial provision has now been made for the families with damaged children in most though not all countries. But it is wrong in virtually every respect. First, the disaster was in no legitimate sense "inevitable." It was not mere mischance. It resulted from specific actions taken by specific groups of people—businessmen and doctors—and these actions remain, in spite of much concealment, capable of analysis and vulnerable to criticism. It is a popular fallacy to accept the idea that the thalidomide tragedy alerted the world to the danger that drugs can cross the placental barrier and affect the foetus. This was commonplace knowledge *before* the thalidomide tragedy; and before it also drugs were tested on pregnant animals and given clinical trials on pregnant women. The knowledge and scientific procedures to give protection were available. The disaster might well have been averted everywhere. Unarguably, the havoc wrought could have been much less than that which occurred.

Second, in the aftermath of the avoidable, the law was neither so benevolent nor so efficient as the lawyers would like to maintain. On the basis of arguments that have long been used to justify the lawyers' trade, it can be said that the thalidomide issue is exactly the kind of problem the common law should have been able to deal with. Several thousand children were irreversibly poisoned because of the actions of other citizens who conceived themselves to be pursuing a legitimate profit. There was nothing criminal about the matter, nothing for the police. The question was a civil one: did the drug companies fail in some duty of care towards the children? The drug companies, not unnaturally, said no. Many parents of the children concerned believed that the companies *must* have failed. Such disputes are supposed to be the pith of the legal system; it may not be the best medium for discovering truth but it is supposed to be the best means of resolving a dispute. Yet the case histories in this book suggest, with varying force, that the law was at best an imperfect instrument and, at worst, positively alien to the welfare of the weaker party. That the proceedings in Britain, for instance, did not solemnize an injustice was due not to the law but to the press, to ordinary citizens, and to a few enlightened businessmen. The legal failures in the thalidomide affair have, however, produced hardly a ripple of concern in the profession and much indignation against the press for prying into affairs that do not concern it.

Secrecy cast a long shadow in the thalidomide affair, first over the discovery of what went wrong, medically and legally, and then over publication of the truth. Much of the story in this book has lain for fifteen years under veils of legal censorship. It is a story about a cover-up as well as about a drug disaster. It is less a scientific horror tale—though that element is present—than a parable about the predicament of the individual who is asked to pay the price for progress.

1 Sound the Alarm

The Women's Hospital, Sydney, known locally as Crown Street, is a rambling, late-Victorian building set in the middle of one of the city's inner suburbs, surrounded by streets of terraced houses, pubs, and factories. It is a busy, efficient hospital, handling each year some 4,000 pregnancies referred from all over Sydney, which makes it the largest obstetrics hospital in Australia and probably in the Southern Hemisphere.

The post of medical superintendent, Crown Street, carries considerable prestige in Australian medical circles and is an important step in a specialist's career. In 1960, the medical superintendent was John Newlinds, a young and up-and-coming obstetrician, keen on efficiency and modern hospital management. Looking at how he organized his day, Newlinds was concerned at the amount of time he seemed to spend listening to drug-company salesmen tell him at length about drugs that were not original or that were supposed to have characteristics he knew from previous experience would not be substantiated in use. One of Newlinds's first acts in his new job was, therefore, an order about salesmen: he would see them between 9:30 and 10:30 each Thursday morning; each salesman would have one appointment a year; if at the end of the appointment Newlinds decided that the salesman had been wasting his time, then that man forfeited his next appointment. This might have made many a salesman nervous, but not Walter Hodgetts, who sat in Newlinds's office on Thursday, August 18, 1960, talking confidently about a new drug. Hodgetts was senior New South Wales representative for Distillers Company Biochemicals (Australia) Limited, the Australian end of Distillers Company (Biochemicals) Limited, of Britain. DCBL was owned by the giant Distillers group, a very successful company engaged principally in the production of gin, vodka, Pimm's Cup, and above all, scotch whisky; it is difficult to name a brand that it does not own, or a country in the world where its liquor is not sold. Hodgetts, a

5

blunt but friendly man, was a first-class salesman, and he felt he had a good case for persuading Crown Street to try out Distaval, a sleeping pill that had already been on the market in Britain for two years, as a sedative for use during labour.

But Hodgetts was somewhat disconcerted to notice that Newlinds was not listening very closely. Hodgetts did not know the reason, but it was a simple one: Newlinds was doing a clinical trial at Crown Street with the drug Torecan (thiethylperazine), marketed by Sandoz as an antinauseant, a remedy for morning sickness. Sandoz was paying for the work, and Newlinds planned eventually to write a paper for the *Medical Journal of Australia*. He had, therefore, little interest in another sedative. He listened to Hodgetts for some time out of politeness, then said, "All right. We'll give it a try from the dispensary." Hodgetts took out a bottle of two hundred 100 mg. tablets of Distaval and left it on Newlinds's desk. Later that day Newlinds sent it to the hospital pharmacy, where the chief pharmacist glanced through the literature and then put the bottle on a shelf. Hodgetts was pleased: the interview had turned out better than he had expected. For DCBL to have got Distaval into a hospital like Crown Street so early in the marketing of a new drug was quite a coup.

As senior New South Wales representative, Hodgetts had the choicest territory: Sydney's major hospitals, and Macquarie Street, one of the city's oldest areas, known for its early colonial architecture, its magnificent view of Sydney Harbour, and the fact that it accommodates the offices of most of Sydney's specialists—an antipodean Harley Street. So one of Hodgetts's other early calls was on Dr. William McBride, who has one of the largest obstetrics practices in Australia. McBride, a quiet, intense man with an attractive wife who is also a doctor, and four children, was then only thirty-three but already remarkably successful. His ability to drive himself—he worked a fifty-five- to sixty-five-hour week—and his undisguised professional ambition, had caused a certain amount of envy in Sydney's tight but competitive medical world. But McBride was recognized as a leader in his field, and if Hodgetts could convince McBride to use Distaval, other obstetricians would undoubtedly follow his example. McBride heard Hodgetts out, agreed to try Distaval in his practice, and to let the company know what he thought about it. It is likely that McBride would have prescribed Distaval only as Hodgetts had suggested—as a sedative during labour—had not an unusual case then occurred at Crown Street.

About two weeks after Hodgetts had called on McBride, a woman whose last period had been on June 24 was admitted to Crown Street as an emergency case. She had been vomiting for several days. All standard methods of stopping this had failed, and the physical effort of the vomiting was threatening to bring on a miscarriage. Thinking about what to do next, McBride remembered Distaval and decided to try it. The hospital pharmacy filled the prescription, and after the second dose the vomiting stopped. (The patient gave birth to a normal child in April 1961.) McBride was very impressed and began to prescribe Distaval for pregnant women who complained of morning sickness, nervousness, or inability to sleep. The drug appeared both effective and without side effects.

Then on May 4, 1961, McBride attended the birth of a baby called Wilson. Mrs. Wilson had been going to Crown Street from early in her pregnancy and there had been no reason to expect that the birth would be other than normal. But the delivery team was upset to see that the baby was malformed. It had upper-limb abnormalities. The radius bone was absent in each forearm. In addition, there was a bowel atresia—the bowel had no opening. McBride transferred the baby to the Royal Alexandra Hospital for Children for an emergency operation for the atresia, but this was unsuccessful and the baby died a week later.

Baby Wilson's death disturbed McBride—no doctor with a vocation likes to lose a patient—but he was also puzzled by the nature of the child's malformations. Although the average malformation rate in live births is some 2 per cent, which means that two to three malformed babies are born at Crown Street each week, McBride had not seen a baby with this particular combination of malformations in his seven years at the hospital. Still, there was no reason to think that this was anything other than a cruel statistic, and McBride's advice to the parents was the same as he gave in all cases like this: go ahead and have another child as soon as possible. His suspicions that Baby Wilson's abnormalities were artificially induced came later.

Like all good hospitals, Crown Street has a mortality committee—a group of senior medical men who meet regularly to consider the hospital's mortality figures and to discuss ways of reducing them. So in May 1961, Baby Wilson became a statistic, and then a tiny coloured pin on a map of Sydney that the medical superintendent, Dr. Newlinds, had been examining with concern since the beginning of the year. He had no wish to cause unnecessary alarm, but the fact was that Crown Street's congenital malformation rate was running at about five times that of Australia's second largest women's hospital, in Melbourne, and at about three times the national average.

To try to establish a cause, Newlinds had bought a large-scale map of Sydney, and had asked his wife, then paediatrics registrar at the hospital, to mark with a coloured pin the address of the mother of each malformed child born at Crown Street. Newlinds hoped that from this exercise a geographical factor would emerge that would offer some clue as to what was causing Crown Street's high malformation rate. To his alarm, a cluster of pins soon surrounded the atomic reactor at Lucas Heights, an area south of Sydney. Could the malformations be the result of exposure to atomic radiation?

In case this theory should reach the newspapers and cause panic, Newlinds kept the map under cover and instructed his staff to say nothing about it to anyone. But as the pins on the map grew in number, other explanations as plausible as the atomic reactor soon appeared. The pins were thicker in suburbs that had large gas holders. Was town gas a factor? There were more pins to the south of Sydney Harbour—which divides the city roughly in two—than to the north. Since the citizens of the southern suburbs were less prosperous than those of the northern suburbs, was there an economic cause: were poor parents more likely to have malformed children than rich parents? And suburbs with a heavy concentration of southern European immigrants produced a heavy concentration of pins on the map. Was there a nationality factor at work?

By July 1961, when he photographed the map, removed the pins, and wrote the whole exercise off to experience, Newlinds had discovered a simple answer to all these questions. The number of pregnant women from any one area coming to Crown Street to have their babies depended largely on how general practitioners in that area regarded the hospital. A doctor who had worked at Crown Street before going into general practice was more likely to refer pregnant women to that hospital than one who had not. More referrals from one area than another meant more births from that area in Crown Street and a correspondingly higher number of malformed births. "The areas with a lot of pins were areas where the doctors liked us and sent their patients to us," Newlinds says. "It was as simple as that. The geographical factor was meaningless. We decided that we were probably getting all our malformations in one crop—like a penny can come up heads for a long sequence—and that taken over a longer period, the rate would even itself out."

But at first it showed no sign of doing so. On May 24, McBride attended the birth at Crown Street of another malformed child, Baby Wood. Its malformations were strikingly similar to those of Baby Wilson, even including the bowel atresia. Baby Wood was also transferred to the Royal Alexandra Hospital, and this child, too, died after an operation.

It sometimes occurs in obstetrics that a doctor goes for years without seeing a bad case of a malformed child and then sees several in a short period. McBride now tried to convince himself that this was what had happened to him. But on Thursday, June 8, fifteen days after the birth of Baby Wood, McBride delivered a third malformed child, Baby Tait. Again this child had limb deformities similar to the two earlier cases, and again an atresia of the bowel was present. Since the two earlier operations had proved unsuccessful, it was decided to keep this baby at Crown Street, and it died soon after in the hospital nursery.

McBride was now very worried. Newlinds, who met him in the hospital corridor after Baby Tait's birth, asked him if he had any idea of what was going wrong. McBride was non-committal but said he would consider the matter over the coming holiday weekend, the Queen's birthday, and would see Newlinds the following Tuesday. Over Saturday, Sunday, and Monday, June 10, 11, and 12, 1961, McBride read up on bowel atresia, on malformations, and because of a growing suspicion, on drug-induced abnormalities. "There was not much available on this last one. The 1960 CIBA symposium on drug-induced abnormalities seemed to sum it all up. But I had, of course, all the hospital records of the three mothers, and from these one striking factor emerged: none of the women had taken any drug during pregnancy except Distaval. By Monday night, I was certain in my own mind, even though I couldn't yet prove it, that Distaval was responsible for the malformations. That was all it could be."

McBride used the local trade name for the drug. Internationally it was better known as thalidomide.

2 When Is a Rat Asleep?

Practitioners of many scientific disciplines are concerned in the making of synthetic drugs. The chief ones are the organic chemist, who creates new compounds, and the pharmacologist, who establishes their effects, and, if possible, the causes, in experimental animals in the hope that they may give indications of what might be expected in man.

Pharmacology is generally considered the central discipline, blending into toxicology, which specifically deals with prospects of death or injury. The chief pharmacological procedure is simple enough in outline: to look for effects in animals, and to estimate the dosages that may produce similar effects in the more complex human system.

Generally, pharmacology proceeds on empirical—or "suck-it-and-see"—methods, for there is not much in biochemical theory to produce anything more than vague hints about the likely effects of new molecular structures. Curiously, that may have seemed less valid twenty years ago, when thalidomide was devised, because a number of confident theories were then still current that only later came to grief. But even then, there was only one way to find a sleeping drug—or hypnotic—which was what thalidomide was supposed to be. That was to try out a substance on animals and see if it made them sleep. And here is the first narrative oddity about thalidomide. Only its begetter, Chemie Grünenthal of Stolberg-am-Rhein, was ever able to perceive its hypnotic effect in animals. And to do so, even Grünenthal was forced to redefine the very nature of sleep.

The Western pharmaceutical trade consists to a large extent of firms which, like Merck and Bayer, can trace their origins back to the nineteenth-century years in which science-based industry began its conscious development. Drugs, for several millennia, had meant fairly simple concoctions from nature, and traditional experience made reasonably sure that ugly surprises were not too likely. It was something very different when Bayer introduced the first barbiturate hypnotics in the closing years of the nineteenth century. Here began the business of chemical structures that nature and traditional medicine did not make available. The spread of barbiturate use soon showed that the consequences for human behaviour were not simple. The production of heroin—an analgesic vastly more powerful than its natural relative, morphine, and capable of moderating even the pains of terminal cancer—showed still more dramatically that new benefits might be accompanied by fearsome side effects. That there have not been more disasters is perhaps due chiefly to the resilience of the human system—and somewhat to the considerable abilities of the pharmaceutical firms. Rather against the general trend of Western capitalism, these firms have resisted movements towards diversification and amalgamation. They have tended to retain their character as specialized concerns, depending for their prospects upon the prowess or otherwise of their large and long-established research teams.

Neither Grünenthal nor its British licensee, Distillers, was part of this tradition. Grünenthal, an offshoot of a soaps, toiletries, and cosmetics firm, was formed shortly after the Second World War to take part in the short-lived antibiotic boom. Antibiotics, which began with penicillin, are in one sense a pharmaceutical "throwback." A limited number are refinements of substances produced by living organisms. They could not have been isolated in bulk without modern chemical technology, but they are produced by methods that closely resemble the ancient skills of brewers. During the early postwar years, they were a very exciting market, and they attracted a good many newcomers into the pharmaceutical industry, until by the mid-1950s, the number of antibiotic producers became so large that it no doubt appeared logical to branch out into synthetic drugs—a potentially limitless field. This Grünenthal did by clearing out a section of its packing plant and hiring a research staff of some half-dozen scientists and technicians. They were placed under the command of Dr. Heinrich Mueckter, who had qualified as a doctor in the 1930s and joined Grünenthal in 1946 after several years' experience in the German army's virus-research organization.

One of the first members of the research team was Wilhelm Kunz, who had qualified as a pharmacist after wartime service as a sergeant. His job was to synthesize organic compounds in the hope of finding new drugs that Grünenthal might exploit, and thus reduce the company's reliance upon American antibiotics made under licence. Kunz was given a contract that entitled him to a small percentage of the return on anything he might find.

Effectively, Kunz was head of chemical research, a position in which a major drug firm would expect to employ a graduate scientist with an extensive and distinguished research background. A German pharmacist, like a British or American one, is concerned not so much with investigating nature as with compounding new substances into usable medicine. No doubt Kunz was a competent pharmacist. But his lack of scientific background may perhaps account for his relative lack of curiosity about the career of the most famous—or notorious—compound he devised during his time at Grünenthal. Even today, Kunz shows only the sketchiest knowledge of what investigations Grünenthal applied to thalidomide. And like a good sergeant, he appears to have regarded the interaction between scientific policy and marketing policy as being the concern of Dr. Mueckter and the "officers." They showed little inclination to discuss such matters with him, and Kunz did not object.

Setting out as a chemical researcher in 1954, Kunz had a vast field in front of him. Organic chemistry—originally the chemistry of compounds occurring in living things—is also described as the chemistry of carbon, and its huge scope is due to the fact that carbon, the sixth element, is endlessly fecund in bonding itself to other kinds of atoms, and in linking up its own atoms into long and complex rings and chains. There were perhaps a million such carbon-based compounds known in the mid-1950s, and there are perhaps two million now.

An organic chemist creating new compounds resembles a child making ever-varying shapes from a kit of modular parts. It is possible to follow his work in outline, because in spite of the sophistication of the process, its basic rules can be stated in quite simple fashion. Each molecule created is a framework of carbon atoms bonded with other atoms, and the rules of the game are the number of bonds that each kind of atom requires. In the case of the building blocks that compose Kunz's thalidomide molecule, there are: thirteen atoms of *carbon* (C), requiring *four* bonds each; two of *nitrogen* (N), requiring *three* bonds each; four of *oxygen* (O), requiring *two* bonds each; and ten of *hydrogen* (H), requiring *one* bond each. This can be stated as the formula $C_{13}H_{10}O_4N_2$, or it can be drawn in terms of the chemist's traditional structural diagram (for convenience, the benzene ring at the left has been drawn in the conventional Kekulé notation):

The double lines represent double bonds, which carbon (to complicate things slightly) has rather a penchant for. The diagram is usually drawn in a simplified form in which the carbon and hydrogen atoms, the "meat and potatoes" of organic chemistry, are assumed rather than drawn out:

When Kunz first produced this pattern, he had no inkling of the human distress it would cause. It is not, as organic molecules go, a very complex structure. But it contains some toxic subtleties that even after twenty years remain mysterious in action and whose detection in those days would have taxed the resources of a research department considerably more sophisticated than Grünenthal's.

One conspicuous feature, however, might have set a train of suspicion into motion. To understand this, one must recall that the *two*-dimensional diagram represents a molecular shape existing in *three*-dimensional reality. Many of the possible molecules based upon carbon will be symmetrical in space: that is, a mirror image of the molecule will look just the same as its original. Octane, much valued in motor fuel, is a simple example. Symmetry will be lost, however, if at any point in the structure there stands a carbon atom that has a different kind of atom or atomic group attached to every one of its four bonds. This happens in thalidomide at the point where the farthest right-hand "ring" joins onto the rest of the molecule:

Here there is a carbon atom that, clockwise from the top, is attached to a *single hydrogen*, to *carbon with two hydrogens*, to *carbon double bonded with oxygen*, and finally to *nitrogen*. Such a molecule is asymmetric. A mirror image will differ from the original, and the structure may exist in either a "right-handed" or a "left-handed" form. The compound therefore may consist entirely of left-handed molecules (−), or laevo-, thalidomide, entirely of right-handed molecules (+), or dextro-, thalidomide, or as "(±)-thalidomide," also known as the "racemate," where (+) and (−) molecules are present in equal quantities.

This phenomenon of "optical isomerism" is profoundly involved in the life process. It has been known for many years that nearly all compounds encountered in living organisms are asymmetric, and may exist in either (+)- or (−)-form. Almost always, the organism uses only one form, and discards or fails to make the other. Therefore, drug molecules that happen to be asymmetric generally differ somewhat in their behaviour, according to optical form. As a general rule, drugs are administered in the (±)-form—and the living body is left to deal with the situation as best it can—because optical separation on an industrial scale is costly and laborious, and it is fairly rare to encounter a drug in which the difference in action is so large as to justify the extra cost.

But why should anyone have thought the (±)-form of thalidomide might be a worthwhile drug? The American firm Smith, Kline & French—enormously more distinguished in research capacity than either Grünenthal or Distillers—made a careful examination, and rejected it as worthless. Dr. George Somers, Distillers' first and only chief pharmacologist, has said that on the basis of the animal tests he himself would have "thrown it out of the window." (Neither Somers nor any other pharmacologist was on the staff of DCBL when acquisition of the wonder drug from Grünenthal was initiated.)

It may now be impossible to get the whole truth of what happened in

Grünenthal's laboratory, for most of the company's research records have disappeared. But something at least can be pieced together, and one must start with a clear definition of what a drug is, namely, a substance used to procure some desired alteration in the biochemical balance of the body.

There are many substances that may be introduced to the body—at least in pharmacological doses—without producing any biochemical change. They are *pharmacologically inactive*. But any positive effect is likely to be accompanied by side effects, because the interdependence of life processes is such that it is almost impossible to modify them in one direction and one only. Therefore, the safety of a drug is always a relative concept. It is a matter of balancing known and beneficial activity, and the need for that activity, against known and harmful activity, all the while making hopeful obeisances to the inevitably mysterious future. By this logic, an apparently inactive compound, or placebo, cannot have *any* safety value, for to ingest a foreign substance always carries some potential risk, and there must be a known benefit to outweigh that.

Thalidomide's use was to be as a hypnotic (sleeping pill) or tranquilizer. But that was not what Kunz had in mind when first making it. He was trying to find simple ways of making peptides, the long chainlike molecules of which proteins are composed, and which were then of interest to antibiotic manufacturers. Thalidomide was no great advance in peptide chemistry, but the molecule intrigued Herbert Keller, Grünenthal's pharmacologist, for he said it was a "structural analogue" of the barbiturates, and might therefore be active as a hypnotic. In truth, such comparisons give only the vaguest hints about likely chemical action. (After thalidomide's true character was revealed, CIBA's research team denied with vigour—and some authority—that there was any similarity between the structure of thalidomide and the previously established hypnotics.) But the structural analogies that Keller perceived seem to have set into motion a most determined laboratory effort on Grünenthal's part.

The simplest check for hypnotic influence in laboratory rats employs the "righting reflex," which makes an alert rat twist itself upright again if tipped on its side. But even massive doses of ($\pm$)-thalidomide do not have a sedative effect that abolishes the righting reflex in rats. Grünenthal's available scientific records do not say whether this simple test—usually used as a preliminary screen—was made with thalidomide. However, if it was, Keller and his colleagues were not put off by the neg-

ative showing. They tried the more elaborate "holding reflex" test orig-
inated by the CIBA scientists Gross, Tripod, and Meier. This places a rat
on a small treadmill, where it must maintain its place by running.
Under hypnotic effects of varying strength, the rat's holding reflex de-
generates, and it sooner or later tumbles off. The advantage of the test is
that it can be calibrated so as to make quantitative comparison among
different drugs. Again, thalidomide, in the holding-reflex test, showed
no activity whatever. Even large doses did not affect the rats' capacity to
hold positions on the treadmill. At this point, a vague structural analogy
would not have been enough to sustain most research programs. But the
Grünenthal team asked themselves not whether there was any value in
their drug, but whether there was any value in the established tests.
They asked (in Mueckter's words) "whether the condition of sleep is distinguished by loss of co-ordination capacity."

Logically enough, perhaps, this led to the evolution of a test for sleep-
inducing capacities in which there was no need for actual sleep to be
produced. Its mechanism was exceptionally elaborate, and it does not
seem to have found much favour with subsequent experimenters. The
basic item of equipment was a "jiggle cage": a container for a few mice
hung upon a spring in such a way as to bounce when the inmates moved
about. Eight jiggle cages were arranged around a bath of sulphuric acid,
and very light levers were attached to the cages, pointing inwards over
the rim of the bath. Each lever was so arranged as to multiply tenfold
the movements of its jiggle cage. From each lever a platinum wire was
suspended, so that with the cage at rest, the wire was just above the surface of the acid. Any movement in the cage would cause the wire to
plunge into the acid bath—and each wire was rigged up to act as the
anode in a 24-volt electric circuit. Beneath the surface in the centre of
the acid bath was another wire, rigged to act as a common cathode for
all the anodes. Current could flow only if one or more of the jiggle cages
were to shake, whereupon it would flow from anode to cathode through
the sulphuric acid, causing electrolysis. Those who managed to retain
"co-ordination capacity" during their schooltime chemistry lessons will
recall that such electrolysis generates hydrogen gas from sulphuric acid.
In the paper they published describing this apparatus, the Grünenthal
men claimed that they had established, by "numerous preliminary experiments . . . that mice of similar age, sex, weight, etc.," would produce a constant amount of hydrogen gas while going about their
business in an undrugged state. A decline in hydrogen produced would

indicate a decline in jiggling, reflecting a change in the behaviour of the mice. (In fact, the polarity of the electrodes was reversed in the original diagram, so that it was not hydrogen but oxygen that would have been collected and measured. The apparatus would still have functioned under these circumstances but with a sensitivity of only about half what it should have been. In retrospect, it is astonishing that no licensee seems to have spotted this elementary error, and suspected it to indicate more general scientific incompetence.) It was quite an ingenious way to get a collective reading of animal activity. However, since a perfectly good method of doing so already existed—using photo-electric cells to count the interruptions of light beams—it might be regarded as a victory of ingenuity over intelligence.

Kunz, Keller, and Mueckter now calibrated their test in remarkable fashion. They said that the hypnotic, or sleep-inducing, dose of a drug was the amount that reduced hydrogen production by half. There is no reason to suppose that animals were actually asleep at that point, and every reason to suppose that they were not. Some years later, two pharmacologists working for the American firm Richardson-Merrell—which, to its subsequent regret, purchased a thalidomide licence—described this definition of sleep as "arbitrary." Still, on the showing of the hydrogen-release test—at least in the hands of Grünenthal, so far its only exponents—thalidomide emerged as a potent substance indeed. A dose of 100 mg./kg. (milligrams per kilogram; a kg. is about 2.2 lb.) of body weight, which by more traditional methods showed no effect whatever, was apparently sufficient to procure the necessary halving of hydrogen output.

The Grünenthal men called this the "hypnotic dose" of thalidomide, and they went on to use it as a bench-mark for comparisons with a number of other hypnotic and sedative drugs. The result was a table that portrayed thalidomide as a miraculous substance, and made any rival products look very poor stuff indeed. Its most devastating part was the final column, giving in milligrams per kilogram the one-shot dose required to kill 50 per cent of a batch of test animals: this LD (lethal dose)$_{50}$ is the pharmacologist's index of acute toxicity.

Here was a powerful hypnotic, nearly as strong as Doriden (already shown to work in man) and more powerful than methylpentynol, one of the latest tertiary-alcohol hypnotics. Its power was comparable with that of Luminal, a classic barbiturate. Its action began faster than any of them, and lasted nearly as long as Luminal, which is one of the longest-

	SMALLEST HYPNOTIC DOSE (MG.)	START OF EFFECT (MINS.)	DURATION (MINS.)	SMALLEST NARCOTIC DOSE (KG.)	INITIAL EXCITATION STAGE	LD_{50}
Thalidomide	100	5	240–300	>5,000	none	>5,000
Luminal	40	30	300	150	++	300
Valamin	50	10	60	375	+	725
Doriden	75	30	200	400–500	++	600
Methylpentynol	150	15	210	500	+	750
Sodium bromide	500	80	360	7,000	none	800

acting barbiturates. Yet all this was done without any trace of the initial stage of nervous excitement—a great trial to elderly users of barbiturates—and with no trace of narcotic effect. Most wonderfully, all this happened quite without danger, for no dose of thalidomide, however huge, was enough to cause death.

Without doubt this table is the origin of the illusion that thalidomide was something capable of overturning many decades of pharmaceutical experience: an effective drug and quite without side effects. (Absence of acute toxicity does not provide an infallible prediction of general salubriousness: indeed, nothing can do that. But it is not a bad initial guide.) How seriously are these findings to be taken? Regrettably, Grünenthal's records of the original experiments vanished even before the German court proceedings in 1968 during which the origins of thalidomide were partially investigated. However, no one since has produced anything remotely like them.

The most serious work of which records survive (though so far unpublished) was done by Smith, Kline & French, when Grünenthal tried to sell them the American licence for thalidomide. During 1956, the SKF research organization in Philadelphia made both animal and human tests, spread over a period of several months. It was able to confirm Grünenthal's claim that thalidomide, code named SKF No. 5627, had no measurable acute toxicity. Otherwise its results seem as if they relate to some totally different substance.

Even at a dose of 5,000 mg./kg.—fifty times Grünenthal's "hypnotic dose"—the SKF team saw no signs of sleep in mice. However, it went on to see whether there might be some collective effect on the behaviour not apparent in individual mice. Instead of the Grünenthal hydrogen-release test, SKF used the well-established light-box test, in which light beams are so arranged in a cage that the animals break them when they move about, and the incidence of breakage can be recorded with photo-electric cells and analysed statistically. In January 1956, thalidomide was administered to groups of mice that, after a thirty-minute period, were recorded for ten minutes per group in the light box. The result was that: "SKF No. 5627 in oral doses of 200, 300, 400 and 500 mg./kg. failed to produce significant depression of spontaneous motor activity. . . . The low doses tended to produce an *increase* in spontaneous motor activity" (emphasis added). The lowest "low dose" recorded is *twice* that of the hypnotic dose claimed by Grünenthal.

In November 1956, the SKF pharmacology department reported again on thalidomide, this time at doses of 500, 200, and 100 mg./kg. One group at each dose level was tested five minutes after receiving thalidomide, and another thirty to forty minutes afterwards. The report said:

> *Summary.* Five to fifteen minutes after oral administration SKF No. 5627 slightly reduced (not to a significant degree) motor activity. Thirty to forty minutes after administration this effect had disappeared. The results suggest that SKF 5627 might have a slight depressant effect upon motor activity, with apparently a short duration of action. . . .
>
> *Activity.* Depression of spontaneous motor activity—no.

The SKF team went on to say that so far as it could discover, thalidomide had no capacity to block a conditioned-escape reflex (suggesting it had no tranquillizing potential), no antiemetic activity, no antihistamine activity, and only slight to moderate antispasmodic activity (something that Grünenthal had claimed to see in considerable measure). They found that thalidomide was about equal to the tranquillizer Miltown (meprobamate) in its capacity to protect mice against electroshock seizures, and had some capacity to potentiate the action of the hypnotic Evipal. So, after a multiple battery of tests conducted by a highly competent laboratory, thalidomide appeared to be without interesting pharmacological activity. For this reason Smith, Kline & French turned it down.

Only Somers of Distillers, working almost alone and under conditions of great pressure (for he had only just been hired to set up the DCBL pharmacological unit), was able to find some degree of action with the light-box test. (He found that he could not make the hydrogen test work at all.) And even Somers, as we have seen, would have "thrown it out of the window" on the evidence of animal tests alone.

Why should Grünenthal have been so confident about the hypnotic potency of thalidomide? Here, the question of its molecular asymmetry becomes relevant.

Once thalidomide's capacity to produce deformity became known, many highly qualified research teams began to investigate. One of them was the biochemistry department of St. Mary's Hospital, London, then led by Prof. R. T. Williams, who had an international reputation in chemistry, biochemistry, and toxicology. He and his chief assistant, Dr. R. L. Smith, immediately decided to check the behaviour of thalidomide's optical isomers, as well as the racemate. They were first to publish the fact that (−)-thalidomide behaved differently from (±)-thalidomide in animal tests. The (±)-form, they confirmed, produced no observable effect in mice. But (−)-thalidomide produced inertia, narcosis, and—at about 700 mg./kg.—death. In other words, it was about as toxic as Doriden and other standard hypnotics.

Later, Smith was able to show that (+)-thalidomide exhibited an even greater toxicity in mice. Like most other scientists, he assumed that the lethal capacity of the optical isomers was not known to Grünenthal when they made their claim that thalidomide was devoid of toxic effects. "That is a toxic molecule," says Smith, making the point that a scientist encountering such biochemical behaviour would expect to undertake a great deal more investigation before announcing the existence of a satisfactory, let alone miraculous, drug. But Wilhelm Kunz, the begetter of the molecule (who no longer works for Grünenthal), has admitted that the greater potency of optically separated thalidomide *was* well known to Grünenthal before the drug was launched upon the market.

Curiously enough, this subtly deadly substance is not, in principle, hard to make. Thalidomide can be produced by merely heating a commercially available compound called (−)-phthaloylisoglutamine, which is normally used as an intermediate in the synthesis of peptides. By controlling the application of heat (which causes the natural (−)-form to racemize) it is possible to obtain (−)-thalidomide, (±)-thalidomide, or something in between. Kunz confirms that heating phthaloylisoglutamine was one of the ways used to make thalidomide during the research programme, although it was too expensive to use for bulk production.

We now have a historical and toxicological problem to unravel in assessing Grünenthal's thalidomide research, and this is complicated by the fact that acute lethality is not a drug action that can be studied experimentally in man. Nobody outside the Third Reich in wartime has attempted to establish an LD_{50} in human beings, so that although there is every reason to think that (−)-thalidomide and (+)-thalidomide have one, no one knows what it is.

Many pharmacologists deal with this problem by saying that as a general rule animal tests are meaningful only if they display the main action of the drug. (This is the view of Dr. Edward Paget, formerly of ICI, the multi-national chemical and pharmaceutical concern, and SKF, now head of the Inveresk Research Institute, Scotland.) By this rule, the supposed atoxicity of (±)-thalidomide is a pharmacological illusion. Both the main action *and* the LD_{50} are "off the scale." Yet when the action of thalidomide can be found in animals at all, it is readily associated with toxicity.

Man, considered as a test animal, has many drawbacks stemming from his elaborate consciousness—and this is especially so when hypnotic effect is to be measured. For instance, if a person is convinced that a substance will help him sleep, this alone may relieve the anxiety that is keeping him awake. Therefore man is vulnerable to placebos that leave animals unaffected.

The exact hypnotic effect of thalidomide in man was never reliably measured during its therapeutic career, and it now cannot be, because quite apart from effects during pregnancy, its known capacity to produce the nervous degeneration called polyneuritis should now prohibit its administration to healthy people. Dr. Louis Lasagna, an expert on hypnotic actions, ran a "blind" clinical study at the request of Richardson-Merrell (a blind test is one where the patient is not told what effect the drug is supposed to produce) and found—rather to his surprise—considerable hypnotic effect. The SKF team found some effect when people *were* told that thalidomide was a sleeping pill, but it seemed little better than a placebo of which the same description was given. Mueckter of Grünenthal rather startled DCBL by saying that whenever he used thalidomide, he always took it in a mixture containing a barbiturate.

Whatever the precise hypnotic value of (±)-thalidomide in humans, it must depend upon the proposition that man as a species is exceptionally sensitive to the chemical's deformative powers. (Pregnant women usually took 100 mg. daily, which corresponds to 2 mg./kg. in a woman of average weight. When this is compared to the huge levels administered to animals without the same ill effect, we can calculate that human sensitivity to thalidomide is about 100 times greater than that of laboratory rodents. In some cases just one 50 mg. pill taken by a pregnant woman produced a deformed child.) In such circumstances, it is venturesome to suggest that anything much can be concluded about the possible dangers to mankind from experiments with animals that exhibit no effect at all. *Only in Grünenthal's published table of animal results can the wondrous phenomenon be perceived of a highly potent drug with no sign of toxicity. In no one else's hands have these phenomena been brought together by experimental data:* without that astonishing and much-ballyhooed conjunction, it seems hardly possible that thalidomide could have swept the European medical profession as it did.

The conclusion that the Grünenthal men saw what they wanted to see—that they somehow conflated the properties of two different kinds of thalidomide—is difficult to avoid. And it is relevant that Grünenthal made an equally sensational claim at around the same time. This concerned a form of streptomycin that Mueckter and his team named Supracillin.

Streptomycin is a potent antibiotic, and of great value in the treatment of some serious diseases. Yet unlike penicillin, which has few serious side effects, it is highly toxic in humans, and especially attacks the nerves between brain and ear, often resulting in deafness.

Grünenthal claimed to have eliminated this problem by combining streptomycin with a vitamin called pantothenic acid, whose lack is known to cause animals and humans to grow up with hearing defects. The claim was a remarkable one, because the analogy between streptomycin damage and vitamin deficiency is not apparent. Somers of DCBL spent a great deal of time trying to verify Grünenthal's claim that Supracillin would not destroy the hearing of cats. To Mueckter's displeasure, he managed at last to show that the claim was *entirely baseless:* a conclusion that began to produce some scepticism about Grünenthal's scientific claims at DCBL, where up to then they had been taken more or less as gospel.

In the case of thalidomide, careful investigation should have suggested that Kunz's new molecule was no more than an intriguing phenomenon worthy of further study: that is, a potential hypnotic whose action was unusually dependent upon separation of the active isomer. That almost certainly is the highest value that a sophisticated research team would have placed upon thalidomide—though in practice, as we know, Smith, Kline & French valued it even lower than that.

Whether such a team might have been more successful in ferreting out thalidomide's most dangerous secret is a question best discussed after some further lines of evidence have been brought in. The crucial point is that in Grünenthal's actual behaviour there was little sign of the scientific curiosity that might have made such an achievement possible.

On the strength of the bizarre hydrogen-release tests (published in the journal *Arzneimittelforschung* [Drug Research] in May 1956) and limited clinical trials (none of them using blind-checking techniques, and most of them conducted by doctors in regular commercial relationships with Grünenthal), the company rushed to the market place with an energetic propaganda campaign celebrating the appearance of a pharmaceutical miracle. No attempt was made to explain the workings of this miracle, beyond the banal observation that glutamic acid—from which thalidomide is partially derived—is of importance in the functioning of the nervous system. Many successful drugs are, of course, mysterious. But their originators usually display more curiosity than this.

No attempt was made to discover how thalidomide might be metabolized in the body. And the simplest chemical properties of the substance were so little understood that Mueckter could say in public that it was an "unusually stable compound," whereas, in fact, it is so dramatically unstable that even a highly skilled St. Mary's team found difficulty in handling it at all. The result was that a huge and disastrous scientific experiment was conducted upon the German people—and extended, by DCBL, to Britain. It was an experiment conducted with unusual incompetence, and its dire effects penetrated eventually to most parts of the medically developed world.

All useful drug programmes are in a certain sense experiments upon the human race. In the words of Somers of DCBL, "the final test will always be in man"—and he might have said, in some particular man, woman, or child. At its simplest, this means that the biochemical variations between human and animal species are so great that even if a drug shows no ill effect in animals, it may still do so once human use begins. More fundamentally, the statement recognizes the real nature of scientific knowledge. For scientists or philosophers no longer maintain that scientific knowledge consists of a set of immutable "laws," from which logical proofs can be projected into the future. That was perhaps the situation for a while, when the Victorian systems of inductive logic flourished in the illusory belief that Newton's physics had described the

universe once for all. Hard experience—particularly the effect of relativ-
ity theory and quantum mechanics upon Newtonian physics—has returned us to a less comfortable position, resembling that taken by David
Hume in the eighteenth century, when he maintained that past observations of the sun rising, no matter how numerous, do not enable us to
prove that it will rise again tomorrow. A working scientist does not need
to have read the *Treatise of Human Nature* to perceive that our knowledge
of the future is a series of more or less useful assumptions, any of which
may be modified at any moment by experience.

When we describe a drug as "safe," therefore, what we should really
say is that it is a drug that has not yet been found *unsafe*.

A firm marketing a drug is in a complex situation. For commercial
reasons, it must urge the virtues of the drug as vividly as possible. But at
the same time, the sales force and the medical staff must remain acutely
alert to any hint of an untoward effect that may require the hypothesis
of safety to be modified or even abandoned. Drug companies, it is no
surprise to learn, maintain that their skills and traditions fit them to rec-
oncile such tensions fruitfully. "We never let go of a drug," says Dr.
Robert Hitchings, head of Burroughs-Wellcome Inc. and chief progeni-
tor of the classic antimalarial drug Daraprim. "However long it's been
on the market, we never stop monitoring it." His remark illustrates the
essential continuity of the process. It is natural for lay people to conceive
of drugs as being invented, "proved safe," and thenceforward marketed
freely. But no experienced pharmaceutical scientist would think so. Dr.
Gerhard Zbinden, formerly of Hoffmann–La Roche and now a professor
in Zurich, maintains that the point at which maximum vigilance is required typically comes when the drug has been on the market for two or
three years, after the sales curve has had time to rise and its effects have
had time to show themselves.

Needless to say, not everyone agrees that the major drug firms are
quite so good as they themselves say they are, and there have been
plenty of controversies over drugs that have been kept on the market
despite considerable evidence of worrisome side effects. We shall now examine the manner in which Chemie Grünenthal put thalidomide to its
"final test in man"—and here the reader should bear in mind that later
sellers of the drug chose to rely very heavily in their assumptions of
safety upon the fact that Grünenthal apparently did not find any adverse evidence from clinical experience in Germany. Yet the whole
Grünenthal operation was quite clearly in a class of its own.

3 How to Sell a Wonder Drug

Grünenthal's first step towards marketing thalidomide was to arrange for clinical trials. The company sent the drug to a number of doctors with the request that they try it on their patients and note the results. Some of the replies were incorporated in the report of a "symposium" held at Grünenthal's offices on December 16, 1955. This "K17 symposium" (named after Grünenthal's code label for the drug) became the company's main source of information about thalidomide and, in the end, something of a Bible for all defenders of thalidomide. Even in 1972, the report of it was flourished in the Court of Appeal in London by John Wilmers, Q.C., acting for DCBL, who claimed that it was "an important scientific document, as anyone could see by looking at it." Grünenthal quoted the symposium to prospective licensees all over the world as evidence of the work done in developing and testing the drug, and they referred to it in articles in medical journals. Yet the symposium was principally a public relations exercise. The report contained a good deal of material dressed up in scientific form, but whether it really constituted a description of an adequate experimental drug programme is by no means so clear as Wilmers suggested.

The report begins by setting out the generalized references to glutamic acid and the nervous system, continues with Mueckter's redefinition of the state of sleep, mentioned earlier, and describes the astonishing hydrogen-release machine and its even more astonishing results. There is no chemical description of thalidomide and no account of its absorption, metabolism, or excretion. There is no shred of a hypothesis as to the possible working of its mysterious hypnotic action, or anything that might cast light on its remarkable lack of toxicity, and there are no results of long-term trials to show whether toxicity might appear if the patient took the drug for, say, a year or longer.

About the only test in the symposium report that could pass for an objective assessment is one on the basal metabolic rate (BMR) of certain hyperthyroid patients after the administration of thalidomide. The BMR test is a measurement of the body's oxygen consumption; it is a useful, if rough-and-ready, guide to the speed at which the engine is turning over. Apparently, the hyperthyroids, whose engines were running too fast, were slowed down somewhat by thalidomide. This could be interpreted as suggesting that there was some kind of generalized sedative effect from the drug. It could also provide a hint of antithyroid behaviour, something that, if confirmed, was already known in the 1950s to be associated with birth defects. The rest of the report consists of a series of more or less glowing opinions from German doctors who had used thalidomide on their patients. None of them had made any serious attempt at a controlled test or a double-blind test (a test where neither doctor nor patient knows what drug treatment the patient is receiving) so there is no way of knowing whether the healthy sleep, sedation, and new tranquillity observed were simply placebo effects produced by the enthusiasm of the doctors administering the drug. And, of course, there is no mention of the fact that some of these doctors, including the most enthusiastic, Dr. Herman Jung, had a financial arrangement with Grünenthal.

Dr. Jung was on a retainer of about DM 200 a month (then about $60) from Grünenthal. In a clinic in Cologne, he had given thalidomide to twenty patients, for only four weeks. Yet his admiration for the drug appeared overwhelming.

He had, for example, used it on four youths who were suffering from moral tension as the result of masturbation. In confidential chats, they had revealed to him that after taking thalidomide their desire to masturbate had decreased, their moral tension had evaporated, and they felt much better. Also, said Dr. Jung, thalidomide had cured premature ejaculation in a number of married patients whose wives were reported to have expressed great satisfaction with the results. On the basis of his trials, Dr. Jung reported to Grünenthal at the beginning of June 1955 that he considered thalidomide ready to be marketed: "We have a substance that, at the correct dose level, has no undesirable side effects. I believe that [thalidomide] is a satisfactory drug and that with the necessary promotion it will succeed in the pharmaceutical market." (Jung went on with his trials and later found that thalidomide sometimes produced dizziness, constipation, shivering, and a buzzing in the ears, but his basic faith in the substance remained unshaken for some time. Moreover, his first report had become a main plank in Grünenthal's sales platform.)

Another major report of the symposium of a favourable clinical trial came from Dr. Heinz Esser, of Düsseldorf. Dr. Esser gave thalidomide to three hundred fifty patients—but never for longer than twelve weeks. He found no narcotic effects, no effect on the blood count, kidneys, or liver. "Unwanted side effects were absent except for slight constipation in bed patients," he reported. Later, Dr. Esser considered the constipation side effect sufficiently severe to justify his decision to cease prescribing thalidomide for his patients.

Shorter reports were more mixed in reaction. Dr. Edwin Baumann of Rottenburg gave thalidomide to fifty-five patients for an average period of four to six weeks. He began by saying he was impressed but his later comments were less favourable. He excused himself from further trials because he believed he had found another barbiturate-free sedative, which, unlike his experiences with thalidomide, had no tendency to leave a "hangover" feeling. A Dr. Fegeler, of Münster, a dermatologist, said that thalidomide was "an excellent hypnotic for patients with itching who demand such an aid." But he failed to report how many patients had taken part in his trials, how often he had administered the drug, and in what doses. A Dr. Gottschick of Bad Pyrmont used thalidomide for patients with brain injury and found that it produced an effect "that may be compared with that produced by leucotomy," which was hardly what Grünenthal were planning. On the other hand, Dr. Gottschick said, another patient did not respond at all well.

The only senior doctor who had taken part in the trials, Dr. Gerhard Kloos, director of the Lower Saxony Hospital, Göttingen, reported mixed reactions. Some of his psychiatric patients felt better after taking thalidomide, but three of his doctors who took the drug themselves reported a hangover, nausea, and dizziness. This tallied with the experiences of Dr. Karl Vorlaender, then a lecturer at the University Clinic, Münster. He reported that in his patients, thalidomide produced giddiness, nausea, wakefulness instead of sleepiness, and addiction after about three weeks. Vorlaender felt that the drug needed many more trials over a longer period of time in order to produce results of any significance, and he suggested that he pass it to the head of his clinic for this to be done. Grünenthal rejected his offer.

Clearly the symposium had not been the unqualified success that Grünenthal later made it out to be. In fact, Grünenthal's managing director, Jacob Chauvistré, said that there was a lot more work to be done on thalidomide before it was ready for marketing. So Grünenthal sent the drug out to more doctors. Only two reported favourably. A Dr. Stärk gave thalidomide to ninety patients in a Swiss tuberculosis sanatorium, and a Dr. Walkenhorst to patients awaiting encephalograms. Both found the drug effective. But Dr. Stärk had given thalidomide to fifty of her patients for less than a week, and Dr. Walkenhorst had administered only single doses.

The other reports were highly critical. Three doctors from the Free University of Berlin reported significant side effects. The most damaging report came from Dr. Ferdinand Piacenza, head of the Wasach Sanatorium, near Oberstdorf. He said that he had been forced to break off his trials because of "absolute non-toleration." He described various side effects including, significantly, symptoms of what he thought was an allergic reaction. Mueckter wrote to him, "We have never had such a negative report as yours. . . . The only explanation is that the [reactions] are a disturbance in the nervous system following too high a dosage over a long period of time."

In his authoritative study on drugs, Professor Zbinden stresses that the evaluation of a drug's toxicity is a complicated research problem which "begins with the first pharmacological test and continues *as long as the compound is used*" (emphasis added). The dangers of a drug sometimes manifest themselves in obscure and subtle ways and sometimes only after the drug has been in use for a considerable length of time. But here, on the contrary, thalidomide was making some of its dangers known in obvious and open ways *before it had even been placed on the market.* For Grünenthal knew by now that among the side effects of thalidomide were giddiness, nausea, shivering, buzzing in the ears, constipation, a "hangover," wakefulness, and an allergic reaction. Most important of all, Grünenthal itself recognized that thalidomide could cause "a disturbance in the nervous system following too high a dosage."

Yet when Grünenthal finally launched thalidomide, it did so with an advertising campaign aimed at selling it over the counter in pharmacies rather than by prescription—which made it difficult for doctors to regulate the dosage or to monitor its effects—and stressing that the drug was "completely non-poisonous . . . safe . . . astonishingly safe . . . non-toxic . . . fully harmless . . ." and even that it could be taken "in higher dosages" than recommended without any danger. This was untrue and Grünenthal knew it. But this sort of dangerous overstatement appeared the only way to promote the drug successfully. For in the three years since thalidomide had been discovered, formidable competition had appeared in the tranquillizer market. Other companies had got in first with all sorts of barbiturate-free drugs, and thalidomide was still nowhere near ready to market: its clinical trials had been sporadic, had left many questions unanswered, and had led to serious misgivings about side effects. It looked as if thalidomide was stuck on Grünenthal's shelves and would remain there.

Then in the late summer of 1957, the West German health authorities forecast that there would be an Asian flu epidemic that autumn. One of the thalidomide preparations that Grünenthal had devised was called Grippex (derived from grippe—a French word for flu), a mixture of thalidomide quinine, vitamin C, phenacetin, and salicylamide. On September 2, reasoning that Grippex would sell well in a flu epidemic, Grünenthal decided to put thalidomide and its mixtures on the market, and the drug went on sale on Tuesday, October 1, 1957. After some deliberation Grünenthal had chosen the brand name Contergan. It was a name that was to have many derivatives, among them Contergan Forte, a stronger version of the product; Contergan Saft (literally "Contergan juice"), which was for mothers to use in sedating their infants (marketed in Sweden under a name meaning "Babysitter"); and the final and most horrifying derivative, "Contergan baby," as the victims of the drug are known in Germany.

Thalidomide was exported to eleven European, seven African, seventeen Asian, and eleven North and South American countries. (It was never sold in the United States for reasons we shall explain later, but it was distributed on clinical trial and caused at least six deformed births.) In addition, it was produced by a number of companies under licence, under a total of fifty-one names, such as Softenon, Softenil, Distaval, and Neurosedyn. Apart from a few imitations of the drug in Italy and Japan, Grünenthal was responsible for all thalidomide preparations sold throughout the world. Directions for marketing the drug in other countries were provided by Grünenthal, which always exercised a major influence on all advertising material. In fact, most of this was printed in Stolberg, and the little that was not was checked before printing by Grünenthal's foreign marketing department.

The policy for marketing thalidomide was set out originally in a memorandum from Grünenthal's scientific research department on September 26, 1957. The theme for all promotion was to be that thalido-

mide was "completely non-poisonous" and "completely safe." This was
a sensational claim. No sedative had ever been called "completely safe"
before, and when these words appeared in 50 advertisements in the
major medical journals, in 200,000 letters sent to doctors, in 50,000 circulars sent to pharmacists, and on the instruction leaflet in the thalidomide packet, there was the feeling—despite scepticism in some
quarters—that Grünenthal must indeed have made an important scientific breakthrough. This belief had an almost instant effect on sales, and
by the end of the first year, Grünenthal was selling about 90,000 packets
of thalidomide a month. It was an astonishing launch, but it had only
scratched the surface of Germany's huge market for sedatives, and it appeared to Grünenthal's delighted executives that the prospects for their
new product were almost unlimited.

So from the very beginning, they were reluctant to modify the theme
of their advertising campaign lest the magic be lost. When the more
cautious or more sceptical doctors complained that the only drug that
could be "completely non-toxic" and "completely harmless" was one
that had no effect at all, even a beneficial one, Grünenthal agreed only
to insignificant changes, or what it called in an internal memorandum
"retaining the previous theme while appearing to reduce the emphasis."
In practice, this meant changing "completely harmless" to "harmless,"
but instructing the sales staff in their sales talk to "emphasize non-toxicity" by using lines such as, "In hospitals, regular tests on patients of thalidomide are superfluous."

It did not take long for the first complaint about thalidomide to arrive. In December 1958, Dr. Gustav Schmaltz, of Frankfurt, who had
not been using the drug in trials but had been prescribing it for his patients, wrote saying that thalidomide had caused giddiness and slight
disturbance of balance in the elderly. Grünenthal replied, "We feel
obliged to say that this is the first time such side effects have been reported to us. . . ." This was simply not true. All through the early clinical trials, from 1955 to 1957, there had been criticism of the drug on just
these points—dizziness and disturbance of balance—from, for example,
three of the nine doctors whose reports had been quoted at the thalidomide symposium. The only reason there were not more complaints was
that the drug had not been in use long enough, by sufficient numbers of
people, for its side effects to become apparent.

Enough time had elapsed by the following year, 1959, the breakthrough year for thalidomide in Germany. The company's advertising

campaign was having its effect, and sales figures increased dramatically. By May 1959, Grünenthal's gross income from the drug was nearly DM 100,000; by December it had quadrupled to nearly 400,000 (then about $96,000) and thalidomide was well on the way to capturing the German market. But 1959 was also the year that complaints from the German medical profession about thalidomide grew from a whisper into an indignant and persistent roar.

Salesmen are a drug company's eyes and ears in the world. They meet the drug's users; they hear the gossip first. So it was that the first complaints were in scattered reports from Grünenthal's sales representatives. In March 1959, Dr. Heinzmann of the Koblenz sales office reported that a pharmacist had complained of abnormally cold hands and feet after taking thalidomide. In April, Dr. Horst Frenkel, working in a clinic in Königstein, told a Grünenthal representative that he had noticed several side effects in patients using thalidomide. In July, a report by Grünenthal representative Johannes Zila described a visit he had made to a pharmacist in Düsseldorf: "A few customers complained of constipation and one customer thought that paraesthesia had developed from the use of Contergan. The pharmacist thinks that Contergan could have a harmful effect on circulation." In August, Zila reported two more cases of side effects, but these paled beside a blistering letter to Grünenthal from Pharmakolor AG of Basle, Switzerland:

> To date twenty well-known doctors have told our representatives that when they themselves or their patients took one tablet of thalidomide they found themselves still under its effect the next morning, suffering from considerable sickness, involuntary trembling of the hands, etc. Dr. Ludwig, head of the second medical department, Burgershospital, Basle, told us yesterday that he gave his wife a tablet of Softenon Forte [thalidomide]. He adds: "Once and never again. This is a terrible drug."

If this powerful—but, as it turned out—perfectly accurate assessment of thalidomide worried Grünenthal, there was no sign of it. For when Dr. Ralf Voss, a well-known Düsseldorf nerve specialist, wrote to Grünenthal in October 1959, Dr. Mueckter and Dr. Günther Sievers, of Grünenthal's medical department, dismissed his query about thalidomide's side effects with a reply at best cavalier, at worst a direct untruth. Dr. Voss wrote: "In my practice there is a sixty-three-year-old man who has been using Contergan Forte regularly as a sedative for a year to a year and a half. In the last six months, polyneuritis has developed, the genesis of which is so far unexplained. Is anything known about whether Contergan can lead to damage of the peripheral nervous system?" Grünenthal replied: "Happily we can tell you that such disadvantageous effects have not been brought to our notice." In other words, Grünenthal, despite its representatives' reports, despite the letter from Pharmakolor, and despite Dr. Piacenza's report three years earlier, was saying to Dr. Voss, no, we have never heard of this.

Dr. Voss was not silent for long. At the end of November, he wrote again. He now had three patients with peripheral neuritis, and all three had been taking thalidomide regularly for a year or longer. He believed, he said, that there was a definite connection between the long-term use of thalidomide and peripheral neuritis. Grünenthal would not have it: "We have no idea how these cases of peripheral neuritis could have been caused by Contergan. We shall pay appropriate attention to this matter in the course of further clinical studies." There were no further clinical studies. Instead, Grünenthal's sales promotion campaign was stepped up still further. In the first quarter of 1960, Grünenthal representatives called on nearly 20,000 physicians and 250,000 leaflets were sent out stressing thalidomide's safety, referring to it as "non-toxic," "completely harmless even for infants," and "harmless even over a long period of use."

Peripheral neuritis is a serious illness. It may occur anywhere in the body. For example, it may begin with a prickly feeling in the toes, followed by a sensation of numbness and cold. The numbness spreads, often above the ankles, and eventually is followed by severe muscular cramps, weakness of the limbs, and a lack of coordination. The patient becomes unable to judge the position of his limbs by their feel, and his gait becomes unbalanced and uncoordinated. Some of these symptoms improve or disappear when the cause is removed, but much of the damage is irreversible. Dr. Voss, who of course knew this, was deeply worried about Grünenthal's attitude. He said later, "I had the strong impression that the Grünenthal doctors did not doubt the validity of my observations but were merely anxious to prevent as far as possible their being made public."

Voss decided to take matters into his own hands. He began collecting evidence in the cases he had diagnosed, and by April 1960, he was ready to act. He prepared a paper on three of his cases, all of whom had been taking thalidomide daily for a year, and planned to present his paper at a conference of neurologists in Düsseldorf April 30–May 1. His work had not been secret and a Grünenthal sales representative, Dr. Ruth Dittmann, heard of it and reported it to her superiors. Grünenthal moved rapidly. Dr. Sievers called on Voss and confirmed the details of his cases. He then attended the Düsseldorf conference to hear Voss speak. Sievers's report made gloomy reading for Grünenthal.

> Dr. Voss stood up at the front of the auditorium and described three patients with peripheral neuritis, all of whom had taken Contergan for a long time. He asked the conference members, specifically Professor Scheid and Professor Bay, whether there was any connection. Neither of these two men had anything to say, but an unknown Düsseldorf intern said that he had noticed that four or five patients who were known as hypertonics had collapsed after taking Contergan.

Dr. Voss's lecture went unnoticed in the lay press but not in the medical world. Grünenthal began to get more and better-detailed complaints. Dr. Paul Ervenich of Duisburg's St. Anna Hospital complained that patients for whom he had prescribed thalidomide had reported nerve damage "of the most severe kind." He had sent one of these patients to the Neurological Clinic in Essen, which had said that thalidomide was very probably the fundamental cause. And from Grünenthal's sales office in Essen came a multiple complaint: "All our medical representatives have sent in reports from doctors who have confirmed cases of peripheral neuritis."

There was now a real possibility that the hostility building up in the medical world would force the authorities to place thalidomide on prescription, where its use could be restricted, its side effects monitored, and its effectiveness assessed. Grünenthal did not welcome this and fought to prevent it. "Unfortunately we are now receiving increasingly strong reports on the side effects of thalidomide, as well as letters from doctors and pharmacists who want to put it on prescription," the company's sales department wrote. "From our side, everything must be done to avoid this, since a substantial amount of our volume comes from over-the-counter sales."

Grünenthal's sales manager, Dr. Klaus Winandi, suggested the tactics: the company should appeal to doctors' and pharmacists' profit motivation. Representatives should spell out to them how much they stood to lose: "Bring economic aspects into the conversation, and this will provide an opportunity for explaining to the doctor that such a harmless sleeping draught should really remain exempt from prescription. . . . In a similar way, one will probably also be able to meet any objections from pharmacists. A hint can be dropped that the consumption of thalidomide will boost sales, which would certainly drop if compulsory prescription were to be introduced."

While the company's salesmen set about this task, the clinical research department was also doing its best to protect the drug that Grünenthal came to call "this apple of our eye." Dr. Günther Michael, head of the section, warned: "Sooner or later we will not be able to stop publication of the side effects of Contergan. We are therefore anxious to get as many positive pieces of work as possible." To this end some rather remote stones were not left unturned. On March 30, 1960, a Grünenthal representative reported that initial approaches to a doctor in Iran had been unsuccessful. "However, since the Iranian doctor is very materialistic in his outlook, concrete results should be forthcoming soon." The head office was left to interpret this cryptic sentence in any way it wished. In point of fact, the representative in Iran seemed to be pursuing the right course, because what Grünenthal wanted above all was *quick* results. The company spelled out its policy on trials in a letter to the Portuguese licensee, Firma Paracelsia, of Oporto: "To be quite clear about it: a quick publication, perhaps in three months, with the reports of fifteen to twenty successful cases who have tolerated the drug well, is more important to us than a broadly based, large work that will not appear for eight to twelve months. From this, you can see what kind of testers we have in mind."

The experience of the doctor in carrying out clinical trials seemed to matter little. One, Dr. Konrad Lang, had never previously tested a drug before it came on the market but undertook to try thalidomide on children at the University Clinic, Bonn. Forty children, most of whom had brain damage, were given the drug under Dr. Lang's supervision for periods of up to nine weeks *without the permission or knowledge of their parents.* The doses were ten to twenty times higher than Grünenthal's recommended dose for adults. One child had a circulatory collapse, one child died from a congenital heart defect, a twenty-one-month-old baby with convulsive disorders lost her vision temporarily, and a three-month-old baby died from heart failure. Dr. Lang considered it very questionable that any of these reactions was connected with thalidomide, and reported to the company: "In general terms Contergan could be described as a rapid-acting sedative particularly suited for use with children." (Later, after he had heard from colleagues of their unsatisfactory experiences with thalidomide, Dr. Lang stopped using the drug.)

Pending favourable reports, Grünenthal did what it could to suppress or delay publication of unfavourable ones. Its tactics with Dr. Frenkel, the neurologist from Königstein, were not atypical. When it learned that he was preparing a paper for publication describing his experiences with twenty patients, all of whom, he believed, had thalidomide-induced peripheral neuritis, two representatives paid him a visit. It would be a great help to the company, they said, if he were to withhold his article. Dr. Frenkel said he had already sent it to *Medizinische Welt*. Then withdraw it, the Grünenthal men suggested. Frenkel refused. Would he at least delay it? No, Frenkel said.

But the publication of Dr. Frenkel's report *was* delayed, seemingly inexplicably; it was some time before the reason emerged. A Grünenthal memorandum explained: "The friendly connection with Dr. Matis [editor of *Medizinische Welt*] contributed to the delay in treatment of the submitted manuscript." (Dr. Matis later denied that he had allowed Grünenthal to influence him, but agreed that he had forwarded Frenkel's paper to Grünenthal for its comments. Many scientists have experience that when an editor submits their papers to hostile reviewers, there is often a delay in publication.) In the meantime, Matis published in *Medizinische Welt* an article written by a woman doctor who had previously done some work for Grünenthal. It noted: "The particular advantages of Contergan reside in its atoxicity and in the lack of side effects after long use."

Even the Drug Commission of the West German Federal Medical Association appeared to have little influence on Grünenthal. When it took up the question of thalidomide's side effects, Grünenthal fought back by sending its representatives to see public-health officials and convince them of the "complete harmlessness" of the drug. The sales promotion material was not modified, thalidomide was still represented as "nontoxic," and it was not until November 2 that a new label was designed with the following statement: "As with most drugs, a more or less prolonged use of Contergan may evoke hyper-sensitivity reactions in certain predisposed patients. . . . Immediately after withdrawal of the drug, these allergic reactions will disappear." This was untrue and Grünenthal knew that, but as a company memorandum put it, "We intend to fight for Contergan to the bitter end."

On December 31, 1960, the first description of thalidomide-induced peripheral neuritis to appear in any medical literature was published in the *British Medical Journal*. In a letter headed "Is Thalidomide to Blame?" Dr. A. Leslie Florence of Aberdeen described four cases of peripheral neuritis in patients who had taken thalidomide and inquired whether "any of your readers have observed these effects after long-term treatment with the drug." Grünenthal now knew of at least one hundred fifty cases of peripheral neuritis in which the cause was strongly suspected to be thalidomide. But the remarkable success of the drug—thalidomide now accounted for more than half Grünenthal's total volume, and Dr. Mueckter, whose salary was geared to sales, was earning at least $1,200 a week—made the company close its eyes to the evidence.

Mueckter described this success and the need to protect it in a letter to DCBL in Britain: "As you probably know, Contergan has now surpassed all other hypnotics in Germany and is far and away above the others. From the sales returns, we estimate that at the present time more than a million people in West Germany alone take Contergan every day. This is doubtless assisted by the fact that in Germany the drug can be bought over the counter without prescription, which I understand is not the case in England." He went on to soothe any anxiety the British licensee might have felt about peripheral neuritis: "This high consumption has resulted in occasional cases of reaction being observed, and these have been judged by specialists to be Contergan allergies. The reactions are partly dermal, with rashes, and partly neural, either central or peripheral. Both varieties of reaction disappear after ceasing use of the preparation."

Again, this was simply not true, as Dr. Voss, the neurologist, now made clear in a resounding attack on thalidomide in an address before the medical academy in Düsseldorf February 15, 1961:

> I have come to tell you about a new illness that I first came across in October 1959 [he began]. It is a picture of toxic peripheral neuritis after prolonged use of Contergan. I have diagnosed fourteen cases in my practice. The illness begins with a numbness in the toes that is usually not noticed by the patient. This numbness spreads to the ball of the foot, then to the ankles, and finally to the calves, but not beyond the knee.

Many months later, hardly ever at the same time, the numbness begins in the tips of the fingers. *To date, there is not a single case of recovery after the drug has been stopped.*

Voss's lecture rocked Grünenthal. Some of the executives were for putting the drug on prescription immediately, but others favoured playing down the side effects. For a while, the second group had its way. Its attitude was best expressed by Grünenthal's Cologne representative, Johann Goeden. He had suggested that Contergan be mixed with other sedatives so that "if it proves impossible to keep things dark or to ward off attacks, any alleged side effects could then be attributed to the other preparations. But heaven help us if this expedient turns into a boomerang."

Dr. Goeden set out to cover up for thalidomide. On February 21 he visited a clinic in Cologne, where, he reported to Grünenthal, "I took the opportunity to explain our standpoint over the peripheral neuritis problem with Contergan and I did my best to foster confusion on this subject." (This approach did not always work. The director of the medical clinic at Bonn University told the Grünenthal representative quite bluntly that he had prohibited all use of thalidomide, that he felt it should be taken off the market, and that he wished to have no further discussion with Grünenthal.)

Too many cases of peripheral neuritis were being reported and too many papers criticizing thalidomide were awaiting publication for Grünenthal to put off any longer applying for the drug to be placed on prescription. Grünenthal made the application but at the same time intensified its marketing and promotion campaigns under the sales department's slogan: "We must succeed, whatever the cost." An important part of the campaign was to secure favourable publication in medical journals to offset the effect of the flow of unfavourable ones. Here Franz-Josef Winzenried, a professor at the psychiatric clinic of Hamburg University, proved helpful, producing a major paper. This was hardly a lucky accident. The author was an old friend of Dr. Sievers of Grünenthal and early in 1961 had agreed to attend a medical convention in Canada where he would discuss his successful use of thalidomide. On the strength of this, Grünenthal arranged for a contribution of $2,500 to help defray Professor Winzenried's expenses. Now Winzenried's views of thalidomide were published in the June 16, 1961, issue of *Medizinische Klinik.*

Winzenried made much of the drug's "atoxicity," proved, he said, by the case of a forty-year-old woman who had attempted suicide by taking 140 thalidomide pills. "The patient slept deeply for ten hours," he wrote, "and then remained for a further six hours in a state of light somnolence. There were no disturbances to respiration or to circulation." Winzenried omitted to mention that doctors had pumped out the woman's stomach and had administered stimulants. The figure of 140 pills was her own and went unchecked. And later, when asked if he himself had ever tried thalidomide, Winzenried said that he had on one occasion but had stopped because the next day his skin itched and he was constipated. Also, the very day after his article was published he saw his first case of thalidomide-induced peripheral neuritis. He told Grünenthal about this and later cases he observed, but they still continued to use reprints of his article for sales promotion.

Actually, Professor Winzenried's paper was too late to help Grünenthal. April had marked the zenith of the company's fortunes. May brought the first indications of disaster. In that month, three extremely critical articles about thalidomide appeared in German medical literature. On May 6, Dr. Frenkel's article on Contergan side effects was published in *Medizinische Welt;* on May 12, *Deutsche Medizinische Wochenschrift* published a paper on polyneuritic syndrome after long-term thalidomide administration, by the neurologist Professor W. Scheid, and in the same issue of that journal, there was an article by Dr. H. J. Raffauf of Essen, asking: does thalidomide cause nerve damage?

By the end of the month, the number of cases of peripheral neuritis known to Grünenthal reached thirteen hundred, and at a meeting in London with the British licensee, DCBL, Grünenthal learned that the British company had between seventy-five and ninety cases of its own. In addition, complaints from German doctors about Grünenthal's attitude to their reports grew louder and more persistent. Grünenthal's thalidomide sales graph, which had shown a steep and steady climb since the introduction of the drug four years earlier, for the first time turned downward. The company's reaction can only be described as amazing.

Doctors who questioned Grünenthal's attitude were abused as trouble-makers. Dr. Hubert Gigglberger, of Regensburg, who told Grünenthal that it was "irresponsible" not to have withdrawn the drug, and that he doubted the company's trustworthiness, was labelled "trouble-maker No. 1" of the South German area. The local company representative wrote to Stolberg, "We have to pull out this sick tooth before the infection spreads." Could the services of a private detective help? Two months earlier, Grünenthal had hired such a man, Ernst Jahnke, of Essen, to place under surveillance certain patients with peripheral neuritis who might raise compensation claims against the company. The aim was to try to prevent any civil lawsuits because of the damage that the cases, with their attendant publicity, could cause Grünenthal. Now the company ordered the detective to extend his attentions to doctors who criticized thalidomide. The reason appears to have been that some Grünenthal executives genuinely believed that hostility to thalidomide was the result of a conspiracy by rival drug firms. Several doctors, including Voss and Laubenthal, were investigated by the industrious Jahnke, but his reports brought little joy to Grünenthal: "Grünenthal's competitors are showing malicious joy over Contergan's now established faults. But on the other hand, they have evidently not provoked this situation. . . . The whole action is initiated not by the industry but by the physicians."

Now even some Grünenthal executives began to have doubts. The company's clinical research director, Dr. Michael, bared his heart to his colleagues in a memorandum on May 10: "I personally maintain the view that there is no longer any doubt that, under certain circumstances that I am unable at present to understand or explain, Contergan can cause the nervous injuries described. I am convinced that all those who are in the company with us must subscribe to this view. . . . I consider it simply impossible that the company should officially adopt the standpoint that these reports are exclusively a matter of unqualified polemics. . . ."

Another executive, Dr. Günter Nowel, who had been handling Grünenthal's application for thalidomide to be placed on prescription, was shattered to find out just how little he knew about Grünenthal's marketing of the drug. His relations with the health department of the Ministry of the Interior in Düsseldorf had always been cordial. But when he called at the ministry on June 8, he could sense a change in the atmosphere. Dr. Hans Tombergs, a senior ministry official, was cold and formal, and then suddenly accused Grünenthal of manipulating its application for thalidomide to be placed on prescription in such a way as to transfer the blame for the company's tardiness onto the ministry. More specifically, Dr. Tombergs accused Grünenthal of withholding information. Dr. Tombergs said that the company had been informed by Dr. Voss as early as December 1959 that thalidomide produced side effects, including peripheral neuritis. Dr. Nowel defended Grünenthal, assuring Dr. Tombergs that Voss had definitely not been in touch with Grünenthal until the autumn of 1960.

But on his return to company headquarters, Nowel quietly checked the records, just to be sure. His anger at what he found comes through in the letter he immediately wrote to his superiors:

> Regrettable result! An exchange of correspondence *did* in fact take place between October and December 1959. And the very first letter from Dr. Voss points out that peripheral neuritis had been observed in patients after the use of thalidomide over a long period. Making a representative responsible for negotiations with the ministry when he is so inadequately informed results not only in the undermining of the company's reputation but that of the representative himself.

Finally Nowel made an entry on his filing card system: "We are more than to blame."

Grünenthal's lawyers agreed. In July 1961, they advised: "It is quite clear that the trial risk in relation to our guilt is far larger than we could have foreseen in the first instance. In these circumstances, we do not see that we would be justified in going to trial on this matter." So on July 28, 1961, Grünenthal, for the first time, paid compensation to a thalidomide victim, Dr. Kersten Thiele, a minister in Düsseldorf. He received the princely sum of DM 750 (then about $190).

Now even Dr. Mueckter showed flashes of pessimism about thalidomide's future. "If I were a doctor," he told a staff meeting in July, "I would not prescribe Contergan any more." But Grünenthal's private detective, Jahnke, continued to watch victims, doctors, and government officials who spoke out publicly against the drug, and a woman was even smuggled into Dr. Frenkel's clinic on the pretext that she was suffering from peripheral neuritis. She was unable to report anything in Dr. Frenkel's behaviour that could be used against him.

On August 1, 1961, thalidomide was placed on prescription in the German states of North Rhine–Westphalia, Hesse, and Württemberg. (On August 16, *Der Spiegel,* in reporting this, made public in the lay press for the first time the extent of peripheral neuritis damage caused by the drug.) But as late as October 1961, it was still possible to buy thalidomide over the counter in at least seven other German states. Abroad the picture varied. At a meeting at Stolberg in September 1961, Grünenthal told its licensees from Britain, the United States, and Sweden about the risks and seriousness of peripheral neuritis but concealed the fact that it now knew of 2,400 cases in Germany alone. And in letters to licensees in *developed* countries it urged them to stop using such expressions as "nontoxic" in their literature about the drug. But in publicity material for countries in *West Africa* thalidomide was still described as "completely harmless."

Grünenthal now prepared itself for a flood of lawsuits for compensation. In April 1962, Grünenthal's lawyer, Hilmar von Veltheim, estimated that about 4,000 people in West Germany were suffering from peripheral neuritis. Those doctors most concerned with peripheral neuritis considered that the Grünenthal figure was too low and that 40,000 cases would not be too high an estimate.

It was through peripheral neuritis, then, that thalidomide first made known its danger, and if Grünenthal had reacted in a more responsible manner as reports of the drug's side effects poured in, then its other, more horrifying power might have been minimized. But instead of a sensitive response to negative reports about the drug as it underwent its final test in man—Grünenthal's behaviour can be summarized as follows:

• It lied when doctors wrote asking if they had heard of this sort of side effect before.

• It denied all causal connection between thalidomide and peripheral neuritis.

• It tried to conceal the number of cases that had been reported to the company.

• It tried to suppress publication of reports about thalidomide-induced peripheral neuritis by using influence and by creating diversion and confusion.

• It sought to counter critical reports with favourable ones, and to get them, it was prepared to spend money, use influence, and create distortion.

• It fought to prevent the drug's going on prescription, attacked doctors who advocated this control, and used a private detective to try to discover information that could be used against these doctors.

This was the company that six years earlier, in the first week of June 1956, had been host to Dr. Walter Kennedy, chief medical adviser of Distillers Company (Biochemicals) Limited, on a visit to Germany to assess which Grünenthal products might be worth while selling in Britain. One of the first drugs he had looked at was thalidomide.

4 Enter the Soma Merchants

Distillers, the spirits and liquor company that marketed thalidomide in Britain, got involved in the drug industry during the Second World War almost by accident. In 1942, the British Ministry of Supply invited the company to make penicillin at Speke, Liverpool, as the government's agent. After the war, the ministry offered Distillers the penicillin plant, then one of the largest in the world, for about $4 million, a price difficult to refuse. Distillers bought it, and this was the beginning of Distillers Company (Biochemicals) Limited, or DCBL as it was more commonly known.

Despite an auspicious start—it produced the first oral penicillin—DCBL was never very profitable. It provided only about 5 per cent of Distillers' volume, and running through the parent company's annual reports was a refrain about "uneconomic prices" and the "highly competitive conditions" of the drug industry. Clearly what was needed was expansion into more profitable drug lines, and in the mid-1950s it appeared more convenient to buy the British rights to a drug already developed by a foreign pharmaceutical company than to try to develop one itself. This was the reason for Dr. Kennedy's visit to Grünenthal.

Kennedy came away with an exciting report of a new sedative that Grünenthal had labelled for convenience "K17." Kennedy reported to the DCBL director, E. G. Gross: "K17 . . . has been licensed in America but not yet in England. If all the details about this are true then it is a most remarkable drug. In short it is impossible to give a toxic dose; it has no narcotic effect; it has no influence on breathing or circulation; no ganglion blocking properties, nor does it produce muscle relaxation. . . . If these details are exact it is, in fact, unique."

Kennedy's glowing account of K17 arrived on Gross's desk at a crucial moment. This was Britain's era of the sleeping pill. About one in eight of all National Health prescriptions were for sedatives, and about one million people took some sort of pill each night to help them sleep—a $5-million-a-year market, expanding all the time. In addition, the report coincided with some fundamental thinking at DCBL's parent company, Distillers, sparked off by none other than Aldous Huxley. Huxley had been writing a series of articles for *The Sunday Times*, and in the last article, which appeared on June 10, 1956, he predicted the benefits the inhabitants of his Brave New World would enjoy from a new drug which, in his novel of that name in 1932, he had called "Soma." Huxley said that from earliest times man had taken mind-transforming drugs: alcohol, nicotine, opium, and cannabis. Now science offered the possibility of safer and more powerful drugs. "Will the pharmacologist be able to do better than the brewers and distillers?" Huxley asked. "It seems reasonable to suppose it."

This excited the interest of N. A. Herdman of Distillers. He wrote enthusiastically to Gross, at DCBL. "The ultimate target would be the production of the ideal tranquillising agent to replace alcohol among those people who would prefer to 'transform their minds' by this alternative means," he said, exhibiting a visionary capacity of a kind that seems out of place in the dour world of distilling. "I would put forward the suggestion that DCL through DCBL should engage forthwith in an extended programme of fundamental pharmacological research. As a halfway target this research should be able to produce for marketing by DCBL a number of products of a therapeutic nature."*

So, incredible as it may seem, one of the factors that led to thalidomide's being marketed in Britain was the belief that it might eventually become an alternative to whisky.

Gross took the point, and thought of K17. He also saw the need for speed. He wrote back to Herdman: "I have a feeling that the market is already becoming a little overcrowded and it will not be long before there are as many of these things as there are brands of whisky."

He also got off a memorandum to DCBL's technical director, J. J. H. Hastings. "If we decided to launch this product we should have to do it quickly." By July 5, Gross was on a plane for Germany hoping to bring back a bulk sample of K17 for testing. The first steps towards marketing thalidomide in Britain had been taken.

Gross went to work on what he clearly saw as the most important task if DCBL was to get hold of this valuable property: the task of convincing

*Herdman resigned from DCL before DCBL began to sell thalidomide.

the German manufacturers that DCBL, a relative newcomer to the pharmaceutical industry, had the resources and the drive to exploit the British and Commonwealth market to the full. On August 20, he sent Grünenthal a draft agreement. This was to last five years, during which the two companies would swap future discoveries free of royalties. DCBL would pay a 5 per cent royalty on the sales of K17. Clearly DCBL had decided that it wanted to go ahead with marketing thalidomide in Britain. Yet at this stage, it had seen no technical information on the drug except the report of a Grünenthal "symposium"—which, as we have seen, was basically a promotional exercise to arouse interest among doctors and pharmacists in Germany—and it had carried out no independent tests. (Dr. Kennedy, an asthma sufferer, had tried the drug on himself and reported that Mrs. Gross had taken it for nervous tension, but these can hardly be considered independent trials.)

Yet not only did DCBL appear ready to go ahead without tests, but there is also evidence that it was their very belief that thalidomide would not need elaborate tests that made the drug so attractive to the company. DCBL had been considering other Continental drugs for sale in Britain under licence and had looked at certain products of the Union Chimie Belge, the Belgian drug manufacturers. Dr. C. N. Brown, Kennedy's deputy in the medical department of DCBL, came down squarely in favour of thalidomide because "the three UCB products will require pharmacological and clinical trials"—the implication being that thalidomide would not.

This suited DCBL because at this time it had not only no research team of its own but no pharmacologist either, and had to hire one, Dr. George Somers, *after* it had begun negotiations for thalidomide.

Although Somers found that the drug was being readied for marketing when he joined DCBL, he made some inquiries of his own, and sent the results to the *British Journal of Pharmacology* in September 1959. Unlike the SKF team, he found some evidence—as measured in the light box—of reduced activity in mice given the drug, but he did not believe that this was sufficient to justify calling thalidomide a hypnotic in animals.

Privately, he told us he thought the effect in animals very slight to have impressed a pharmacological investigator, but he *was* impressed by the reports of clinical success from Germany, and he assumed that Grünenthal had somehow encountered a vigorous human effect without being led to it by pharmacology—a case of a drug "discovered in the clinic." In addition to acute toxicity tests, he studied "sub-acute" toxicity in rats for four weeks, seeing no ill effects. Somers's paper ventured the guess that thalidomide's non-toxicity might be due to poor absorption. He would have liked to investigate this by studies relating the intake of the drug to blood levels, but no methods of measuring blood levels were known at that time. Not until the following year, 1960, did he succeed in having a biochemist added to his staff: a young man who spent several months wrestling with the absorption and metabolism of thalidomide but who found the substance very difficult to handle. By then, thalidomide had been on the market for nearly two years.

Grünenthal had pressed DCBL into signing a contract not for the five years DCBL had wanted, but for the unusually long term of sixteen years. The most startling clause, however, was that DCBL agreed to begin marketing thalidomide within nine months of the date of signature. Since the contract was signed in July 1957, this meant April 1958. Accordingly, the whole complicated process of getting the drug on the market had to be done swiftly.

DCBL now set the target marketing date for thalidomide for January 1958 and, realizing that it would have to give the new drug some tests, wrote to Grünenthal on March 8 ordering 6,000 tablets for clinical trial and 500 grammes of pure substance for "animal experiments, formulation, etc." By May, the drug had been issued to five specialists, but by mid-September, the results were still not available and "may not be available in time for marketing in January."

On September 4, 1957, the executives of DCBL and the executives of Grünenthal met formally for the first time. DCBL's domestic sales manager, C. A. Barnes, later expressed his doubts about Grünenthal's ethical attitude: "The intention is to launch this product with so-called scientific data and literature to the medical profession. There appeared to be no medical objection to blatant claims which might not be able to be wholly substantiated. . . ."

But if these doubts caused any second thoughts at DCBL, there is no evidence of it, for by November, the company was preparing its own propaganda campaign to launch thalidomide on the British market. The name Distaval had been chosen and the theme of the campaign decided: it was to be absolute safety. Advertisements were to stress this with phrases such as "non-toxic" and "no known toxicity."

To his credit, one man at DCBL expressed misgivings about this advertising. The development manager, R. Grasham, thought "no known toxicity" was "rather sweeping" and wanted it replaced with "exceptionally low toxicity." But his recommendation was not adopted. The actual wording in advertisements became "side effects are virtually absent" and thalidomide was described as "non-toxic" until DCBL was forced by events to suspect that its new product was by no means the wonder drug it had hoped it would be.

Distaval went on sale in Britain on April 14, 1958. (Later thalidomide was also marketed under the names Asmaval, Tensival, Valgis, and Valgraine.) It was advertised as "completely safe," and an answer to the "mounting toll of deaths due to barbiturate poisoning."

The most devastating claim of all was made in 1961, when DCBL sent doctors a leaflet that recommended thalidomide for use in psychiatry, geriatrics, neurology, dermatology, paediatrics—and obstetrics, where *"Distaval can be given with complete safety to pregnant women and nursing mothers, without adverse effect on mother or child. . . ."*

Where did this belief, the crux of the thalidomide tragedy, originate? It came directly from Grünenthal, which had always maintained that thalidomide was highly suitable for use by pregnant women and nursing mothers. Yet the very best that could be said about Grünenthal's knowledge of thalidomide's effects on the reproductive system was that it was speculative. Replying to a doctor who wrote from Heilbrunn asking whether thalidomide in a pregnant mother's blood might pass through the placental membrane and reach the child inside her womb, Grünenthal wrote that there was no evidence suggesting that the drug would do so. A Finnish doctor asked a series of extremely well-directed questions, and Grünenthal's answers, four years after its drug went on the market, reveal an astounding degree of ignorance:

1. When thalidomide is given to women patients, does it pass the placenta? *Not known.*
2. Can the preparation have a harmful effect on the child in the event of its getting to the embryo via the placenta? *Unlikely.*
3. In what part of the organism is thalidomide broken down? *Probably in the liver.*

Yet by 1955, if not sooner, it was scientifically quite well known that any substance with a molecular weight of less than 1000 could be expected to cross the placenta and appear in the foetal blood—and the molecular weight of thalidomide is only 258. A general practitioner could not be expected to be sure of this by 1961, but surely Grünenthal should have been aware of it.

As to the question about where thalidomide was broken down, Grünenthal's honest answer should have been that, as it had not made studies of absorption and metabolism, it had no idea of the answer.

But the unloveliest aspect of this set of answers concerns the second one: could thalidomide harm an unborn child? Grünenthal, by misrepresentation, had made it appear that experimental work had been done upon that very question. In fact, such work had not been done. But if it had, the teratogenic effects of thalidomide (teratogenic means "monster-making"—that is, creating deformities) would almost certainly have come to light sometime between 1956 and 1958.

During this period, Dr. Augustin Peter Blasiu, who had a retainer from Grünenthal and was in charge of a private nursing home in Munich, administered thalidomide to 370 patients. Of these, 160 were *nursing* mothers. On May 2, 1958, Blasiu published an article in *Medizinische Klinik* in which he said: "Side effects were not observed with either mothers or babies." The tone of the article was favourable to thalidomide, but Blasiu throughout was referring to women *who had already given birth.* There was no mention of pregnant women receiving the drug, nor would Blasiu have given it to them. As he said later: "It is my basic rule never to give sleeping pills or tranquillizers to mothers-to-be." (This is a rule a great many doctors have always followed, although it was temporarily weakened by the propaganda for "atoxic" thalidomide. The reason traces back almost to the origins of medicine: the only therapy that should be applied in pregnancy is that which deals with a threat to the life of mother or child.)

Grünenthal seized upon Blasiu's article and, shortly after it came out, sent 40,245 doctors a leaflet containing extracts from it, together with a carefully worded letter implying that thalidomide was safe for use in pregnancy:

> *In pregnancy* and during birth the feminine organism is under great strain. Sleeplessness, unrest, and tension are constant complaints. The prescription of a sedative and hypnotic that *will hurt neither mother nor child* is therefore often necessary. Blasiu has given many patients in his gynaecological department and in his *obstetrical* practice [thalidomide]. Depth and length of sleep were good and patients could easily be awakened from deep sleep. [Thalidomide] had no effect on the nursing baby.

Emphasis has been added for clarity, though even without it the impression must be that Blasiu had observed the effect of thalidomide with women throughout the process of pregnancy. In 1968, at the trial of Grünenthal executives for involuntary manslaughter, Blasiu said in evidence that, had he seen this letter, he would have "most emphatically resisted" its circulation and its reference to his report. "I consider that this letter . . . is unfair, misleading, and irresponsible," he said. Both Grünenthal and DCBL have since claimed that they never recommended thalidomide for use in pregnancy as such. Both say that the use of the qualifying word "obstetrics" would be interpreted by any doctor as meaning that thalidomide would be safe for women during *the final stage of pregnancy*. There are three answers to this: The first is that doctors did not so interpret the information, as the many who prescribed it for women in the *early* stages of pregnancy could testify. Second, it uses hindsight. When the claim was made, neither Grünenthal nor Distillers knew that thalidomide was safe at *any* stage of pregnancy. But the most powerful argument against defining obstetrics as the care of women in the final stage of pregnancy is that to do so is wrong. Both the Royal College of Obstetricians and Gynaecologists and the West German Federal Medical Association say that the practice of obstetrics *commences with conception* (and sometimes even before, when, for example, a woman has difficulty in conceiving).

We must now ask: what would have been the effect if any substantial proportion of Blasiu's patients had, in fact, been pregnant women? Many teratogenic substances tend to be variable in their effects on animals and human beings—which is exactly why their action is often difficult to prove. But thalidomide was amazingly powerful; in the words of the London Hospital pharmacologist, Dr. Herxheimer, it is "flamboyantly" teratogenic in humans. Some medical scientists believe that thalidomide in the sort of doses used for hypnotic effect might be almost 100 per cent effective as a teratogen if taken regularly during the first three months of pregnancy.

Grünenthal, in order to sell its drug, thought it useful to give the impression that a clinical trial with pregnant women had been made. That certainly strengthened the "hypothesis of safety" as publicly perceived. Had Grünenthal actually thought to have such a trial conducted, and had it been competently organized, it would have been very likely that teratogenic effects could have been picked up with the suffering confined to a dozen cases or so. But Grünenthal not only failed to conduct a clinical trial to examine thalidomide's safety in pregnancy, it failed as well to carry out any reproductive studies on animals. Other drug companies, *at that time*—the period when Distillers and Grünenthal were promoting thalidomide as safe for pregnant women without knowing whether it was or not—were doing such studies, and it is worth while examining some examples in detail.

In 1954, the year that Grünenthal first synthesized thalidomide, Wallace Laboratories in the United States published its first scientific papers on the pharmacology of a compound called meprobamate, soon to become well known as the tranquillizer Miltown. Miltown was sufficiently like thalidomide in application for both Grünenthal and Wallace's German agents to consider the two drugs competitive.

The acute toxicity of Miltown was assessed in both rats and mice, and the mode of the drug's absorption and its metabolic fate were established in some detail. Unlike Distillers and Grünenthal, Wallace Laboratories did not consider that acute (one-shot) toxicity studies, plus sub-acute studies involving dosage over a three-week period, were sufficient assurance with which to go to market. Dr. Frederick Berger, the "designer" of Miltown, reasoned that any drug sold as a tranquillizer was likely to be used for long-term therapy. Therefore, he and his team made chronic toxicity studies in which they administered Miltown daily to rats for periods of more than a year. No ill effects were seen.

And a drug of this kind, Berger thought, might be used by pregnant women. Therefore a reproductive study was made, which began by mating male and female rats from the chronic-toxicity studies. The fertilized females were kept on Miltown throughout gestation, birth, and suckling of their young. The litters were then counted and examined for physical condition and compared with the litters of rats fertilized at the same time that had not been given Miltown. No abnormalities of number or condition were observed.

The paper in which Berger and his colleagues described their work was published and available in British scientific libraries at the time DCBL put Distaval on the market. It is not, of course, knock-down proof that Distillers was negligent in failing to do reproductive studies. There are a number of complexities to take into account, beginning with the responses of different kinds of creatures to thalidomide. In human beings, and in some other species—especially monkeys—thalidomide produces highly visible deformities. But in many others, including the rat, we have seen that it scarcely ever does so. (This was one of the first problems encountered by the DCBL pharmacologist, George Somers, and others, when after the tragedy they tried to check the teratogenic effect by animal testing. Not until Somers tried thalidomide in the New Zealand white rabbit could he obtain deformed offspring.) The rat responds to thalidomide by "resorption." Typically a female rat will have nine or ten embryos attached to the placental membrane in her womb. If thalidomide is administered during pregnancy, some of the embryos will stop developing—whereupon their physical substance is "resorbed" into the placenta, leaving a small scar behind.

In the two years following the withdrawal of thalidomide, some twenty independent studies were made with thalidomide in pregnant rats. In no published case did the animals tolerate the drug without some reduction in litter size. Even at fairly modest doses of 100–150 mg./kg., some workers got resorption rates as high as 50 per cent. (The mouse, the other standard experimental animal, also "resorbs" as a general response to thalidomide, though some experimenters have produced deformations.) Thalidomide is far from being the only substance that produces resorptions in rats. Indeed, it is possible to produce numerous resorptions in rats with the hypnotic Doriden (which has *not* been known to cause reproductive damage in humans) or with such commonplace substances as caffeine and aspirin. For this reason, simple reproductive studies in rats, such as Wallace Laboratories made with Miltown, are no longer regarded as suitable for assessing likely teratogenic effects in humans.

To do so now, it is realized, would be to produce too many "false positive" results, thereby condemning many useful substances. In modern teratogenic studies, a "tougher" embryo is required—one that is not apt to be wiped out of existence by a fierce teratogen like thalidomide but will stand up to its action and survive in a deformed state. Various kinds of rabbits and monkeys meet this demand.

This is an important scientific and commercial point, and it accounts for the statement often made by scientists, *that the animal tests necessary to prove thalidomide teratogenic were not in general practice before the disaster.* True, they were not. *But that does not mean that animal tests could not have suggested that thalidomide might endanger unborn children, because it had been established before thalidomide that resorption indicated the possibility of teratogenic potential.*

Suppose thalidomide had been tested in the same way that Miltown was tested. Given competent experimenters, it is certain that a significant decrease in litter size would have been observed. Nobody would have known the whole truth about thalidomide from that alone. But it would certainly have been enough to negate the idea that thalidomide was safe for pregnant women. In any well-run company, such a finding would have been bound to lead to an intensive further scrutiny of thalidomide (or possibly, of course, to the abandonment of the drug; thalidomide was only a sleeping pill, after all, and there was no shortage of such drugs in the mid-1950s).

It is instructive to examine the way that another British drug firm handled a similar problem at a stage slightly earlier than thalidomide. In 1955, ICI developed a drug that was intended to control anaemia by supplying iron to the body in readily usable form. Dr. Edward Paget, then in charge of toxicology at ICI, knew that the drug was likely to be used by pregnant women, because anaemia is a frequent ailment of expectant mothers. (Distillers, of course, must have known that it would be possible for thalidomide to be ingested during pregnancy, because they prepared it in a form specifically recommended to minimize menstrual tension: a woman might take it in anticipation of menstrual tension, or for tension that turned out not to be menstrual, when in fact she was pregnant.)

Not all physicians in the mid-1950s realized that the drugs might damage a foetus while leaving the maternal organism unharmed. Most teratogens then known—aminopterin, for example—were fairly dangerous poisons, and while many doctors observed the ancient precaution that drugs should be used in pregnancy only to relieve a pressing danger to life, others subscribed to the theory that drugs circulating in the mother's body would not cross the placental membrane and affect her child.

Dr. Paget did not imagine that to be the case, and there were numerous studies, going back at least to 1917, to show that birth defects could be produced in animals by altering the mother's biochemical balance in a way that might not cause *her* any observable discomfort—most simply, indeed, by the negative means of depriving her of certain vitamins. A line of work that particularly impressed Dr. Paget had first been published in the late 1940s by three scientists working in South Africa, T. Gillman, J. Gillman, and C. Gilbert. They investigated a dye called trypan blue—the name being derived from its one-time use in combating the trypanosome organism of sleeping sickness—and found that it and several similar dyes could produce birth deformities in rats, though not necessarily other species, at dosages far too low to have any toxic effect on the mother rat. This work, first reported in the *South African Journal of Medical Science* in 1948 and after that in many other places, rapidly became something of a teratological classic. The point that impressed Dr. Paget—as a practical pharmaceutical scientist, rather than an academic teratologist—was that it showed dramatically that absence of acute toxicity could not be taken to imply an absence of reproductive danger.

He did not have sophisticated teratogenic tests available. But he was familiar with the idea of reproductive studies, and so he fed his new drug to pregnant rats at dose levels equivalent to the therapeutic dose in humans. He counted the litters and inspected the individual newborn rats for abnormalities. He observed no significant differences from his undosed control groups. Dr. Paget would be the first to agree that his work did not *guarantee* that the anaemia drug would be safe. Nothing, indeed, could provide such a guarantee with any drug. And it is now apparent that many subtle teratogens might slip past so crude a test. But there is nothing subtle about thalidomide's action. Either by resorption or malformation, it wreaks reproductive havoc in the majority of almost any species. So Dr. Paget believes that a reproductive study with thalidomide in rats would probably have produced warning signals: "You would not have got deformities. But if you got a reduction in litter size, you would dissect the female rats. And if you found a lot of resorption scars, that would be enough to make you raise an eyebrow."

In Dr. Paget's view, *one* such eyebrow-raising factor can be enough—until satisfactorily explained—to negate the hypothesis of safety. While he was at ICI, he says, the company had a promising drug on which a considerable sum of money had been spent, and which turned out to cause eye defects in one species of test animal. The effect was not found in any other animals. But it was considered necessary to abandon the drug without making trials in man. Of course, such a calculation may be affected by the relative importance of the drug—and here it is useful to look at the "raised-eyebrow reflex" as seen in the behaviour of another British-controlled firm in pre-thalidomide days.

During 1950, Burroughs-Wellcome was completing the animal testing of Daraprim, an antimalarial drug that had been chiefly developed in the firm's American laboratories. Since antimalarial drugs are likely to be used for long-term medication, it might be used during pregnancy.

Burroughs-Wellcome therefore ran reproductive studies, done in the firm's London laboratories. Rats given Daraprim showed a mild but significant incidence of resorption, maintained throughout pregnancy. Dr. Robert Hitchings, who was chiefly responsible for Daraprim, was worried, but he did not wish to abandon the drug because malaria was then a major scourge in tropical countries. (Burroughs-Wellcome, owned by the non-profit Wellcome Foundation, has traditionally had an interest in tropical medicine.)

A substantial programme was launched to investigate the reproductive effects of Daraprim in several species. In addition to work in the firm's own laboratories, an independent study was commissioned from Dr. Alfred Thiersch of the University of Washington, Seattle. After testing Daraprim in several species, including dogs, Dr. Thiersch—who already had considerable experience with teratogens—found that the rat resorptions appeared to be unique. It did not seem likely that the drug would be teratogenic in man.

Nonetheless, special precautions were taken with clinical trials of Daraprim, and all pregnant women who used the drug were regularly checked and their children examined for illness or deformity. After a quarter century's use, no evidence has yet been found that Daraprim is teratogenic in human beings. So it was in no way unusual for reproductive studies to be made with drugs in the days before thalidomide was invented, though practice varied among companies and, of course, among different drugs. There would be no point in doing reproductive studies with a drug designed to combat the effects of senility. But the scientific record makes it clear that many scientists considered that drugs in the sedative/hypnotic/tranquillizer bracket, such as Miltown and thalidomide, should be checked for reproductive dangers.

Chlorpromazine, patented by the French firm Rhône-Poulenc in 1954, was the first of the "major tranquillizers" to be used to treat serious psychic disorders. As the hydrochloride, it is best known by the trade names Largactil or Thorazine. Mme. Françoise Courvoisier, leader of the team that developed the drug, conducted a reproductive study in rats. No ill effects were seen, and chlorpromazine does not appear to produce teratogenic effects in humans.

Miltown, following shortly afterwards, was the first of the synthetic "minor tranquillizers," intended to deal with neuroses. As we have seen, it was tested for reproductive effect in rats. (And incidentally, Berger's original reproductive investigations were repeated two years later by another Wallace Laboratories scientist, who used much larger batches and extended his observations to the second generation. This, too, was done before there was any knowledge of thalidomide's teratogenic capacities.)

The greatest "family" of minor tranquillizers and hypnotics are the benzodiazepine drugs, developed by Hoffmann–La Roche and known best as Librium, Valium, and Mogadon. Librium, the first of them, was introduced to the market *after* thalidomide but *before* the teratogenic effects of thalidomide were known. The basic scientific papers upon its properties, toxicity, etc., were published by Hoffmann–La Roche's Roche Laboratories in the United States in 1959.

There was no special reason to think that Librium (or, for that matter, Miltown) might be dangerous to the reproductive system. Nonetheless, Roche Laboratories' published work shows the results of some fairly elaborate reproductive studies with rats, in which animals were maintained at various doses, and their offspring were checked for any signs of physical or other abnormality. A proportion of the mother rats was dissected and examined for signs of resorption scars.

All the results were negative: in the admirably cautious words of the Roche paper, Librium was not pronounced certainly safe insofar as reproductive effects were concerned, but it could be said that "no evidence was found to suggest that the effects of methaminodiazepoxide [Librium] upon the reproductive system may be dangerous."

We asked Roche to explain why it had decided to investigate Librium in this way, since there was no particular reason to suspect it might cause such damage. The answer casts a curious light upon the claims of innocence made by Grünenthal and Distillers (and upon the confidence with which the lawyers for plaintiffs against them later accepted those claims). Since 1944—ten years before thalidomide was first synthesized —it had been *routine procedure* in Roche Laboratories to make a reproductive study in animals with any substance intended to be sold as a drug for human use.

DCBL did not have the standards of Hoffmann–La Roche, but there was a stage during the history of the company's marketing of thalidomide when its eyebrow should have been raised, but the chance to have averted the tragedy was missed. The results of one of DCBL's own clinical trials were published in the *British Medical Journal* on January 10,

1958, three months before thalidomide went on sale. The trials had been conducted by two eminent medical men, James Murdoch and G. D. Campbell, then respectively senior registrar and research fellow in the Department of Therapeutics at Edinburgh University and at the Royal Infirmary, Edinburgh. Murdoch, in particular, was an acknowledged authority on tranquillizers, and his boss, Professor Sir Derrick Dunlop, was a powerful figure in medical circles. The trials indicated by measurement of the body's uptake of radioactive iodine that thalidomide in doses of 100–200 mg. might block the action of the thyroid gland. Evidence that a drug can interfere with so vital a part of the human hormone balance is not to be taken lightly. (DCBL has since claimed that the dose of 100–200 mg. was unrealistically heavy and that the results conflicted with others available. But the upper dose was precisely that which Dr. Louis Lasagna later found in a controlled trial to be necessary to bring about *any* pharmacological action from thalidomide.)

So Murdoch wrote, "It would seem unjustifiable to use the drug for long-term sedative or hypnotic therapy, pending the results of a more detailed study of its long-term effects in a larger series of patients, notably those suffering from mild or moderately severe hyperthyroidism." He pointed out that the way thalidomide worked was unknown. And—a very telling cut—he put "a tendency to sleep in five patients," a reaction DCBL considered to be the drug's *main* purpose, under the heading *"Side Effects."* There is evidence that Murdoch's findings were originally phrased in even more forthright language but were watered down at DCBL's request. Four months earlier, in August 1957, Murdoch had sent a draft of his report to Dr. Kennedy at DCBL. As Kennedy recalled later, "There was another sentence suggesting that the manufacturers should not go ahead with things of this kind until extensive trials had been done. . . ." Murdoch had hit on the vital weak spot in the whole DCBL involvement with thalidomide.

Kennedy read the draft report and immediately wrote a stiff note to Murdoch, whom he knew very well. "With regard to your final sentences I can assure you that it is our definite intention to treat this whole matter with restraint and complete professional propriety." (It was, of course, not lack of propriety that Murdoch was criticizing, but lack of knowledge.) But the only counter to Murdoch's report that Kennedy could muster was: "I am sure you will agree that drug action in acute or advanced conditions is not to be equated with trials on healthy volunteers." This was not really much of an argument since Murdoch's basic point still stood: the drug's mode of action was unknown. Kennedy concluded: "I feel that this should allay any misgivings you might have especially as we are determined to eschew the term 'tranquillisers.' Anyway, I hope it does, and in consequence you will be able to delete or modify that final dig."

Murdoch then agreed only that he would "attempt to modify the final sentence." Kennedy replied: "With all respects, I must say that I think your last sentence in the discussion might be omitted. I am quite prepared to accept that it is a reasonable recommendation for you to put to us as a responsible party, but I feel that to publish it to all and sundry is, shall we say, unnecessary. . . . I cannot help feeling that your admonition is a bit of a swipe at us, and while I am sure that it is a good-natured one on your part, I am doubtful that all readers of the *Journal* would take it in the same way." Murdoch relented, and deleted the sentence.

Kennedy did not immediately pass on to his managing director, D. J. Hayman, Murdoch's recommendation that more testing was needed before launching the drug on the market, and in his memo he somewhat underplayed Murdoch's conclusions. "Dr. Murdoch only warns against the possibility of trouble in long-term therapy," he wrote, "while many of the cases will be short term." This was true, but the crucial point was that some cases would be long term. And then Kennedy added reassuringly, "The name Distaval does not appear in the [Murdoch] paper and the chemical name used is the German one. . . ."

No doubt Kennedy considered he had justification for this action: he genuinely thought that Murdoch's work was wrong. He had earlier arranged a trial with Dr. Raymond Greene, a distinguished Harley Street endocrinologist. Greene agreed to do some trials at New End Hospital, North London, to check the antithyroid effect of thalidomide.

When Murdoch's paper appeared in the *BMJ*, DCBL put its position to Greene in a frank manner. "I do not know whether you are in a position to make any comment at this stage," Kennedy's assistant, Dr. Brown, wrote, "and if so whether you would think it worth while to make it in the form of a letter to the *BMJ*."

Brown even gave a hint of the line he hoped the letter might take: "I think it is a little unfortunate that in Dr. Murdoch's paper the effects which we consider to be the main pharmaceutical action of the drug are described under the heading of 'Side Effects' and the anti-thyroid effect, which we would like to think is a side effect of no great significance in normal dosage, is featured as its main action."

Three days later Greene's letter went off to the *BMJ:* "We are not yet ready to pronounce a final judgement but our preliminary results suggest that the effects of the drug [on the thyroid] . . . are negligible compared with those of carbimazole." And later: "Is it not a little unfair to describe as side effects these actions for which the drug was introduced?"

So DCBL brushed aside Murdoch's recommendation for more detailed studies on thalidomide before it was marketed. Yet anyone interested in the worries expressed by some scientists in the 1950s—that there was "increasing evidence that the unborn child can be injured by agents well-tolerated by the mother"—might well have gone on to notice that endocrine (and particularly thyroid) upsets appeared to be associated with human birth defects. (Even with hindsight there is no good reason to think that thalidomide's teratogenic effect is endocrine based, but if medical science could not sometimes get the right result for the "wrong" reason, life could be very dangerous indeed.)

After thalidomide was withdrawn both Grünenthal and DCBL argued that even if some chain of circumstances had led them to make a reproductive study—say, as the result of Murdoch's findings—the likeliest result would have been to clear thalidomide. The claim they make is that such a study would almost certainly have been done in the rat, in which even resorption, let alone visible deformity, does not occur until unrealistically huge doses of thalidomide are administered. Certainly some scientists working with thalidomide after the tragedy found it difficult to procure resorptions. And when George Somers, alarmed by some of the first evidence of human damage, tried to home-in accurately on the effect by dosing rats in days 8–12 of pregnancy, he did not get significant resorptions until he used a substantial 800 mg./kg. dose.

But at this distance, the closest we can get to a record of what *might* have been, had suspicion dawned earlier, is to look at DCBL's nearest equivalent to the simple reproductive screening that—as we have seen—was done with some notably similar drugs. Distillers did this only *after* the human alarm was given in late 1961. Somers by this time had some groups of rats on long-term thalidomide dosage and pairs from each dose level were put to breed. Undosed control rats averaged 7.8 rat pups per litter. Thalidomide at 20 mg./kg. cut this by a quarter, to 5.9. At 100 mg./kg., the average litter size was 5.0, and at 500 mg./kg., it was only 3.6. Clearly thalidomide was doing something dramatic to the rat's reproductive process. If anything, the results were as obvious when rats were only started on thalidomide immediately after mating. The controls averaged 9.9 rat pups per litter. On a dose of 200 mg./kg., this fell by nearly a third to an average of 6.8. At 400 mg./kg., the average litter was only 5.3. These are scarcely outlandish doses for animals in which the drug's main action is barely perceptible and which suffer no acutely toxic effects from it. These did not, of course, specifically reveal any malformations. But could a drug firm aware of them have allowed—no, have *recommended*—thalidomide's use by pregnant women until some further study had been made?

The fact is that DCBL exhibited a naïve desire to believe only the best of thalidomide, that DCBL accepted everything that Grünenthal said about it with absolute trust, and that to promote this apple of its eye, DCBL was prepared to turn a vacuum of knowledge about thalidomide into specific assurances of safety.

This was a corporate failure rather than an individual one, so it is proper to say that this approach made at least one DCBL employee uneasy from the very beginning. George Somers, the DCBL pharmacologist, remains universally respected among his scientific colleagues, who find it inconceivable to think that the worst drug tragedy of modern times might be ascribable in any way to any failings on Somers's part. (For what it is worth, that perception is shared by the present writers.) Somers often urged caution on his DCBL colleagues about dosage, marketing techniques, and general use of the drug. For example, when Murdoch's warnings about thalidomide's side effects on the thyroid were being brushed aside, Somers was urging: "I agree with the *BMJ* report that we must take caution in this matter . . . a decision on the dosage being limited to 200 mgs and for avoiding prolonged administration is probably wise at present until we have more experience with the drug."

But Somers was later to discover something much more alarming about thalidomide than Murdoch's suspicion that it could affect the thyroid. The drug that had been trumpeted as "non-toxic" and "completely safe" was, he found, in certain circumstances, poisonous.

In his laboratory at Speke, Somers and three assistants carried out a series of tests with thalidomide in powder form compounded with sugar and other sweeteners. Grünenthal already had a liquid or suspension version of thalidomide on the market called Contergan Saft (Contergan juice) and was pushing it as a safe and reliable sedative for children. Some German parents were using it to keep their children quiet while they went to the movies, and—even more amazingly—in a children's clinic in Dortmund, it was being administered to noisy new-born infants. DCBL was interested in entering this lucrative side of the thalidomide market too, and had ordered some of the Grünenthal preparation for testing.

The results of these tests must have stunned Somers. The liquid preparation of thalidomide was poisonous. The reason thalidomide had been believed non-toxic was, it turned out, that not enough of it was absorbed into the bloodstream. Micro-fining it and mixing it with a sugar solution allowed it to be absorbed more easily, and once absorbed, it was poisonous.

In Somers's own carefully considered but highly alarming words written later: "We do not therefore regard the formulated suspension as prepared by Grünenthal to be a safe preparation like the tablets and we are of the opinion that there is a very real danger of deaths occurring following overdosage." This was a new blow to DCBL. Sales, especially to hospitals, had been poor. This had been attributed to the fact that sales representatives had no published work to which they could refer to support their claims except "Continental reports which are so lightly regarded." Now Somers had to tell the New Products Committee of DCBL that thalidomide liquid was toxic and that this fact was "of primary importance . . . in relation to our advertising claim for Distaval." In other words, how long could DCBL go on saying that Distaval had "no known toxicity" when there was evidence that this was not true?

Somers was by now a deeply worried man. Some of the liquid had gone out for clinical trial and he was perturbed that this had occurred before he had done his tests. He tackled Kennedy about it. "The results, you will appreciate, might have been dangerous, in particular because people regard Distaval as being a non-toxic drug." Emergency action had to be taken to withdraw the samples sent out for trial.

To add to Somers's worries, early in 1959, a doctor had reported the case of a young man taking thalidomide who had complained he experienced an itching in the palms of his hands and the soles of his feet. Somers decided to look at the effects thalidomide might have on the nervous system, and by mid-1960, DCBL's medical department had on record reports of five patients who were suffering from peripheral neuritis—intermittent severe pins and needles or cramps in fingers and toes—after prolonged use of Distaval.

If there had been closer consultation between the British and the German companies, then DCBL might have learned that Grünenthal had received a series of reports of thalidomide having caused peripheral neuritis, rashes, boils, loss of speech, and epilepsy. But even from its own experience, DCBL now knew that its wonder drug, whose major selling point was its safety and almost complete absence of side effects, was in fact dangerous and, in addition, could cause serious illness. What did DCBL do about it?

Throughout June 1960, a series of memos flew among DCBL executives. Surprisingly, they seem mainly concerned not, as one might imagine, with giving serious consideration to withdrawing the drug pending further tests but rather with anticipating publication in medical journals of the fact that Distaval was toxic.

Kennedy's deputy, C. N. Brown, thought the time had come when it would be "wise" to modify DCBL's claims for Distaval. He suggested substituting for "no demonstrable toxicity" the phrase "low or very low toxic effects." It was decided that all references such as "non-toxic" and "free from toxicity" would be deleted from DCBL publications about Distaval—but not until the next reprinting!

Somers was the only DCBL man out of step and he was pressing for publication of all his findings: "I think you are of the opinion that a danger exists and we should present the facts as soon as possible." But DCBL was unhappy about losing its major claim for Distaval—that it was a safe sedative or hypnotic. At least one executive, the managing director, D. J. Hayman, made it clear he thought the safety angle was getting out of proportion. And as late as May 1961, more than a year after Somers had discovered that thalidomide in sugar solution was toxic, Hayman admitted that DCBL was still circulating from time to time an abstract of Somers's earlier report, which said that he had been unable to find that thalidomide had any lethal dose whatsoever.

Somers appears to have done his best to persuade DCBL to publish all his latest findings. He tried the "self-interest" approach: "Some day someone is going to make the observations we have made with different formulations of thalidomide. They may publish them and cause us some damage. If we have already drawn attention to these matters . . . we will be in a much stronger position."

Hayman was unmoved: "I cannot see any reason why we should ex-

tend the debate outside the scope of Grünenthal-DCBL." Hayman won
and Somers's report was never published. In fact, Hayman saw no reason why a liquid version of thalidomide should be kept off the market,
despite the fact that it was toxic, and was all for pressing ahead despite
Somers's findings:

> I understand that it has not yet been possible to develop a for-
> mulation which compares favourably in terms of toxicity with
> our tablets. Whilst it is obviously desirable to do so, I really feel
> that the dangers of issuing a product of this nature have got
> out of perspective. In addition to our own findings which, I
> believe, indicate that the suspension is considerably safer than
> any other comparable product on the market, we do know that
> Grünenthal have sold many thousands of bottles of a product
> less satisfactory than our own formulation. We should take im-
> mediate steps to market a preparation of this type at the ear-
> liest possible date. . . .

So the liquid version of thalidomide went on sale in Britain in July 1961.
DCBL's marketing line for the liquid version of the drug was to describe
it as "specially flavoured to suit all palates" and to recommend it as
being "particularly suitable for administration to children."

The issue of the *British Medical Journal* for December 31, 1960, brought
into the open the other problem that had been worrying Somers: peripheral neuritis. It published the letter from Dr. Florence of Aberdeen placing on record four cases where patients had reported symptoms of the
complaint after using thalidomide over a long period.

DCBL was now heavily occupied with a sudden flush of reports of
more cases of peripheral neuritis. January and February 1961 saw more
and more doctors concerned with this severe and frequently incurable
side effect of thalidomide. February alone brought 8 definite and 5 suspected cases to the London office of DCBL, in Wimbledon, and the company began to consider at last putting "a little more emphasis" on the
risk of peripheral neuritis "in the hope that the number of cases will diminish if doctors are aware of the possibility."

This plan did not meet with the unqualified approval of the sales side
of the company. J. Paton, a sales executive, wrote: "It is not our job to
educate the medical profession how to look out for various conditions.
From a sales promotion point of view, the more we write on this side effect, the more it is likely to get out of perspective." It is not hard to spec-

ulate about the reasons for this alarming attitude. By the end of March 1961, DCBL had sold nearly 64 million thalidomide tablets. April turned out to be the best month for sales in three years.

So the sales representatives were instructed: "[The] possible occurrence of peripheral neuritis is a remote one and in no way detracts from the main selling point of Distaval. . . . It has a toxic effect of which you should be aware . . . but there is no need to alarm the medical profession or discuss the matter unless it is raised."

But by July, DCBL knew of more than 100 cases of peripheral neuritis in Britain. August brought 15 more cases, September a further 13. Doctors began to complain that DCBL had tried to conceal important information from the medical profession and that Distaval advertisements were misleading. On July 15, the *Pharmaceutical Journal* reported that a death from suicide had been recorded as having been due to an overdose of Distaval.

But Brown, the deputy medical adviser, for one, remained optimistic. "In spite of the doubt about this case," he wrote, "it seems there is nothing we can do about the verdict . . . so I think we must proceed with care in making claims about no untoward results being recorded after overdosage with Distaval. The drug is so firmly established now that with a little care in re-wording our claims I think we can still tell essentially the same story as before."

And this is what DCBL proceeded to do. In October (by which time it knew of more than 120 cases of neuritis), it issued a brochure called "A New Assessment of Distaval." It recommended Distaval for every age group from infants and pregnant women to geriatric cases and stressed its consistent safety and low toxicity. It admitted that some cases of peripheral neuritis had been reported but dismissed them with: ". . . it arises only in a small percentage of cases and can be expected to resolve provided the drug is withdrawn promptly on the onset of symptoms."

In the November issue of the *BMJ*, the British company stretched truth to its limit with an advertisement that read in part: "There is no case on record in which even a gross overdosage with Distaval has had harmful results. Put your mind at rest. Depend on the safety of Distaval." Unfortunately for DCBL, the very same issue carried three more letters describing cases of peripheral neuritis, and this discrepancy brought a complaint to the editor of the *BMJ*.

So the warnings were there: from the results of the Murdoch-Campbell trial to the growing flow of complaints about peripheral neuritis—

not itself pointing to reproductive damage, but many scientists would take such an assault on the nervous system as grounds for general suspicion. (Molecules not being men, toxicology can, and must, work by McCarthyite methods of smear, and guilt through association.)

The one last chance DCBL had—not to avert tragedy; it was already too late for that—to confine the scale of the disaster came with its follow-up procedure to its clinical trials. We have seen how important the major drug companies regard their ability to react to reports of their drugs in actual use, never ceasing to monitor them.

We shall return to Distillers later to see how their monitoring procedure mysteriously broke down, but now we turn to the United States, where, after a late start, preparations were under way to market thalidomide on a scale that would dwarf that in the rest of the world.

5 America on the Brink of Disaster

Grünenthal had been deeply disappointed that the American drug company Smith, Kline & French had decided after two years' investigation not to go ahead with thalidomide. The Germans were eager to exploit their wonder drug throughout the world, and although competition in the United States would be fierce—many different types of sleeping pills were already well established there—if Grünenthal could squeeze thalidomide into just a small corner of the American market, the profits would be huge. What Grünenthal needed was an American licensee prepared to push thalidomide in the United States as vigorously as Grünenthal had done in Germany. Grünenthal next tried Lederle, without success, and then began negotiations with the Vick Chemical Company, famous for Vicks VapoRub. Vick, the parent company of William S. Merrell, changed its name in 1960 to Richardson-Merrell Inc. For convenience, that is the name used in this account. Richardson-Merrell regularly appeared at about number 300 on *Fortune* magazine's list of the 500 largest industrial corporations in the United States, and at the time it attracted Grünenthal's interest, it had some $200 million in resources, a vast production capacity, and a sophisticated distribution network that enabled it to disseminate drugs on a large scale to the North American public. It had a reputation for resourceful promotion, but it had never quite been able to make the foremost rank of American pharmaceutical concerns, and during the 1950s, it had passed through a series of organizational traumas. Initial discussions went satisfactorily, and in September and October 1958 Grünenthal signed agreements with Richardson-Merrell granting it exclusive rights to market, and later manufacture, thalidomide in the United States.

Thalidomide was Richardson-Merrell's second "wonder drug." The other was Mer 29, which it developed in response to the growing belief that high blood cholesterol levels were linked to heart disease, the biggest single killer in the United States. The two new drugs were seen within Richardson-Merrell as agents of corporate regeneration—a chance, as one executive put it, of breaking into "the truly big time"— and they shared much in common. Many of the same personnel in the company guided both drugs through their animal tests and clinical trials, devised their promotional campaigns, and negotiated their submission to the Food and Drug Administration. The story of how Richardson-Merrell dealt with thalidomide would not be complete, therefore, without brief reference to the disaster it caused with Mer 29.

Mer 29, or Triparanol, as it was called, went on the market on June 1, 1960. Within its first year, it became Richardson-Merrell's biggest-selling prescription drug, and in the twenty-two months before its withdrawal, it was used by nearly 400,000 Americans. Yet at the time, there was no conclusive evidence about the role of cholesterol in heart disease, no evidence that Mer 29 had any beneficial effects on patients with heart problems but, on the other hand, clear evidence that the drug had little margin of safety.

In February 1960 an FDA pharmacologist, Dr. Edwin Goldenthal, had urged that because the drug had such a small margin of safety, permission to market it should be withheld pending clinical investigations over a period of years. Dr. Goldenthal was ignored, and on April 19, the FDA approved Richardson-Merrell's application to market Mer 29, adding a rider to the approval letter: ". . . Our action in allowing this application to become effective is based solely on the evidence of the safety of the drug. All claims are on your responsibility."

These claims included "the first safe agent to inhibit body-produced cholesterol" and "the first to lower excess cholesterol levels in both tissue and serum, *irrespective of diet.*" This latter claim gave the drug great sales appeal: patients who loved high-cholesterol foods could, Richardson-Merrell claimed, stay on them provided they regularly took Mer 29. One of the company's advisers predicted that Mer 29 could become like vitamin therapy, taken daily for life. At nearly 20 cents wholesale a pill, the potential market for Mer 29 was, the company estimated, $4.25 billion a year.

The dismay in Richardson-Merrell can be appreciated, therefore, when reports of side effects began to arrive. These included vomiting, nausea, and loss of hair. The company's response was defensive; as the following memorandum to its drug salesmen suggests: "When a doctor says your drug causes a side effect, the immediate reply is, 'Doctor, what other drug is the patient taking?' Even if you know your drug can cause the side effect mentioned, the chances are equally good the same side effect is being caused by a second drug."

Not all the reports of the side effects came from doctors and patients. Early in 1961, Merck Sharp & Dohme, one of the major American pharmaceutical companies, reported to Richardson-Merrell that when it had used Mer 29 in a comparative study its test animals had developed cataracts in their eyes. Richardson-Merrell replied that these results were questionable, because Merck Sharp & Dohme had made its own supply of Mer 29, and this could have been impure. It suggested that Merck Sharp & Dohme should re-do the tests. When the FDA raised the whole question of eye damage, Richardson-Merrell replied that an eye infection could be the explanation. It claimed that the company's own tests showed no eye damage whatsoever. Yet at that time, Richardson-Merrell knew that twenty-five out of twenty-nine rats in their laboratories had developed corneal opacities after being given Mer 29 and that the same type of opacity had been observed in two dogs in a study the company had completed in February 1960.

In September 1961, there were staff changes in the FDA. A new FDA officer, Dr. John O. Nestor, demanded from Richardson-Merrell a complete dossier on eye changes in humans and animals who had taken Mer 29, and any information the company had concerning effects on skin and hair. Nestor knew nothing of Merck Sharp & Dohme's findings and was unaware of the true extent of the havoc being wrought by Mer 29, but he nevertheless felt that what he *did* know warranted an immediate suspension of FDA approval for the drug. Instead, in the apparent belief that the FDA had no legal rights to enforce the drug's withdrawal, FDA officers agreed to a compromise with Richardson-Merrell—the company would issue an FDA-approved warning to doctors calling their attention to the side effects and cautioning them not to exceed the recommended dose.

How long this would have staved off the eventual exposure of Mer 29 will never be known because a chance meeting in a Cincinnati car park in February 1962 between Thomas M. Rice, an FDA inspector, and Larson Jordan, a telephone company employee whose wife, Beulah, had once worked for Richardson-Merrell, hastened matters. As they shared a car ride, the two men discussed press reports about the Mer 29 warning letter. When Jordan mentioned that his wife had been shaken by her experience of working with Richardson-Merrell, Rice went to see her and heard an alarming story. In May 1959, Beulah Jordan said, she had finished a report on eight monkeys being tested on Mer 29. The company then asked her to make alterations in her report so as to imply, first, that the experiment had continued for two months longer than in fact it had and, second, that the monkeys had suffered no ill effects. She also told Rice of one monkey whose condition had deteriorated dramatically under the influence of Mer 29. This monkey had then disappeared from the laboratory without being autopsied but, she alleged, had appeared in the Mer 29 application to the FDA as having survived unharmed. Rice reported this interview to his superiors, and on April 9, 1962, in an unprecedented move, the FDA descended on Richardson-Merrell's Cincinnati plant with a team of inspectors. Two days later the company agreed to withdraw Mer 29 from the market.

In July 1963 a grand jury began hearing criminal charges against Richardson-Merrell and associated companies; one of their pharmacologists, E. F. van Maanen; laboratory chief William King; and vice-president Harold Werner. Indicted on counts of knowingly making false, fictitious, and fraudulent statements to the FDA about Mer 29, the defendants entered a *nolo contendere* plea in March 1964 on between two and six counts in the indictment. Such a "no-contest" plea requires the defendant's recognition that it is tantamount to a plea of guilty.

The lengths to which Richardson had been prepared to go to get the drug on the market are revealed in the charges. Count three, for example, dealt with Richardson-Merrell's reports of a chronic toxicity study in monkeys. The company had reported that monkey No. 51 was given Mer 29 at one dose level for six months and at a lower dose level for a further ten months, but what the FDA inspectors uncovered was that the higher dose of Mer 29 had never been administered to monkey 51 and the lower dose had been administered for a shorter time than claimed. *In toto*, the experiment had lasted for 7 months and 26 days and not the 16 months stated in the application to the FDA. Monkey 35, on the other hand, had been designated a control for the "16 month study," although in fact for the first 6 months, No. 35 had been given a drug similar to Mer 29 and had not been used as a control at all. The company's application to the FDA claimed that monkeys had not lost body weight when in fact they had, and that a monkey had suffered no liver or gall bladder damage when in fact it had.

Federal Judge McGuire fined the company a total of $80,000, and

Werner, van Maanen, and King—all active in company affairs when thalidomide was prepared for the market—were sentenced to six months on probation. Nearly 500 civil lawsuits followed the criminal indictment, and the Americans who had suffered—and were still suffering—from the appalling effects of Mer 29 were awarded damages against Richardson-Merrell reported as being about $200 million. This, then, was the company that Grünenthal licensed to market thalidomide in the United States.

Thalidomide must have appeared very attractive to Richardson-Merrell. It had been on the market in Germany for nearly three years with brilliant commercial results and no admitted evidence of drawbacks. And when cleared by the FDA it could eventually be sold over the counter in the United States without prescription. Its use in pregnancy, including early pregnancy, was to be, therefore, just one of an astonishingly large range of conditions for which Richardson-Merrell hoped thalidomide would be prescribed. It planned to recommend the drug for the treatment of anxiety and apprehension associated with, in alphabetical order: abdominal pain, alcoholism, anorexia, asthma, cancer, cardiovascular and hypertensive disease (including cardiac neuroses), dental procedures, emotional instability, enuresis, febrile conditions, functional bowel distress, hepatic disease, marital discord, menopause, nausea and vomiting, nervous exhaustion, nightmares, poor school work, premature ejaculation, pruritus ani, psychoasthenia, psychomotor restlessness, and tuberculosis. If thalidomide was not an elixir to cure all the ills of mankind, then it was certainly intended to make them incomparably easier to bear. Yet, at the time it signed the agreement with Grünenthal, Richardson-Merrell knew little of thalidomide beyond what the Germans had told it. It had made no studies of its own and, like Distillers, had relied on Grünenthal's work—despite the fact that FDA regulations prohibit American drug companies from relying on European firms in this way.

Within Richardson-Merrell, where thalidomide had been given the code name Mer 32 (its trade name was to be Kevadon), this lack of knowledge was openly recognized. On February 2, 1959, an internal memorandum noted: "We have no specific human safety data. We will have to collect them partly for our own information and partly to satisfy the requirements of the Food and Drug Administration." Richardson-Merrell did conduct animal tests, including some similar to those carried out by Smith, Kline & French—the ones that showed thalidomide had no interesting pharmacological activity—and in general, their results agreed with those obtained by SKF. So when Richardson-Merrell showed these results to Dr. Louis Lasagna, an authority on hypnotic actions, and asked him to conduct a clinical trial in humans, Dr. Lasagna's response was to say that Richardson-Merrell was wasting its money; the drug would obviously be inactive.

In fact, Dr. Lasagna later found some evidence of thalidomide activity in humans, which raises the intricate problem of comparing drug effects in animal and human systems. Human results are, of course, generally taken to outweigh animal results; so balanced against the fact that thousands of Germans appeared satisfied customers, the report of Richardson-Merrell pharmacologists Kuhn and van Maanen, doing some routine checks on a drug that their management was already determined to buy, must have seemed like a pharmacological quibble, and it clearly failed to carry decisive weight with Richardson-Merrell.

On February 11, 1959, less than four months after securing the licence from Grünenthal, Richardson-Merrell began testing the drug on human beings by distributing thalidomide to private physicians for experimental use on their patients. Three months later, it expanded this trial to include pregnant women. At that time, Richardson-Merrell had no information about thalidomide's effects in early pregnancy, but it repeatedly assured doctors that the drug was safe for everyone, *including* pregnant women. While these human exposures were under way, Richardson-Merrell undertook animal tests. Since its human trials included pregnant women, it would have been logical for Richardson-Merrell to have included tests on pregnant animals. It already knew a considerable amount about the dangers of drugs to the foetus. With Mer 29, for example, it had done animal reproductive studies itself, commissioned an independent laboratory to do likewise, and finally decided to print a warning on the Mer 29 label saying that the drug was not suitable for use in pregnancy.

Yet with thalidomide, Richardson-Merrell observed no such caution, even though it had asked one of the doctors taking part in its trials to assess the drug's effectiveness in treating women suffering from nausea in early pregnancy. Nor, as we shall see, did Richardson-Merrell take the opportunity to investigate thalidomide's effects on the foetus when the *American Journal of Obstetrics and Gynecology*, before it would agree to publish an article on thalidomide's use in pregnancy, asked the vital question—did the drug cross the placental barrier? The FDA itself asked for such information, but none of these inquiries prompted Richardson-Merrell to set up animal reproductive studies, a technique with which, it must again be emphasized, the company was perfectly familiar.

But the result of one animal test the company *did* do was alarming. Thalidomide in syrup form administered to 11 rats (6 females and 5 males) killed all 6 females. Thalidomide administered to 30 male rats killed 22 the same day and 1 two days later. In a follow-up study, 37 rats were tested; 32 died the same day and 5 the next. To rule out the possibility that rats were exceptionally sensitive to thalidomide, Richardson-Merrell repeated this toxicity test on a dog. Within two hours of being given thalidomide, the dog trembled throughout its entire body, twitched, retched, and vomited. For the next two hours and forty-five minutes it was normal. Then it became very active, but it could not coordinate its muscles and staggered around the cage. Next morning it was found dead.

These results indicated with absolute clarity that thalidomide was indeed toxic, and in high doses could be lethal to rats and dogs, and therefore that it did have an LD_{50}. Yet Richardson-Merrell did not reveal these findings to the FDA and pressed ahead with its clinical trials on humans, expanding them until the number of doctors taking part and the number of thalidomide pills they dispensed constituted records. The figures are certainly impressive. According to the U.S. Department of Health, Education and Welfare, Richardson-Merrell distributed 2,-528,412 thalidomide tablets to 1,267 doctors, who gave them to some 20,000 patients—in containers that bore nothing more than directions for use. Actually, the trials were not clinical ones in the true sense of the term. To begin with, the "investigational program"—as it was called within the company—was run by the sales and marketing division, not by the medical department, and although the medical department had a veto over the salesmen's choice of doctors to carry out the trials, the very fact that salesmen were allowed to select the doctors was unusual in the American drug industry. Also the salesmen were told not to offer placebos—fake pills that are a vital part of a blind trial needed to ensure that the patient's reaction is genuine and not imagined—but to wait until the doctor requested them himself. In fact, Richardson-Merrell's approach must have seemed casual to many of the doctors, for when thalidomide was eventually withdrawn, it emerged that several hundred of them could not get in touch with patients to whom they had given the drug because they had kept no records of the fact. In short, several of the main reasons for the "investigational program" seem to have been not clinical at all, but to develop a marketable product, to perfect the best possible sales story for the national introduction of thalidomide into the United States, to encourage favourable publication of thalidomide's properties, and to establish throughout the country local studies whose results could be spread among hospital staff members.

Some idea of the dimension of the Richardson-Merrell human-trials programme can be gained by comparing that 20,000 figure with the fact that no other American drug company had ever tested a new drug on more than 5,000 patients or had used more than 200 doctors.

It is generally assumed by people outside the pharmaceutical industry that the Food and Drug Administration protected Americans from taking a drug until it had been proved both effective and safe. This was not necessarily so. Richardson-Merrell was administering a toxic preparation that turned out to be capable of producing the most horrifying malformations and that could also cause crippling peripheral neuritis and other complaints, and it began this distribution nineteen months before it filed its application to the FDA for permission to sell thalidomide to the general public. In fact, one of the reasons *for* the trial programme involving 20,000 or more Americans was, it was said, to gather evidence of the drug's effects to present to the FDA.

Some justification for the use of the general public as guinea pigs can be sustained, it is argued—for after all, the final test of any drug must be in man—if a person taking the drug does so voluntarily. At that time, the American Medical Association had consent forms that it suggested doctors should ask patients to sign before giving them a drug that was on clinical trial. Richardson-Merrell did not give these forms to doctors taking part in the investigational programme for thalidomide, so unless the doctor himself told the patient what was going on, it is unlikely the patient realized the real role he was playing.

Richardson-Merrell had set a release date for thalidomide of March 6, 1961. It had amassed sufficient raw material to manufacture 15 million thalidomide pills, actually produced about 10 million ready for nation-wide distribution on release day, and as we have seen, had handed out more than 2.5 million as part of its "investigational program." It is en-lightening, therefore, to examine exactly what Richardson-Merrell had learned about its wonder drug, both from its own research and from

Grünenthal and other licensees, and what, according to the generally accepted standards of the American drug industry at that time, it *should* have known.

To begin with, some of the basic clinical actions of thalidomide still remained a mystery—not only to Richardson-Merrell, but also to Grünenthal. In March 1960, Grünenthal admitted its ignorance in an internal memorandum: "The better known thalidomide becomes, the more people ask questions. Mostly they ask about its metabolism and breakdown in the body. This also interests Merrell in the USA. Unfortunately we have practically nothing on this." On the other hand, it was already known in the American drug industry that more than 200 different drugs, not including anticancer agents (which are often teratogenic) and endocrine drugs, affected the foetus in various species. (In fact, this information was so readily accessible that after thalidomide was withdrawn in the United States, Richardson-Merrell was able to compile a list of these drugs by going through the published scientific literature; and, in fact, they knew that their own drug, Mer 29, had an effect on the foetus.) The Richardson-Merrell pharmacologists Kuhn and van Maanen knew that a drug like thalidomide could cross the placental barrier. Yet knowing that thalidomide *might* affect the foetus, Richardson-Merrell did no animal reproduction tests or controlled clinical trials on mothers during the sensitive period of pregnancy to see whether in fact it *did*. More than two years after it had bought the rights to thalidomide from Grünenthal, Richardson-Merrell did not know of one single instance in which thalidomide administered in the sensitive period of pregnancy to either an animal or a human being had proved to be safe. True, the company had no reason to think that thalidomide was *not* safe in pregnancy, but it turned its lack of knowledge into *positive assurances of safety:* thalidomide was safe, it had no harmful side effects, and it could be given to pregnant women in all trimesters of pregnancy.

At least ten, maybe sixteen, and possibly many more women (the number is uncertain because parents may not have realized that their child's malformations were due to Kevadon) gave birth to thalidomide babies in the United States. What responsibility should Richardson-Merrell have carried for these births? The company argued that it had entered into the investigational programme in good faith with the intention of ascertaining the risks of thalidomide and of weighing the benefits against the risks, that it had no reason to suspect that thalidomide was dangerous, and that it had merely made an innocent mistake. We believe that this defence does not stand up.

Richardson-Merrell's application for its new drug, Kevadon, arrived at the old FDA building in Washington, D.C., September 12, 1960. New drug applications are distributed in turn to the FDA's medical officers, and this one went to Canadian-born Dr. Frances Kelsey, forty-six, a pharmacologist as well as a physician, newly arrived from Vermillion, South Dakota, where she had been in general medical practice for three years. It was her first case at the FDA, and she began by sending Richardson-Merrell a routine acknowledgement. Richardson-Merrell expected no trouble with the application and went ahead with plans for launching the drug nationwide. On October 25 and 26, the company held an employees' meeting in Cincinnati to explain its "Kevadon Hospital Clinical Program."

A brochure prepared for this meeting made it clear from the outset that the purpose of the clinical programme was to sell and not to investigate thalidomide. The first "Objective of the Job" listed in the brochure was to "contact teaching hospitals . . . for the purpose of selling them on Kevadon and providing them with a clinical supply." The salesmen responsible for the success of the Kevadon programme were advised to appeal to the doctor's ego, making him think he was important enough to be selected as one of the first to use Kevadon in that section of the country. The salesmen were equipped with data about suicide and accidental overdosage of barbiturates, and it was emphasized that the real "hooker that makes the doctor sit up and take notice" was Kevadon's lack of toxicity.

Frances Kelsey, by now busy preparing her first response to Richardson-Merrell's new drug application, might have been interested to know that the salesmen's brochure *"cautioned"* them: "Bear in mind that these are not *basic* clinical research studies. We have firmly established the safety, dosage and usefulness of Kevadon by both foreign and US laboratory and clinical studies. This program is designed to gain widespread *confirmation* of its usefulness. . . . You assure your doctors that they need not report results if they don't want to. . . . Be sure to tell them that we may send them report forms or reminder letters but these are strictly reminders and they need not reply." The salesmen were instructed with equal firmness to tell the doctors that Kevadon would be on the market early in 1961—perhaps as early as February. But—to judge from Kelsey's reply to the Kevadon application written November 10—a huge gulf existed between the company's plans for thalidomide and what Kelsey had in mind. Everything about the application seemed to her to be inadequate:

1. The animal studies were not reported in sufficient detail, and the study on the absorption of the drug in rats was not supported by evidence.

2. The company had failed to report the clinical studies in full detail. In addition, an insufficient number of cases had been studied. Kelsey also observed that many of the 3,156 cases cited were in foreign literature reports and "in many instances the reports do not represent detailed studies to determine the safety of the drug."

3. Chronic toxicity data were incomplete, leading to the obvious conclusion that "no evaluation can be made of the safety of the drug when used for a prolonged period of time."

4. The application contained rather limited information about the drug's stability.

5. Side effects were passed over lightly. "The impression is left that the 'hangover' frequently observed by Lasagna was due to overdosage, yet in double blind studies this investigator was unable to elicit a therapeutic response with lower doses."

6. There were no data to support the claim advanced in a report by one Dr. Ray Nulsen that expectant mothers suffering from nocturia (excessive passing of urine in the night) had no difficulty arising or returning to sleep after taking thalidomide.

Despite the implications of Dr. Kelsey's letter—particularly that processing the Kevadon application might take considerably longer than Richardson-Merrell expected—the company was determined that its programme was not to be disturbed. An interdepartmental memorandum to all Kevadon representatives headed "Cease Fire—You Made It" said that no new studies should be set up as they already had more than they needed. Significantly, they were also told that during their follow-up calls, some doctors might ask for more thalidomide. However, "we do not want to continue these studies after the doctor has already convinced *himself* of Kevadon's advantages, but we are willing to send him a small additional supply to keep Kevadon in front of him until it becomes commercially available."

An internal FDA analysis of the Kevadon material submitted by Richardson-Merrell at the end of 1960 made it clear that as far as the

FDA was concerned, this might be a long time. The analysis was harshly critical of Richardson-Merrell and accused the company of unacceptable ignorance of what was scientifically legitimate. The author of the FDA memorandum was Frances Kelsey's husband, F. E. Kelsey, a pharmacologist who also worked at the FDA. He wrote: "The section entitled 'Chemical Comparison of Thalidomide and Glutethimide' is an interesting collection of meaningless, pseudoscientific jargon, apparently intended to impress chemically unsophisticated readers. The selection of one chemical difference between two compounds as the 'most important chemical difference' is absurd. What is the most important difference between an apple and an orange?" As for the company's submissions on absorption studies, "the experimental procedure used is either undescribed or inadequate. The data are completely meaningless as presented."

The memorandum concluded with Kelsey's belief that Richardson-Merrell was not being honest on a matter that was central to the rationale and success of thalidomide throughout the world: its claim to have proved thalidomide's non-toxicity by comparing it with other sleeping pills. Like Grünenthal, Distillers, and other companies marketing the drug, Richardson-Merrell saw the total non-toxicity of thalidomide as the "real hooker." The people at the FDA, unlike everyone else, from the start never believed this. F. E. Kelsey began by quoting the company's statement that thalidomide had *no* LD_{50} and "no other substance can make *that* claim!" He then turned to Richardson-Merrell's pharmacological comparison between thalidomide and glutethimide (Doriden) and made his most devastating criticism: "The last sentence in this section is an almost classic example of the widely used irrelevancy of size-of-dose comparisons between drugs. Weight is never a determinant of activity or toxicity; this is a property of each drug. For example one gram of a great many drugs is very much less toxic (or effective) than one-hundredth of a gram of a large number of other drugs. Since this is an *elementary* concept of pharmacology *I cannot believe this to be honest incompetence* [emphasis added]."

Events were moving too slowly for Richardson-Merrell, so when, on January 25, 1961, the company's FDA contact man, Dr. F. J. Murray, was unable to speak to Kelsey, he called her superior, Dr. Ralph Smith. Murray told Dr. Smith—quite inaccurately—that the company was waiting only for a review of revised labelling copy that it was all set to print. Dr. Smith promised to investigate, but leaving nothing to chance,

Murray called him six days later to remind him—only to be told then that much more than labelling changes was under review at the FDA. Murray complained that if this were so, then marketing of Kevadon might have to be postponed.

Murray kept up the pressure during February, for only a month remained before Richardson-Merrell's planned release date. But on February 23, there occurred a conversation between him and Dr. Kelsey that in retrospect can be seen to mark the end of Richardson-Merrell's chances of ever marketing thalidomide in the United States. The Kevadon file at the FDA reveals that by then Dr. Kelsey had seen Dr. Florence's letter in the *British Medical Journal* on thalidomide and peripheral neuritis. It is evident from her handwritten note about her telephone conversation with Dr. Murray on that day that she was extremely angry that the company had failed to tell her about peripheral neuritis and that she had had to discover it herself two months after publication.

The order of events noted in the FDA file reveals a lot about Dr. Kelsey's state of mind. Having learned about peripheral neuritis independently, it seems that she wanted to give Richardson-Merrell a last chance to break the news to her themselves. They failed to do so. Her handwritten report reads: "Dr. Murray called (9:30 A.M.) to inquire about status of Kevadon. I explained we were concerned about chronic toxicity experiments with a view to OTC [over-the-counter] release. . . . He inquired as to what I meant by chronic toxicity so I mentioned recent British reports [about peripheral neuritis] and he said he had seen them too and had written for further information."

Dr. Kelsey now demanded evidence from further animal studies and further clinical information. She also asked Richardson-Merrell for a list of the clinical investigators who had been given the drug. Murray tried very hard to dissuade Kelsey from insisting on these requests. He told her that in Britain, Distillers was merely adding a warning about neurological toxicity to its brochure. But Kelsey was adamant; a warning would not do. She wanted to know a lot more about thalidomide before she would proceed with the Kevadon application.

To try to give Kelsey what she wanted, Murray and another Richardson-Merrell executive, Dr. T. L. Jones, flew to Britain and Germany for meetings with Distillers and Grünenthal. The most enlightening meeting was with Dr. Somers of Distillers. Dr. Hans Werner von Schrader-Beielstein, a medical adviser in Grünenthal, was present, and his testy report on what he considered the excessive frankness of Dr. Somers survives:

> Dr. Somers not only gave a detailed and completely unsolicited account of his toxicity investigations [which showed that thalidomide could kill mice] but also handed over his report to the Americans. This situation was unpleasant for us since in view of the divergent results in Germany and England and the future exchange of mouse strains [Grünenthal was claiming that Distillers' mice must be peculiarly susceptible to thalidomide], this matter was still continuing and so we had not yet told the Americans about it. We had to give a short review there and then in order to prevent the Americans from getting the impression that we had purposely suppressed important results.

As far as peripheral neuritis was concerned, the information the two Richardson-Merrell representatives gathered must have been confusing. They learned that thalidomide did indeed cause neuritis. (On his return to the United States, Dr. Jones wrote to Distillers: "I am more than ever convinced that peripheral neuritis from thalidomide is certainly a clinical entity, albeit a bizarre one.") But equally their visit to Grünenthal convinced them, they told Kelsey later, that the incidence of the complaint was low and rapidly reversible. Grünenthal had told them, they reported, that it knew of only 34 cases of peripheral neuritis in West Germany and that the trouble cleared up when the patient stopped taking the drug. But at this time Grünenthal had in its files reports of 400 cases and, further, knew that in many instances this side effect was *not* reversible.

When Murray and Jones reported to Dr. Kelsey in March 1961, they plugged the Grünenthal line: the incidence of peripheral neuritis was low and the complaint was rapidly reversible. She remained sceptical, however, noting, "a brief perusal of a report from California indicated that this was not always the case." She then made a major point against thalidomide: "The field of usefulness of the drug is such that untoward reactions would be highly inexcusable"—meaning that thalidomide was not a vital, or life-saving, drug so that there could be no justification for serious side effects.

Kelsey's notes on the Murray-Jones report also confirm that she was uneasy with the way the whole application had been handled by Richardson-Merrell. "I had the feeling throughout that they were at no time being wholly frank with me," she wrote, but she acknowledged that she might have been prejudiced by the company's advance publicity and by, among other things, "their failure to notify us of the British reports of toxicity." In May, Kelsey explained her position to a physician who had written to her—at Richardson-Merrell's request—in support of the company's claims for the safety and efficacy of the drug: "We do not as yet have sufficient information with respect to this toxic effect to permit a complete evaluation of its safety. . . ." Among other uncertainties, she said she was *not*—and yet again her doubts later proved to be justified—satisfied that the toxic effects of thalidomide were reversible. She made it clear that she was unimpressed with the argument that the fact that the drug had been available in other countries was necessarily proof of its safety. This was, she wrote, "of no particular significance."

In the second week of April, Murray called Dr. Smith at the FDA to warn that his superiors did not believe that Murray was pushing the Kevadon application hard enough and wanted to take a hand in it themselves. If nothing happened soon, the company's vice-president intended to approach the head of the FDA. Dr. Smith denied that Kelsey was avoiding a decision. He added that it often happened that side effects of drugs were not reported until they had been on the market a long time, and it was possible that the incidence of peripheral neuritis was greater than was currently believed. Undeterred, Murray wrote to Dr. Kelsey a few days later with the results of a literature survey on peripheral neuritis showing that the condition was a common side effect with many drugs and that it almost invariably cleared up immediately administration ceased, no matter what the drug. In case she should still feel that barbiturates were safer for hypnotic use, Murray enclosed two copies of a literature search on the side effects of barbiturates. "I again want to stress," he wrote, "that there is actually no proof thalidomide causes peripheral neuritis. The evidence is circumstantial." And he concluded his letter: "In order that we may intelligently proceed with our market plans, I should like to have you advise me of your final decision on this new drug application some time next week."

Dr. Kelsey's stark response on May 5 reflected both her indignation at this pressure and her continuing dissatisfaction with the quality of Richardson-Merrell's evidence:

> In our opinion the application as it now stands is entirely inadequate to establish the safety of the Kevadon tablets under the

proposed labelling. In particular the application does not include complete reports of adequate animal studies nor sufficiently extensive, complete and adequate clinical studies to permit an evaluation of the toxic effects of the drug which have been manifested by reports of cases of peripheral neuritis. On the present evidence we cannot regard Kevadon tablets as safe in the sense that its usefulness as a sedative hypnotic outweighs the toxic effects indicated by the cases of peripheral neuritis. Detailed case reports with adequate follow-up studies will be required to determine whether the condition is reversible. . . . We have taken appropriate note of your contention that it has not been proved that Kevadon tablets actually cause peripheral neuritis, and the fact that the labelling of the drug proposed in your letter of March 29, 1961, fails to make a frank disclosure that the drug has been found to cause peripheral neuritis. In the consideration of an application for a new drug, the burden of proof that the drug causes side effects does not lie with this Administration. The burden of proof that the drug is safe—which must include adequate studies of all the manifestations of toxicity which medical or clinical experience suggest—lies with the applicant. In this connection we are much concerned that apparently evidence with respect to the occurrence of peripheral neuritis in England was known to you but not forthrightly disclosed in the application.

Richardson-Merrell was furious. Murray immediately telephoned Ralph Smith to say he considered the letter "somewhat libellous"—a reference to Dr. Kelsey's suggestion that the company had been aware of the peripheral neuritis problem for some time without informing the FDA—and also went to the medical director of the FDA. Another meeting with Dr. Kelsey was arranged. At this meeting, according to the FDA record, she specified that she would now also need evidence that thalidomide would be safe to take during pregnancy. Her handwritten note on the original memorandum reads: "This was based on peripheral neuritis symptoms in adults."

Richardson-Merrell did its best. To meet this new demand, it arranged to bring a group of investigators to the FDA to discuss their experiences with Kevadon. Kelsey's report of this meeting, which took place on September 7, 1961, was again critical. She said that none of the investigators had any knowledge of what the drug might do to the foetus if used in pregnant women. Lasagna, who thought the drug might be given a try, "admitted that it would be highly desirable to know of the effect of this drug on the foetus." At the end of September, Richardson-Merrell sent the FDA some information on the administration of thalidomide during pregnancy, but it was largely late pregnancy.

Dr. Murray's last attempt to get approval of the Kevadon application was made in a telephone call to Ralph Smith on September 26, 1961. Murray requested the FDA to give him an estimate of when the application would become effective because Richardson-Merrell wanted to go to market by mid-November, he now said. After checking with Dr. Kelsey, Smith told Murray that neither he nor she could predict when the application would be approved, and that in the meantime the label should carry a warning excluding pregnant women from those who could take the drug.

Over the years, the question has been repeatedly asked: did Frances Kelsey behave merely as a cautious bureaucrat? Or more bluntly, did she get thalidomide right for the wrong reasons? Getting something as momentous as thalidomide right for the wrong reasons is a perfectly respectable position, but what emerges from the record is that she got it right largely for the right reasons. True, she did not *predict* that thalidomide would cause birth deformities, but she *did* ask the question. She was, by chance, especially interested in foetal damage because during the 1940s she had worked with her husband on the antimalarial drug quinine, which had been found to possess teratogenic activity. But the record clearly shows that this was not her main preoccupation. It was even more fundamental. She wanted to know—and was clearly never satisfied that she did know—about the way in which thalidomide behaved in the body; its stability, its effects on human metabolism, even its basic chemistry and pharmacology. She grasped the vital point that because the drug appeared to have little or no effect on animals in the hands of many investigators, experience based on animal experimentation was less impressive than if the animals had proved more sensitive to thalidomide. She was also very unhappy with Richardson-Merrell's attitude, antagonized by the pressure she felt herself to be under, and disturbed by their lack of total honesty in some of the material submitted to impress her. These factors perhaps made her more critical than she might otherwise have been, but the record suggests that this hardly mattered. Of course, once the neurological toxicity of thalidomide came to her attention, her demands for proof of safety became even more stringent. Peripheral neuritis is a serious side effect of a drug, particularly one to be used as a mild sedative or hypnotic, and particularly when alternative compounds exist.

Later emphasis on Dr. Kelsey's foresight into thalidomide's power to deform the foetus was due partly to a front-page article by Morton Mintz in *The Washington Post* on July 15, 1962. Headlined HEROINE OF FDA KEEPS BAD DRUG OFF MARKET, it began: "This is a story of how the skepticism and stubbornness of a Government physician prevented what could have been an appalling American tragedy, the birth of hundreds, or indeed thousands, of armless and legless children." The article went on to say that Dr. Kelsey believed that thalidomide was "peculiar" and that in the face of what the drug company believed was a clear and overwhelming case for granting its application, Dr. Kelsey "delayed, and delayed, and delayed." Mintz's article turned Dr. Kelsey into an American heroine; she was awarded a gold medal by President Kennedy and for a while was the centre of press and television attention. All of this tended to obscure the fact that her criticisms of thalidomide had been so basic, so persistent, and so scrupulously scientific that any charges (as were made by a section of the drug industry) that her actions were merely lucky or marked by excessive bureaucratic caution can be dismissed as ludicrous.

What emerged after the appalling defects of thalidomide were revealed was that some of the supporting data put together by Richardson-Merrell were compiled in a manner even more unscientific than Kelsey could possibly have imagined. Ironically, it was one of the few published studies on the use of thalidomide in pregnancy, albeit in the last trimester, that provided alarming evidence of Richardson-Merrell's indifference to scientific veracity. The paper, published in the *American Journal of Obstetrics and Gynecology* in June 1961, appeared under the name of R. O. Nulsen and was entitled "Trial of Thalidomide in Insomnia Associated with the Third Trimester." In 1964 and 1976, depositions taken by lawyers acting for thalidomide children revealed that this article had been written not by Nulsen at all, but by Dr. Raymond Pogge, the medical director of Richardson-Merrell, with the help of his secretary. Nulsen's paper referred to six German publications, but Nulsen could not read German; it referred to an article in the *British Medical Journal*, but Nulsen had not seen it; it quoted Lasagna's studies, but Nulsen did not know who Lasagna was or what he had written. Yet "evidence" from Nulsen's article was used not only in submissions to the FDA but in Richardson-Merrell's promotional material (some of which also failed to mention that Nulsen's "work" concerned the use of thalidomide in the *third* trimester of pregnancy, thus giving the impression that the drug wàs safe in *all* trimesters).

The full extent of the company's indifference to the quality of the clinical investigations it had promoted emerged only in 1976 when Dr. Nulsen was examined under oath by Craig Spangenberg, the lawyer representing a number of thalidomide families, for the second time.

In 1959, Ray O. Nulsen was a doctor practising in Cincinnati, Ohio, the home town of Richardson-Merrell; he specialized in obstetrics and gynaecology. Nulsen's association with Richardson-Merrell as a clinical investigator had begun twenty years earlier. Don Merrell, a descendant of the founder of the company, was a Lambda Chi Alpha fraternity brother of Nulsen's at the University of Cincinnati and had asked him to do some clinical trials for the company. Don Merrell was dead by the time the thalidomide contract was negotiated with Grünenthal but by then Nulsen had a number of personal friends at the company, including Raymond Pogge, the medical director. Requests to carry out clinical investigations on new drugs were anything but formal. Nulsen's recollection was that Pogge had either telephoned or invited him to play a game of golf, and had then asked him if he would try out a new drug that might well take the place of barbiturates. Pogge, for his part, testified that Nulsen had been chosen because "he was very co-operative, he was competent, he was geographically convenient."

Nulsen's trial of thalidomide began in May 1959, though from his testimony, "trial" was not an appropriate description for what amounted to the uncontrolled and often unrecorded dispensing of a drug to his patients, many of whom were pregnant women. Much of the time Nulsen did not even do the dispensing. If, for example, a patient ran out of thalidomide and wanted more, she could simply call his secretary, who would put the pills into an envelope for collection from a metal mail box outside Nulsen's office. Despite the fact that thalidomide was an experimental drug and that Nulsen was purportedly one of its clinical investigators, he kept no running record of how much thalidomide he had received. Richardson-Merrell's records show that he was given 109,000 tablets; whenever he ran out, his secretary called the company, and it delivered a new supply.

Nulsen was not surprised when Richardson-Merrell told him it wanted to write a paper describing the results, and to use his name. After all, the "same thing happened on other things" on which Nulsen had worked for Richardson-Merrell over the previous twenty years. That Nulsen shared the company's indifference to scientific validity or accuracy emerged with alarming clarity when he was examined under deposition. Asked what written material was given to Richardson-Merrell so that it might write an article based on his work, he replied, "There were some forms that it received with patients' initials and when they took the medication, and the effects it had, and this was the basis of the article."

Q. Who filled out the forms?
A. One of the girls in the office. [The information had been supplied by the patients themselves.]
Q. Did you sign the forms?
A. I don't know that.

Nulsen had not checked his secretary's arithmetic. The paper began by saying that in the five-month study period the author had delivered approximately 125 patients, of whom 81 had needed thalidomide during their third trimester.

Q. Now did you make some head count to determine that you had actually tested this new drug in 81 patients, with the primary complaint of insomnia in the third trimester?
A. Yes.
Q. Who made the count?
A. Miss Dempsey [his secretary].
Q. Do you have any personal knowledge whether that count was accurate?
A. I didn't recheck her figures. . . . I assumed it was correct.

The facts are that serious doubts were cast on Ms. Dempsey's figures. According to the material that Richardson-Merrell supplied the FDA to support its Kevadon application, Nulsen had given thalidomide to not more than 21 women in the third trimester. But there was, by then, no way of checking this. Nulsen, who rarely kept any records and who passed on his findings verbally to his friends at Richardson-Merrell, said that the records that had formed the basis of the article in the *Journal* had later been destroyed.

Dr. Pogge's secretary, too, appears to have played a large part in the preparation of the account. The secretary, Margaret L. Higgins, wrote to Nulsen in February 1960 enclosing the original and a copy of the text:

"Since you are describing what appears to be a previously unrecognized cause for insomnia, both Dr. Pogge and I think that the text should be submitted to the editor of the *American Journal of Obstetrics and Gynecology.*" The Nulsen (or Pogge-Higgins) article was duly submitted to the *Journal,* whose editor asked for some additional information. He wanted the chemistry of the compound described and particularly wanted to know: "Does this drug cross the placenta . . . ?" If this is not known, he said, then a statement to that effect would have to be added before he would agree to publication. Predictably, Nulsen simply returned the article to Richardson-Merrell, where Pogge and his secretary made what additions and amendments they could to comply with the editor's requests. When examined on oath in 1976, Nulsen was forced to admit that he knew nothing of thalidomide's chemical structure and that he had relied on Pogge to insert the details the *Journal* had asked for. (Pogge, in turn, said he had obtained the information from the company's chemistry department.) Pogge dealt with the query about whether thalidomide passed the placental barrier by saying, "Since the compound does not depress respiration or produce circulatory collapse, there is no danger to the baby if some of it appears in the milk or passes the placental barrier." Nulsen agreed that when he approved this addition to his text, he had in mind that it would be passing the placental barrier in the third trimester. "You were not trying to say it was safe all through pregnancy?" he was asked. "I didn't know that," he replied. Yet when on March 20, 1960—after the article had been written—Pogge asked Nulsen if he would try thalidomide in the next six to eight patients who were suffering from nausea in pregnancy, Nulsen readily agreed. The significance of this was that nausea is, of course, a characteristic of the first—and most vulnerable—trimester of pregnancy.

And, indeed, Ray Nulsen was responsible for the deliveries of at least three living thalidomide children and of two who did not survive. And there may have been more. When in 1964 Nulsen first gave a deposition to lawyers for two thalidomide families, he denied having delivered any child with deformities similar to those that were, by then, recognized as typical of thalidomide. Yet the lawyers later discovered that in January 1961, Nulsen had delivered a child with deformed hands, an imperforated anus, with no apparent testes, and a deformed penis folded back on itself in such a way that the baby was at first thought to be female. This child also had multiple abnormalities of the hips, knees, upper

thighs, and feet. And in May 1961, Nulsen delivered a child—who subsequently died—without arms and legs.

The final irony is that if Nulsen had been conducting a *genuine* clinical
trial, or if Richardson-Merrell had been really interested in establishing
the safe and effective application of thalidomide in a broad spectrum of
circumstances, then they both might have won an honored niche in
pharmaceutical history for being the first to discover thalidomide's devastating effects on the unborn child. Five months after Nulsen delivered
what was probably his first thalidomide baby, Dr. McBride, the Australian obstetrician, made the historic connection.

6 The Warning That Got Lost

Dr. McBride spent the Queen's birthday weekend of 1961 reading about drug-induced abnormalities in babies and examining the records of three of his patients who had given birth to malformed children. By the last evening of the holiday, Monday, June 12, he was certain that the cause of these malformations was thalidomide. True, his evidence was slim: the fact that the only drug all three mothers had taken during pregnancy had been Distaval (the Australian trade name for thalidomide), and his reading. But Dr. McBride was *convinced* he was right. A vital, if unscientific, factor in the make-up of many a first-rate doctor is an intuitive feeling about a case. So he did not hesitate, and early Tuesday, June 13, he went straight to see John Newlinds, the medical superintendent of Crown Street Women's Hospital, Sydney. Dr. Newlinds was shocked at what McBride told him, but it did not cross his mind to question McBride's conclusion. Dr. McBride had been supervisor of students at Crown Street when Dr. Newlinds was a student there, and it was McBride, a former medical superintendent at Crown Street himself, who had urged Newlinds to apply for the position when it became vacant. Dr. Newlinds says, "Everything I know about obstetrics and gynaecology I learned from Bill McBride."

So if Dr. McBride said he considered thalidomide responsible for the malformed births at Crown Street, then that was enough for Dr. Newlinds. He telephoned Mrs. Sperling in the hospital pharmacy and told her to withdraw Distaval from use in Crown Street. "It may have seemed a hasty step, but look at it this way. I believed Bill. Distaval wasn't a life-saving drug. It wasn't penicillin I was withdrawing. It was a sedative and we had lots of others in the pharmacy." So Mrs. Sperling put her bottle of Distaval tablets carefully to one side, and the doctors agreed that McBride would tell DCBAL (the Australian branch of Distillers Company [Biochemicals] of Britain) of the decision to withdraw the drug and the reasons for doing so.

Since no one then realized that the exact sequence of events and their chronology would be so important, no one made comprehensive notes, kept a diary, or recorded his actions. In compiling this account, it has been necessary to fall back on memory—which is fallible—but confirmed where possible by independent testimony and reference to other events that can be more easily dated.

Dr. McBride is certain that he telephoned the office of DCBAL that very week and told them about his suspicions of Distaval. When recalling these events, he at first thought he had spoken to the managing director, William Poole. But Poole denies ever having spoken to Dr. McBride. Dr. McBride now believes that he spoke to the New South Wales sales manager, Frederick Strobl. His reasoning is this: before he became convinced of thalidomide's dreadful side effects, he had kept his promise to let DCBAL know of his experiences with the drug and on May 9, 1961, had written the company a letter saying he was pleased with Distaval's effectiveness. DCBAL had replied thanking him for this testimonial, and the letter had been signed by Strobl. It seems a reasonable assumption that when he telephoned DCBAL, McBride would have asked for Strobl, the one executive of the company with whom he had had previous dealings. (Strobl left Australia after the tragedy, settled in Switzerland, became a film actor, and changed his name. He remembers speaking with McBride but cannot be certain of the date.) The important point is that McBride remembers clearly the substance of the conversation. "I said, 'Look. I know that there is no real proof against Distaval, but why not stop promoting it while we try to find out what is happening.' " McBride says that the executive at DCBAL, whoever he was, replied that Distaval had been widely used in Britain for more than two years, and surely if the drug were causing malformations, these would have shown up long before then. (This is exactly the point that Professor Zbinden makes in his widely respected study on drugs: it is about two years after a drug has been on the market that any dangerous side effects are likely to reveal themselves.) However, the DCBAL man did say that he would pass on Dr. McBride's suspicions to London, and in return asked the doctor not to spread his disquiet because the evidence was very circumstantial. McBride remembers that at no time did the DCBAL man mention that thalidomide was a German discovery, and he came away from the telephone with the firm impression that the drug was a British development, probably DCBL's own.

Dr. McBride's recollection of the conversation and his dating of it seem confirmed by other actions that week which *are* firmly dated. On the same day that he telephoned DCBAL, he wrote a paper for the *Lancet* setting out his theory about thalidomide-induced malformations, and he started tests at Crown Street to try to reproduce in animals the malformations he had seen in humans. Neither step was to produce results.

The laboratory animals at Crown Street—mice and guinea pigs normally used for pregnancy testing—were fed 100-mg. tablets of Distaval crushed and mixed with their food. Since McBride was working in the dark—DCBL had no idea even at this stage how thalidomide was broken down in the body—there was no regulated dose. As Dr. McBride describes it: "We just stuffed it into them." And because the hospital's supply of animals was small, there was no control group, which meant that there was no way of perceiving any sudden drop in the litter rate of the animals fed thalidomide. The white mice were allowed to go to term; the guinea pigs were sacrificed after four weeks. None of the offspring of these animals showed any abnormality, and Dr. McBride felt the first doubt about his theory that was to nag him for the next five months.

When Dr. McBride was only midway through his experiments on the animals, he had a meeting with the local DCBAL salesman, Walter Hodgetts. In 1974, when we interviewed him, Hodgetts was unable to remember the date of this meeting, but from his own written records it was possible to date it exactly—July 6, 1961. Hodgetts says, "I saw Dr. McBride in Macquarie Street. He asked me to go to his surgery because he wanted to talk to me urgently. When we got there, he said, 'I suspect that Distaval has caused some malformations of the phocomelia* type in births at Crown Street.' I was astonished and asked him what basis he had for believing this. He said, 'I've had quite a number of deliveries of phocomelia babies, and when I checked the records, I found that the mothers had taken Distaval and no other drugs.' I told Dr. McBride that I would report this to the company immediately and I did so the same day."

There is considerable disagreement over what occurred next. Hodgetts certainly wrote a report of his conversation with Dr. McBride and

---

* Phocomelia (from the Greek *phōkē*, "seal," and *melos*, "limb"): in which the hands, or feet, or both, start immediately from the main joint (shoulder or hip), like the flippers of a seal.

this still exists. Hodgetts says that he gave the report and an account of the meeting to his immediate superior, the New South Wales sales manager, Frederick Strobl, and then to the managing director, William Poole. "They were very surprised at what I had to say. Immediately, in my presence, Mr. Poole telephoned Mr. Gross [now, after leaving England, chairman of DCBAL and of Distillers in Australia] and relayed to him what I had said." Strobl's version is substantially the same. "Hodgetts came into my office and said McBride had had three cases of deformed births. I went into Poole's office and told him."

Poole categorically denies this. He says that after thalidomide had been withdrawn in November 1961, he held an inquiry in the Australian office to examine McBride's claim that he had sounded the alarm about thalidomide five months earlier. Poole says that it was only during this inquiry that he discovered for the first time that Hodgetts had seen Dr. McBride on July 6 and had made a special report on this meeting to Strobl. He insists that neither Strobl nor Hodgetts had informed him or any other senior officer of DCBAL about this. The first he knew of Dr. McBride's suspicions about Distaval, Poole says, was in October, when he set in motion the events that led to the drug's withdrawal.

Poole's account also conflicts with an incident reported by John Bishop, one of the two DCBAL representatives in South Australia. Bishop, an ex-serviceman who had attended medical school for five years before a shortage of money and a bout of illness forced him to abandon medicine as a career, had joined DCBAL in June 1960. He had four children. A fifth had been born July 23, 1960, just after his return from the sales training course in Sydney. In October, Mrs. Bishop had become pregnant yet again, and had been so upset about it that Bishop had given her some of his sample Distaval tablets to calm her nerves. Bishop says that this is why he is able to remember with such clarity a conversation he had with Poole in late June or early July 1961—at the time Dr. McBride was doing his animal tests at Crown Street, at about the time of the McBride-Hodgetts meeting, and *after* McBride told the Sydney office of DCBAL about his suspicions of thalidomide. Bishop says, "Bill Poole had arrived in Adelaide on an overnight visit. We arranged to have a working dinner at the Australia Hotel. There was Poole, me, and my boss, Creswick. We were pretty pleased with ourselves. The Children's Hospital in Adelaide had just agreed to take Distaval as a sedative for children, and we were telling Bill Poole how good sales prospects looked. Suddenly, Bill said, 'Look, you'd better not count your chickens before they're hatched. We've had a report from a doctor in Sydney about Distaval abnormalities in the foetus.' Bill didn't mention the doctor's name, but he was clearly worried. He was not taking the matter lightly."

A month later Bishop's sixth child was born. She had six digits on one hand. Both hands were at an uneven angle at the wrist joint, turning inwards across the body. Bishop now made the link between having given his wife Distaval and what Poole had said that night at dinner at the Australia Hotel, and decided that his child's deformities must be due to Distaval. (DCBAL accepted this, and the child received compensation along with the other thalidomide children in Australia in 1975.)

If Bishop's account is accepted, it offers further evidence that DCBAL indeed knew of McBride's suspicions about Distaval by July. But Poole, while agreeing that he may well have dined with Bishop at that time, denies ever having made the remarks Bishop attributes to him. Bishop is not shaken by Poole's denial and sticks to his story: he is certain of the date because it was *before* his thalidomide child was born, i.e., before July 28, 1961.

A courtroom trial, with witnesses on oath and subject to the pressure of cross-examination, would have helped to iron out the inconsistencies in these conflicting accounts and would probably have produced a version as close to the truth as is possible in human affairs. But there has been no trial, so the reader will have to make up his own mind which version of these events in Australia he prefers to believe. All that can be stated here with certainty is that by the first week of July 1961, at least two DCBAL employees (Hodgetts and Strobl) and possibly six (Hodgetts, Strobl, Poole, Gross, Creswick, and Bishop) knew that Dr. McBride suspected thalidomide of causing deformed births. Yet Distillers insists that no word of this reached the head office in London until November 21, more than four months later. In the meantime, DCBAL continued to sell the drug in Australia as vigorously as it always had, and it remained on sale in Britain, Germany, and elsewhere. How many mothers around the world took thalidomide in the four months between McBride's first warning and the withdrawal of the drug is not known. (One indication is that in Britain about a quarter of the known thalidomide children were damaged in their mothers' womb during this period.) And it must remain speculation whether DCBL would have regarded McBride's theory as sufficiently convincing and would have withdrawn the drug even if McBride's warning *had* been passed to London when he first made it. But surely it is reasonable to ask: why wasn't it?

We can only surmise that on reflection DCBAL had decided that Dr. McBride must be wrong, a view that, by early September, Dr. McBride himself was almost prepared to share. To begin with, his animal tests had failed to produce malformations. Next, he had a disappointing interview with Professor Rowland Thorp, head of the pharmacology department at Sydney University. Thorp is a contentious character, not over-fond of doctors, and he has been known to deplore the fact that he has only one year out of the six-year medical course to teach them pharmacology. He was also an old friend and colleague of George Somers, the DCBL pharmacologist, and knew him to be thorough and professional. So Thorp was sceptical and abrupt with McBride. How did McBride think that thalidomide could cause deformed births? McBride advanced a theory that thalidomide could be an anti-metabolite, a folic acid antagonist. Thorp brusquely knocked this down. Thorp had laboratory rats, so McBride asked if he would do some experiments with thalidomide using these rats. No, Thorp said, too expensive.

Next, between June and September, 23 mothers who had been prescribed Distaval during pregnancy gave birth at Crown Street and not one had a malformed baby. We now know that thalidomide causes malformations only if taken between the fifth and eighth weeks of pregnancy. But in Sydney in 1961, the fact that 23 mothers who had taken Distaval had normal babies could only mean that McBride had been totally wrong. Then, the final blow: early in September, the paper McBride had sent to the *Lancet* was returned—by surface mail! A covering letter dated July 13 and signed by the assistant editor said that although McBride's theory about thalidomide was interesting, pressure to publish important papers was such that there was no space for this contribution—a fairly standard rejection, if more polite than most. (McBride's paper was eventually published, as part of another, in 1963 in the *Medical Journal of Australia*.)

Everything now seemed to indicate that McBride had acted hastily and unscientifically. No other cases suggesting that thalidomide could cause malformed births had been reported in the medical press anywhere in the world. Professor Thorp, Sydney's leading pharmacologist, disagreed forcibly with McBride's views. DCBAL had not considered it necessary to withdraw Distaval or even cease promoting it. McBride's detractors eagerly looked forward to his admission that he had been wrong.

Then, on September 13, another baby with what are now recognized as typical thalidomide malformations was born at Crown Street, and thirteen days later yet another. In both cases, the hospital records showed that the mothers had taken Distaval during early pregnancy. McBride was now certain that he had been vindicated: thalidomide must be the cause of these malformed births. Again he telephoned DCBAL and this time adopted a tougher attitude. "I told them that I was going to write letters to several medical journals in both Australia and Britain." This time he was assured that his message would be passed to London immediately and he was urged to delay his letters until this was done. While he was waiting for DCBAL to act, McBride pressed his views on anyone he thought might be able to influence the company. One, a salesman new to DCBAL, called on McBride at his local office in Hurstville, an expanding suburb about ten miles south of Sydney. It turned out that McBride and the salesman had been to the same school, Canterbury Boys' High; otherwise, the salesman might have received even shorter shrift than he did. "I went into the surgery and before I could say a word, Dr. McBride said, 'Unless you've got a product that hasn't got Distaval in it, then we've nothing to say to each other.' I asked him why and he said, 'I've told your people about it. Ask them.' " The salesman was very worried and says he reported the conversation to Poole.

On October 29, Dr. McBride went to Young, a country town in New South Wales, to address a medical conference. One of the other speakers was Professor Thorp. Again he tried to convince Thorp that thalidomide could be responsible for the malformed births. Again he set out the facts and again he asked Thorp if he could see any way in which thalidomide could have been the agent. Thorp said, "I would be very surprised." The trouble was that Thorp regarded Dr. McBride principally as a clinician. "He had an *impression* that he was seeing more malformations than he should and he had formed an *impression* that thalidomide was responsible. I told him that as a scientist I would want more evidence than that."

Dr. McBride was not shaken. He decided after his talk with Thorp that the simplest but most effective way of deciding the matter would be for him to go ahead and write to the medical journals in Britain and Australia. The following week he telephoned DCBAL to tell the com-

pany this and, it appears, spoke to Strobl, who in turn told Poole.
DCBAL was now under considerable pressure to act. Hodgetts had gone
to Crown Street Hospital, had been given access to the records, and had
confirmed that McBride was correct in stating that all the phocomelia
births had been to women who had taken Distaval during their pregnancy. Hodgetts says that he even called on some of the mothers to
check this with them. "I reported this to Mr. Poole," he says, "and I told
him that I accepted Dr. McBride's conclusions."

Poole now sent H. O. Woodhouse, the assistant sales manager, to see
McBride in his Macquarie Street office to get from him an official report
on the malformed births and to ask him again to delay writing to any
medical journal until the report could be studied by DCBL's medical
advisers. Woodhouse and McBride met on November 16, and *five months*
almost to the day after McBride's telephone call to DCBAL, and *four
months* after DCBAL had officially recorded McBride's suspicions (in
Hodgetts's weekly sales report), the company at last got around to taking a detailed statement from him. It is essential to quote the report
Woodhouse prepared, both because of the reaction it caused when it
reached London and Germany and because of the significance of its
errors:

> Dr. McBride has been recommending Distaval for morning
> sickness, the usual dose being 1 100-mg tablet first thing in the
> morning and 1 100-mg last thing at night. If necessary 1 100-
> mg tablet may be taken during the day.
> This treatment proved to be extremely satisfactory in this
> condition and few patients complained of drowsiness. How-
> ever, in April, 1961 three babies died soon after birth. All were
> full-term pregnancies. The mothers had not had any infection
> during their pregnancy and were not given any antibiotics.
> The common factor was that they had taken Distaval for
> morning sickness in the dosage already described.
> Each baby had abnormal long bones, e.g. 1. The radius was
> either absent or deformed. 2. The femur was short. 3. Polydac-
> tyly occurred. 4. Macrodactyly occurred. 5. In each case duo-
> denal atresia was present and this was the ultimate cause of
> death. Dr. McBride pointed out the fact that all the above are
> of mesenchymal origin.
> Dr. McBride continued to use Distaval for morning sickness
> and there was no further trouble until September, October,
> 1961 when three more babies died with similar abnormalities.

He feels that six similar cases in one practice are too many to
be purely coincidental, while he does not wish to condemn
Distaval, he does not have any other alternative since it appears to be the only common feature in each case. He does say,
however, that the abnormalities could possibly be due to a
virus.

Dr. McBride had intended writing to the *Medical Journal of
Australia* and the *British Medical Journal* asking whether any
doctors had similar cases; however, he had second thoughts.
But Distaval has been withdrawn from the Women's Hospital.
Dr. McBride consulted Professor Thorp who apparently said
that he found it extremely difficult to believe that Distaval
could be responsible for the abnormalities.

X-Rays of all or some of the babies will be sent to me next
week and Dr. McBride suggests that our laboratories should
carry out animal experiments to see if it is possible to either
prove or disprove these malformations. He would also like to
hear if any doctor in the United Kingdom has any similar
reports.

The mistakes and emphasis in this report are interesting. *"Dr. McBride
has been recommending Distaval for morning sickness. . . ."* The choice of
tense gives no indication that McBride had in fact *ceased* prescribing
Distaval five months earlier. *"In April, 1961, three babies died soon after
birth."* The births were actually in May and June. Dr. McBride may
have been responsible for this error in that he initially remembered the
holiday weekend when he did his reading on malformations as being
Anzac Day (April 25) whereas it was the Queen's birthday weekend
(June 10–12). But the correct dates were on the mothers' records, which
had been examined by Hodgetts. *"Dr. McBride continued to use Distaval for
morning sickness. . . ."* This was not so. *"But Distaval has been withdrawn
from the Women's Hospital."* When? The report does not say. The effect of
these mistakes is that it is not clear that McBride suspected Distaval in
June, that he ceased prescribing it *then,* that Crown Street withdrew it
then, and that all this was known to the Sydney office of DCBAL *at that
time.* We can only surmise that if the report had been wholly accurate,
then London might well have asked Sydney: "Why didn't you tell us all
this back in June?"

Even the statement in the report that McBride had had second
thoughts about writing to the *MJA* and the *BMJ* about thalidomide was
wrong. Dr. McBride, far from confident that this latest visit from

DCBAL would produce any action, sat down when Woodhouse left and wrote to the *Lancet*. In view of his earlier rejection, he advanced no theories but simply noted what he had observed and sought further information. The letter was published December 16, 1961.

> Sir:
> Congenital abnormalities are present in approximately 1.5% of babies. In recent months I have observed that the incidence of multiple severe abnormalities in babies delivered of women who were given the drug thalidomide (Distaval) during pregnancy, as an anti-emetic or as a sedative, to be almost 20 per cent.
> These abnormalities are present in structures developed from mesenchyme—i.e. the bones and musculature of the gut. Bony development seems to be affected in a very striking manner, resulting in polydactyly, syndactyly, and failure of development of long bones (abnormally short femora and radii).
> Have any of your readers seen similar abnormalities in babies delivered of women who have taken this drug during pregnancy?
>
> W. G. McBride
> Hurstville, NSW

Meanwhile, Poole and Woodhouse worked on the report for London of the meeting with McBride and got it into the following day's post. It arrived in London on Tuesday, November 21. It was met with mixed emotions. Brown, Kennedy's deputy in the medical department, thought that it was "a rather disturbing report," but Hayman, the managing director, felt at first that there was no cause for alarm. By Thursday, November 23, DCBL's pharmacologist, George Somers, had arranged to examine the effects of thalidomide on the development of the foetus in rats—the standard reproductive study DCBL should have done three and a half years earlier—and McBride's conclusions had been passed to Grünenthal for its comments.

McBride's report arrived in Germany at a crucial time. There, because of thalidomide's enormous sale, its terrible effects were more apparent than anywhere else. Yet Grünenthal's reaction to the mounting evidence against thalidomide—painstakingly collected by worried doctors—can only be described as incredible.

7 Lie, Suppress, Bribe, and Distort

One year before McBride's conclusions reached Germany, that is, in October 1960, Professor W. Kosenow, of Münster University's children's clinic, and Dr. R. A. Pfeiffer, a paediatrician, presented X rays and photographs of two thalidomide-deformed infants to a meeting of the German Paediatric Society in Kassel. At that time, neither Kosenow nor Pfeiffer, nor any of their colleagues at the conference, had the slightest idea that thalidomide was responsible for the deformities. They regarded the cases as two interesting examples of the rare condition of phocomelia. Previously, pictures of this condition were almost unavailable. Medical text books carried only Goya's drawing of a phocomelic baby in the arms of a Spanish peasant woman, and the late Professor Georg Benno Gruber, of the University of Göttingen, who had devoted his life to studying malformations in human beings, said that before 1961—the year in which the ghastly nature of thalidomide finally emerged—he had seen more babies with two heads than with phocomelia. So no blame can be attached to the paediatricians at the Kassel conference for not suspecting the association between the deformed infants and thalidomide—even though it later emerged that at that time there were no fewer than 136 cases of phocomelia in various hospitals throughout Germany. In the event, it was someone outside the medical profession—Karl Schulte-Hillen, a young lawyer who came from the little town of Menden, near Münster, but who practised in Hamburg—who was instrumental in throwing open the whole matter.

On March 15, 1961, Schulte-Hillen had been to see his sister, who had just had a baby. It had been a painful visit. The baby's arms ended before the elbow and each hand had only three fingers. Six weeks later Schulte-Hillen's wife gave birth to their child, and it, too, had almost the same malformations. In the days of despair that followed, Schulte-Hillen kept asking why? Was there some terrible hereditary disease in the family? There was nothing in the family's history to suggest this. Had something gone wrong during the pregnancy? His wife could think of nothing except, perhaps, that she had been grief-stricken when her father died during her second month of pregnancy and she had taken two "sedative tablets" to quiet her nerves. When no local doctor could provide Schulte-Hillen with an answer to satisfy him, he became convinced that the reason for two deformed births in his family must be a geographical one—the same false trail at first followed in Australia—and that there was some common factor at work in his home town. This was clearly a theory only an expert could evaluate, so Schulte-Hillen made a few inquiries, and one day in June, when his practice allowed him time, he drove to Hamburg University and called on Professor Widukind Lenz, head of the children's clinic.

Lenz was patient and sympathetic. He said he understood the need that the father of a deformed child has to find a scapegoat; he did not think there could be anything in Schulte-Hillen's theory. But he promised to think about it and make further inquiries. Lenz kept his word: the next day he telephoned a Menden gynaecologist he knew—had the gynaecologist heard of the Schulte-Hillen cases? The gynaecologist said he had, and then startled Lenz by saying that he knew of several similar cases of deformed births, not only in Menden but in Münster and other neighbouring districts. Suddenly Schulte-Hillen's theory took on an entirely new dimension.

Lenz was a very busy man, and it was not until August that he managed to find time to drive to Münster to consult Professor Kosenow, who told him of the cases he and Pfeiffer had presented to the conference the previous October. Kosenow also said that he and Professor Degenhardt, a genetics expert, had set up a working group to examine the outbreak of deformed births and to seek a cause. Lenz said he would help by seeing what he could learn in Hamburg. He began by asking colleagues whether they had seen, or knew of, any cases of phocomelia, and simply by word of mouth learned of 16 within a matter of days. With an assistant, he set about counting the number of cases in Hamburg University women's clinic and in the larger Hamburg maternity hospitals. Out of 6,420 babies born between September 1960 and October 1961, they found 8 who had phocomelia deformities. Applying this proportion to the total number of births in Hamburg in the previous two years, Lenz estimated that there must have been at least 50 cases of phocomelia. To put this into perspective, he went through the city's records of all births

from 1930 to 1955—212,000. There was only *1* recorded case of phocomelia. Lenz was stunned: 1 case of phocomelia in twenty-five years, and
then, suddenly, 50 in thirteen months. A rare and terrible human catastrophe had suddenly become an epidemic. What could be causing it?
In September, Lenz read a paper by Dr. H-R. Wiedemann, of Kiel,
describing 27 cases of phocomelia in his area. Wiedemann suggested
that one of the many new drugs coming on the market could be responsible. But he did not press this theory with vigour because he had been
told—incorrectly as it turned out—that there had been no cases of phocomelia in the neighbouring state of Bremen. If a drug had been responsible, the phocomelia would be widespread. So Lenz's first thought
was that something in common use in most households would turn out
to be the cause—a food preservative, an insecticide, or a detergent—and
when he began the painstaking business of interviewing all the mothers
of deformed children, his questions were broadly based: during their
pregnancy what was their household routine, what was their diet, was
there any food they had eaten more of than usual? Convinced that the
mothers had absorbed the teratogenic substance unknowingly, he at first
did not specifically ask if the mothers had taken any *drugs* during pregnancy. But with a scientist's attention for detail, he did note down
everything each woman told him. So we know from Lenz's records that
before November 11, 1961, only one woman mentioned that she had
taken thalidomide, and that was only in the last stages of pregnancy.
But on that date, a doctor's wife told him that she had taken the drug in
high doses both before and during pregnancy. She added that she was
worried even before her baby was born, because the thalidomide had
given her peripheral neuritis and she had been concerned that it might
also have harmed her child. Lenz said later, "I knew that sales of Contergan [thalidomide] had increased greatly over the previous two years. I
now became suspicious that it might be the cause."
    The following day, November 12, prompted by more direct questions
from Lenz, 4 other mothers remembered that they had taken thalidomide during their pregnancy, and receipts and medical records confirmed this. Lenz telephoned as many doctors as he could reach in
Hamburg, described his suspicion and the reasons for it, and asked them
to make their own inquiries. By November 15, Lenz had heard of 14
cases where the mother of a deformed baby had definitely or very probably taken thalidomide during her pregnancy. Lenz realized that 14 cases
did not constitute scientific proof, but, as with McBride, it was a clinical

impression of such strength that Lenz saw no reason for delaying further. He telephoned Grünenthal and was put through to Mueckter. "I told him everything I had done, everything I had learned. I told him all I knew at the time, my suspicions, my conclusions. I said that in my opinion Contergan should be withdrawn from the market immediately."

If Mueckter was disturbed by this call, he showed no sign of it. He replied that this was the first report Chemie Grünenthal had had of any connection between thalidomide and deformed births. He said he would send a representative of the company to see Lenz to get details from him "in a few days or so." Lenz found Mueckter's apparent lack of concern astonishing and told him so. Then, "to relieve myself of the responsibility and to place it where it belonged, I wrote the next day a letter to Chemie Grünenthal setting out the facts." Lenz began by saying he had formed the impression that Mueckter did not attach the importance to the matter that it merited. He went on:

> Since about 1957 a certain type of deformity has occurred in West Germany with increasing frequency. It is a matter, in the first place, of serious defects in the limbs, especially the arms, which are usually mere stumps with two to four fingers or none at all. These malformations of the arms are in part combined with serious leg defects and also with the absence of the outer ear, closure of the auditory passages, heart trouble, and blocking of the oesophagus. There have always been deformities of this kind, but their incidence has been certainly less than 1 in 50,000, probably less than 1 in 100,000. During 1959, 1960, and 1961, the increase in the number of deformities of the type described has been so marked that it has been noticed in numerous places. . . . Last year 1 or 2 out of every 1,000 infants born in Hamburg were deformed in this way. A very intensive search in Hamburg for any factor that could possibly be associated with the occurrence of these deformities has led to the discovery of one single factor regularly present in all these cases. In each of the 14 cases of which I have a reliable account with a complete statement of the drugs prescribed, thalidomide had been taken during the early months of pregnancy. . . . In view of the incalculable human, psychological, legal, and financial consequences of this problem, it is, in my own opinion, indefensible to wait for a strict scientific proof of the harmfulness or harmlessness, as the case may be, of Contergan. I consider it necessary to withdraw the medicament from sale

immediately until its harmlessness as a teratogenic agent in man is conclusively proved.

Lenz posted the letter on November 16, and the same day—that is, before the letter had arrived—Mueckter telephoned. His manner was more open and conciliatory. He said that he had not been "free to talk" during their previous conversation and now wanted to know if the following Monday, November 20, would be a convenient time for the Grünenthal representative to call to see Lenz. Lenz said it would, but asked for a letter confirming the meeting.

Lenz remained concerned at the delay. On Saturday, November 18, the Paediatricians' Association of North Rhine–Westphalia was to hold a conference in Düsseldorf, with a paper read by Kosenow and Pfeiffer on the causes of malformed births. Lenz decided to attend the conference and voice his fears about thalidomide. His chance came in the discussion that followed Kosenow and Pfeiffer's address. He told the paediatricians that he believed that "a certain substance" was associated with an outbreak of deformed births. Fourteen mothers of children with severe deformities had taken it in early pregnancy. Of twenty mothers of normal children, only one had taken the substance and that had been during the late stages of her pregnancy. Lenz said he considered that the drug should be withdrawn immediately and added, "Each month's delay in sorting this out means the birth of perhaps fifty to one hundred horribly mutilated children." He did not name the drug on the floor of the conference, but as the meeting broke up into knots of alarmed conversation, he gave five of his closest colleagues the name: thalidomide.

On Monday, November 20, instead of the one representative of Chemie Grünenthal that Lenz had been expecting, three arrived to see him. They introduced themselves: Dr. Hans Werner von Schrader-Beielstein, earlier Mueckter's deputy and now in charge of the whole thalidomide operation, Dr. Günther Michael, head of the clinical research department, and Dr. von Veltheim, Grünenthal's legal adviser. The strength of the delegation caught Lenz unawares. Unwilling to commit himself without an independent witness, Lenz asked the Grünenthal men to wait while he found one. When no one was available, Lenz made another suggestion: he had already arranged to meet the Hamburg health authorities that afternoon to discuss this very matter; if the Grünenthal men went with him, they could hold a three-sided meeting with everyone's interests protected. The Grünenthal representatives agreed.

The meeting began at 2:30 P.M. Lenz opened proceedings by presenting his fourteen cases, with frequent interruptions from von Schrader-Beielstein and von Veltheim. The atmosphere became heated and one of the health officials intervened to remonstrate with the Grünenthal men over their "aggressive attitude." Lenz, too, was disappointed by Grünenthal's approach. "I had the impression that they had no interest in the facts or the arguments that pointed to thalidomide's being the cause of the deformities. Quite the reverse. Their liveliest interest was in every detail that showed the quality of my research in an unfavourable light." When Lenz pressed ahead, the Grünenthal team turned nastier. They said they would take legal action for "an unjustified attack on our firm," for "behaviour damaging to our business," and for "the murder of a drug by rumour." At 6:00 P.M. when both Lenz and Grünenthal had exhausted their arguments, the health officials stepped in. They asked the Grünenthal group if they were prepared to withdraw thalidomide from the market. They said no. (That very day, November 20, back at the Grünenthal factory, 66,957 circulars went out to pharmacists and doctors all over Germany calling Contergan a "safe medicine.")

The next day, Lenz was confronted at his office at Hamburg University children's clinic by von Schrader-Beielstein and von Veltheim. Was Lenz prepared to hand over his research documents? Having experienced Grünenthal's tactics, Lenz was not willing that the mothers he had interviewed should be seen again by Grünenthal, so he removed all names and addresses from his records before giving the Grünenthal men photocopies of them. The next meeting was arranged for Friday, November 24, at the Provincial Ministry of the Interior in Düsseldorf. It was set for 10:00 A.M., but one of the ministry officials telephoned Lenz Thursday and asked him to arrive half an hour early so that he could go through the evidence with him before the Grünenthal men arrived. Unfortunately, Lenz got caught in a traffic jam and did not get to the ministry until eleven. The Grünenthal executives had spent most of this time repeating that they were prepared to sue anyone who made unjustified attacks on their company. When Lenz did arrive, the meeting started badly. He had brought with him Karl Schulte-Hillen, the young lawyer who had first aroused medical interest in the outbreak of deformities. Von Schrader-Beielstein demanded to know if Schulte-Hillen was there to represent Lenz's legal interests. Schulte-Hillen said no; he was representing himself as the father and uncle of deformed children. The Grünenthal men objected immediately and refused to continue the meeting until Schulte-Hillen, upset, agreed to leave. Lenz considered striking back by challenging the presence of a new Grünenthal executive, introduced as Dr. Nowel, but he then decided to wait. At first the talk was very general—the nature of evidence, how best to prove a scientific hypothesis. Then the reason for Dr. Nowel's presence became clear. "I am a professional statistician," Nowel said. "I cannot judge the medical problems here, but after the report Dr. Lenz has given of his statistics, I can only say that I have doubts about the strength of your material." The ministry officials, however, seemed impressed by Lenz's case, and just before lunch they formally asked Grünenthal if the company was prepared to withdraw thalidomide from the market. The Grünenthal men said no, they had no authority to do so, but they would consult with their office before the meeting resumed in the afternoon.

The Grünenthal men spent two hours on the telephone to their headquarters and opened the afternoon's proceedings by asking Lenz to leave while they made a suggestion to the ministry officials. Lenz left reluctantly. Von Schrader-Beielstein then said he had agreed on a proposal with his headquarters—Grünenthal would attach to all Contergan containers a sticker reading "Not to be taken by pregnant women," and doctors and pharmacists would be warned of the danger the drug could have during pregnancy. "That's as far as we are prepared to go," he said. The ministry officials demurred. Von Schrader-Beielstein launched into another attack on Lenz's evidence, his voice rising as he did so. At this point, Lenz burst back into the room, enraged. He had not been able to avoid overhearing, he said, and it was absolutely wrong for his evidence to be discussed in his absence. Lenz's outburst was uncharacteristic but it had a dramatic effect. The attitude of the ministry officials hardened and when the Grünenthal men became equally hostile, the officials issued an ultimatum—either Grünenthal could withdraw the drug voluntarily, or the ministry would ban its sale. Any attempt to do that, Grünenthal's lawyer, von Veltheim, said, would be met with legal action. With that, the Grünenthal men withdrew. Lenz remained behind with the ministry officials, concerned that legal action would further delay thalidomide's withdrawal. One of them reassured him: Grünenthal had agreed to attach stickers to the Contergan packets; in the meantime the ministry would send telegrams to every doctor and pharmacist in Germany stopping the sale of Contergan until the containers had been altered.

The next day, Saturday, all the top executives of Grünenthal gathered at Stolberg for an emergency meeting. They included Mueckter, von Schrader-Beielstein, and von Veltheim. Those who had attended the meeting with the ministry officials reported on what had happened and said that they had concluded, reluctantly, that Grünenthal had no alternative but to withdraw the drug from the German market. Mueckter disagreed, but then, to the amazement of his colleagues, chose that moment to produce a letter he had received the day before from DCBL in London, relaying the substance of Dr. McBride's conviction that thalidomide had caused deformed births in Australia. Mueckter read the letter aloud:

> We have had a rather disturbing report from a consultant obstetrician of deformities in children which could be associated with the taking of thalidomide by mothers in early pregnancy for morning sickness. . . . The mothers of these infants had all been given Distaval early in pregnancy in a dose of 100 mg. night and morning with an occasional extra dose during the day. There is no history of infection and the administration of Distaval seems to be the only common factor in these cases. I would be grateful if you could let me know whether you have heard of any similar reports. We believe that the cause of the abnormalities in these cases is much more likely to be due to undetected virus infection but nevertheless we feel that the report must be investigated as far as possible.

Hayman, the DCBL director who had written the letter, had, of course, no idea that in Germany Lenz had come to the same conclusions as McBride, and that this made thalidomide a far more likely cause of the deformed births than any "undetected virus infection." But Mueckter knew, and yet he *still* did not want to take the drug off the market. The others felt that the arguments for withdrawal were now overwhelming and protested at Mueckter's intransigence. Very well, Mueckter said, he would take full responsibility himself. The other Grünenthal executives eventually persuaded Mueckter to agree that a circular should be sent to doctors and pharmacists informing them of Lenz's views. Finally there was a long discussion about the technical problems of attaching stickers to all the packages of thalidomide already in warehouses and shops. At 2:00 P.M., believing they had done all they could to protect their wonder drug, the Grünenthal executives broke up for lunch. But events were already out of their hands.

The next morning, Sunday, November 26, the mass-circulation newspaper *Welt am Sonntag* came out with a long, prominently displayed story about Lenz that they had got from one of the doctors who had heard Lenz at the Düsseldorf conference on November 18. The headline on the article read: MALFORMATIONS FROM TABLETS—ALARMING SUSPICION OF PHYSICIAN'S GLOBALLY DISTRIBUTED DRUG. The newspaper cited most of the arguments put forward by Lenz in his letter to Grünenthal November 16 and backed his demands that the drug should be withdrawn immediately. It concluded: "So far it has not been withdrawn. Should this warning, prompted by a sense of medical responsibility, be ignored? It is high time that the authorities intervene and without delay, too." The Grünenthal directors who saw or heard of the *Welt* report hurried to Stolberg, where at a brief meeting they decided to take the drug off the market. A telegram went off to the ministry: WE ARE TAKING CONTERGAN OUT OF CIRCULATION IMMEDIATELY UNTIL SCIENTIFIC QUESTIONS HAVE BEEN ANSWERED. MEASURES FOR THIS HAVE ALREADY BEEN TAKEN. MORE DETAILS TOMORROW ORALLY. The decision was made with such haste that some of those who had been closely concerned with the events over the previous few days were not consulted. Dr. Nowel, the statistician, for example, had spent the day like a dutiful German family man with relatives, in Bochum. He heard of the *Welt am Sonntag* article by accident when he telephoned a doctor friend later in the day. He then rang Leufgens, the managing director, at home and Leufgens told him that Contergan had already been taken off the market.

Early the next morning, Monday, November 27, Grünenthal set about contacting pharmacists, doctors, and wholesalers, and its licensees in other countries, including the United States. The company's attitude was not that it was withdrawing the drug in the public good, but that it had been forced into the decision by the sensationalism of the *Welt am Sonntag* article. "Because press reports have undermined the basis of scientific discussion," Grünenthal wrote to the West German Federal Medical Association's Drug Commission, "we have decided to withdraw Contergan from the market immediately," and a letter to overseas licensees read, "Due to continuous pressure from Dr. Lenz on the health authorities, and above all, because of the press campaign in Germany that we feared might break out and that in fact did break out, we were finally forced . . . to withdraw Contergan from the market." The West German Ministry of Health would have none of this. It issued a firm statement that thalidomide was suspected as the major factor in the outbreak of deformed births, and newspapers and radio and television stations carried the statement with a warning to women not to take the drug.

Grünenthal had telephoned DCBL in London the same Monday to report the decision and to assure the British company that it was taking immediate steps to investigate the evidence. DCBL's managing director, Hayman, spent the morning on the telephone speaking with Grünenthal, DCBL's medical advisers, and his fellow directors. At a meeting of the management committee, his recommendation that Distaval and its associated products be withdrawn was accepted.

Once DCBL decided to end the sale of thalidomide, it moved with commendable speed. Letters announcing the decision went off to the *BMJ* and the *Lancet* and were published in issues for the week ending Saturday, December 2. The principal sentence read: "We feel that we have no alternative but to withdraw the drug from the market immediately pending further investigation." A letter in similar terms went to all doctors in the United Kingdom, and drug wholesalers, retailers, and hospitals were advised of the decision. Subsidiary companies in Australia and New Zealand, and other export markets controlled by Distillers were also notified.

DCBL now added up the damage. The withdrawal of the drug left it with stocks at home and overseas worth about $350,000. It was clear that before it could hope to put Distaval back on the market a lot of expensive research would be involved, and in the end it might not be worth it. Some executives nevertheless remained optimistic. Others were depressed. Hayman wrote: "We have received a great deal of sympathy and praise for our action. Although this is very gratifying it does not of course change the profit picture at the end of the day. . . ."

In the United States, Richardson-Merrell received the news of Grünenthal's decision on November 29. The following morning, Dr. Murray of Richardson-Merrell telephoned Dr. Kelsey at the FDA and, in what must have been a moment of some chagrin for him, told her that thalidomide had been withdrawn from the German market. When Dr. Kelsey asked why, Dr. Murray said that the drug was suspected of causing congenital malformations but that he hoped this association was only coincidental.

Now came the final blow. The most crucial scientific question was the one Mueckter had been asked by the Finnish doctor back in July 1961: did thalidomide pass the placenta so that it could affect an unborn child? Mueckter had replied "Not known," and Grünenthal had done absolutely nothing to find out. Now, when it was too late, Grünenthal put its researchers to work in this vital area. It did not prove difficult. They used radioactively labelled thalidomide which enabled them to track its passage in the bloodstream of mice and watch whether it crossed the placenta. Four weeks after the decision to withdraw thalidomide they had an answer. It did.

Grünenthal was determined not to lose its wonder drug without a struggle. It argued that even if thalidomide did cross the placenta, there was still no evidence that it was responsible for deformed births. Anyone who agreed with this proposition was encouraged to say so publicly. Those who disagreed were described within Grünenthal as "trouble-makers, opportunists, or fanatics." The company's real virulence was reserved for Lenz, and a campaign was started to discredit him and to "influence the press for our purpose." Company minutes of a meeting on December 27 capture the full flavour of Grünenthal's feelings toward the doctor who had caused them so much trouble:

> When considering how many countless psychic traumas have been produced by the contribution to the discussion of Dr. Lenz and still more by the sensational reports of the irresponsible gutter press, I cannot regard Dr. Lenz's behaviour as responsible. What Goethe once said applies to him as well as to Dr. Frenkel: "Idiots and clever people are both equally harmless. Those halfwits and half-educated people who always recognize only half-truths are dangerous."

Lenz was made out to be a dangerous fanatic. Grünenthal's line of attack can be judged from a report written by a Canadian drug company executive after being briefed by Grünenthal on a visit to Stolberg early in December:

> Dr. Lenz is associated with the paediatric clinic of the University of Hamburg and has been interested in genetics for a long time. His father was a famous and popular geneticist in Nazi times, since he had "proven" the validity of the master race concept on genetic grounds. He first broached his suspicions to [Grünenthal] on November 16 but was unwilling to give any details of the cases that had come to his attention. He simply wanted them to take the drug off the market immediately and is supposed to have told Grünenthal that he had a "vision" indicating Contergan as the cause of all these deformities. . . . Although it had been Grünenthal's intention to send out

a warning letter, and their local health authorities had agreed that this was all that was required, the furore in the newspapers grew so quickly and violently that Grünenthal felt they had no choice but to take the product off the market until the question had been resolved.

A journalist specializing in medical questions was engaged by Grünenthal to write articles for newspapers and technical journals putting Grünenthal in the "best possible light." An internal memorandum set out the approach for doctors: "It was decided that all doctors, and especially those in a position to influence public opinion, who make critical statements must be persuaded by the strongest possible means to change their minds or at least must be neutralized. It is extremely important that our PR department in the future make even greater efforts than in the past to keep in close touch with important scientists and leaders of public opinion."

But nothing Grünenthal did could stop the evidence piling up against thalidomide. The next blow for Grünenthal came in the *Lancet* on February 10, 1962. Dr. Alexander Speirs of the Stirling Royal Infirmary had observed during 1961 ten cases of babies born with severe limb malformations. In September—about the same time that Lenz was collecting evidence in Germany—Speirs began to try to find a common factor in the ten cases. He reasoned that as the limb buds of a child in the uterus usually appear at the sixth to seventh week and have formed by the eighth week, whatever had caused the malformations must have operated about this time. So he questioned the mothers closely about the progress of their pregnancy during the first three months: What had they eaten? Had they had any infection? Had they been exposed to radiation? What drugs had they taken? Despite Speirs's persistence, nothing emerged. But when he learned in November of the withdrawal of thalidomide and the reasons for it, he reopened his investigation. He visited the mothers again, showed them thalidomide, asked if they could remember having taken such a drug, and with the permission of their family doctors, had a search made in the local health authority archives for the actual prescription forms written for the women. This produced dramatic, documentary evidence. As Speirs wrote:

> Of these ten mothers, eight took thalidomide during pregnancy. One had a sedative, the nature of which is unknown, and in one case there is no evidence that the mother had any

drug at all. However, it became apparent early in the investigation that statements by the patient or the doctor that no thalidomide had been taken could not necessarily be accepted. In view of this it remains quite possible that the two mothers for whom there was no proof did in fact have this drug.

But the most powerful evidence against thalidomide came from the laboratory of the British licensee, DCBL. There, during February and March 1962, Dr. Somers gave four white rabbits thalidomide from their eighth to sixteenth days of pregnancy. Of the 18 baby rabbits born, 13 bore the horrible and characteristic deformities now associated with thalidomide. Somers was the first researcher to reproduce the thalidomide malformations in animals, and he was anxious to publish. But when Grünenthal learned about these results, they wrote to DCBL suggesting that Somers should not make his findings public "for the time being." Somers, with a scientist's regard for the truth, took no notice, and his paper was published in the *Lancet* on April 28, 1962. "We have succeeded in producing deformities in rabbits remarkably similar to those in humans," he wrote. "It is hoped that the techniques employed will permit a method to be developed which will be of general application in the screening of all new drugs for possible teratogenic effects."

Not everyone at Distillers approved Somers's action, and a directive went out rigorously controlling the publication of papers on Distaval. As one DCBL director remarked: "It is clear that the senior directors . . . have become hypersensitive . . . and in future those concerned at working level must be prepared to steer a very careful course between the advancement of scientific knowledge through scientific publications and the bad publicity for the company that these are likely to generate through the popular press and elsewhere."

In fact, DCBL had not yet decided to give up thalidomide. There had been requests from hospitals for further supplies and the company decided to respond to these requests and keep selling thalidomide to them. Results were disappointing, and the representatives were told to try harder. "Representatives should, from now on, take every opportunity of informing members of the hospital medical staff that Distaval is again available for use in hospitals where the administration to pregnant women or those likely to become pregnant, can be avoided."

DCBL now tried to create a demand for thalidomide to be put on the market again and tried to enlist the help of the *Lancet*. At the seventeenth monthly meeting of the medical department, on March 2, 1962, Brown said that he had spoken to the *Lancet*'s editor, Dr. Munro. "If doctors wishing Distaval replaced on the market will write in asking for it, Dr. Munro will do his best to stimulate discussion and get the subject ventilated in the *Lancet*." The company also instructed its sales representatives to try to persuade doctors to write such letters, but the effort proved useless and sales continued to slump. In December 1962, DCBL finally decided to end its sales even to hospitals, and the "wonder sedative" vanished from the market.

In the United States, Richardson-Merrell had formally withdrawn its application to the FDA in March 1962, when it was apparent that Dr. Murray's hope—that the association between thalidomide and malformed births was only coincidental—had turned out to be unfounded. But the problem of withdrawing the Kevadon tablets distributed as part of the Richardson-Merrell "investigational program" proved very difficult. Richardson-Merrell sent a warning letter to doctors it had asked to test the drug, but 42 said later that they did not receive it. The FDA tried to track down all the thalidomide tablets but was unable even to locate 99 of the doctors who had taken part in Richardson-Merrell's trials. In addition, 410 of the doctors it did contact then made no effort to get in touch with the patients to whom they had given thalidomide *because in many cases they had kept no record of having done so.* The cases of thalidomide damage that have to date been traced in the United States must not, therefore, be considered as representing the true extent of the American tragedy.

Grünenthal, DCBL, and Richardson-Merrell now considered their legal position. Grünenthal began to prepare for the battle clearly in the offing. Its advisers had warned the German company earlier, "There is the strongest probability that we will lose most of the civil law suits brought against us." But far more ominously, the public prosecutor's office in Aachen had started an investigation of the thalidomide tragedy in December 1961, soon after the drug had been withdrawn, and already there were rumours that the investigators believed they had sufficient evidence to justify a *criminal* action against certain executives and scientists in Grünenthal. The company was determined to be well prepared, and von Veltheim proposed "an intensive but very careful and tactful public relations exercise which unobtrusively shows the Grünenthal position in the best possible light in the medical and trade press."

The basic defence was much the same for all three companies. DCBL set it out in an internal memorandum: "Pharmacological investigation for teratogenic effects is not standard practice. Since the withdrawal of the drug DCBL laboratories have spent many months in an attempt to produce congenital malformations in off-spring of female animals to whom thalidomide was administered in high doses during early pregnancy." The first tests had failed, the memorandum says, but later ones succeeded. "From a clinical trial point of view a human trial to test teratogenic effects would, for obvious reasons, not be considered. Investigators must necessarily rely on animal experiments and observations on pregnant women who were given the drug for its normal therapeutic effect." In a nutshell, DCBL's main argument was that they could not have done tests on human beings for teratogenic effects; that it was not customary at that time to do such tests on animals, so they did not do them; and that even if they had done such tests, nothing would have shown up because the only animal in which it is comparatively easy to produce thalidomide's teratogenic effects is the New Zealand white rabbit. (It might be pointed out that New Zealand white rabbits had been in DCBL's animal house for some years and were, therefore, easily available.)

This defence was later to recur in different forms in scientific journals, the lay press, and government letters. Yet we believe that we have shown that it is invalid. Neither Grünenthal, Distillers, nor Richardson-Merrell followed the best drug-testing procedures of the time, despite all the statements to the contrary. Had they done so, question marks would have been thrown up of the kind that—again at the time—persuaded established pharmaceutical firms not to proceed with other new products. All three companies, moreover, made positive assertions for the drug without worthwhile supporting evidence—notably, that it was safe for use in pregnancy. (How the companies' defence worked out under British and American law is another matter, and we shall return to this later.)

While the lawyers took over, those executives who fully comprehended the enormity of the tragedy were horrified. Dr. Somers remembers that when he went into his laboratory and found the 13 deformed baby rabbits, proof of the terrible power of the drug, he was "completely shattered, emotionally and professionally." And when Dr. Keller, a co-discoverer of thalidomide, heard of the evidence, he said, "I feel like a bus driver who has run into a group of children."

In the end, Distillers Company (Biochemicals), the firm that felt it had no cause to reproach itself, left the pharmaceutical business in 1962, selling out to the American firm Eli Lilly. Grünenthal and Richardson-Merrell remain in business. Many of the main characters who figured in this narrative are now in other employment; thalidomide is just a painful memory. Only the victims still occupy the stage.

8 Alone in a World of Horror

Distillers' operation in Australia was formally an autonomous one, separate from the British company. In practice, it worked in close liaison with the British parent company, and at the London headquarters of DCBL there was even an export manager for Australia, John Flawn. So in November 1961, when the Sydney office sent London its report about Dr. McBride and his experience with deformed births, the letter first went to Flawn.

Flawn read it with growing alarm, not only for professional reasons but for personal ones as well. He had been taking thalidomide himself to help get to sleep and had given his wife, Judith, some thalidomide tablets. She was now in the seventh month of her pregnancy, and Flawn realized that if McBride was right, then the child Judith was carrying was in danger of being malformed. He kept this knowledge to himself for three weeks and then, unable to carry the burden alone any longer, told his wife.

It was as well that he did. Alexander Flawn, born on January 9, 1962, was one of the worst-damaged thalidomide children in Britain. He had a deformed and shortened arm with a hand without a thumb. The other hand had one extra finger. His palate had a gaping hole in it. His face was paralysed on one side. One ear was completely missing, the other grossly deformed. For the first eighteen months of his life, he vomited his food across the room with projectile-like force. It soon became clear that his brain was damaged, that he was deaf and dumb, and had poor vision in his left eye. "When Alex was born, I was frightfully brave," said Judith Flawn. "I cut off all my feelings. This was a terrible mistake because I didn't come alive again for seven years."

All over the world, wherever pregnant women had taken thalidomide during the crucial period, deformed babies were being born. In some cases, the tragedy was compounded by other factors. One woman had *two* thalidomide children. One mother, Shirley McCarrick of Los Angeles, was a teen-ager, only sixteen years old and still in high school, when she gave birth to a deformed daughter. One couple from Liége, Belgium, with the help of their family doctor, poisoned their eight-day-old daughter, who had been born without legs. (Charged with murder, they were acquitted to the wild acclaim of a thousand people who had crowded into the courtroom for the week-long trial.)

The type of deformity depended on what stage of development the embryo had reached when the mother took the drug.* Many children had foreshortened limbs, often no more than flippers like casual addenda to the trunk. Eye and ear deformities were common. Frequently there was terrible internal damage, such as anal atresia, a condition in which there is no external opening to the bowel. There were babies with malformed kidneys, others whose genitals were missing or deformed. And a few of the children, like Alex, suffered brain damage. It was as though the jigsaw of life had been jumbled and then the pieces forced into places they could not fit or simply left out altogether.

Although the total number of British thalidomide babies who survived was only 410, Dr. Gerard Vaughan, in charge of the children's unit at Guy's Hospital, London, and Dr. Claus Newman, consultant paediatrician at Queen Mary's Hospital, Roehampton, both think that at least twice as many died at birth, mostly because of internal damage. Many hundreds of other children in Britain, the United States, Canada, Japan, and elsewhere, may, they believe, be suffering from faulty hearts, hearing defects, and other abnormalities that have not been attributed to thalidomide because they do not fit the most typical pattern.

Both doctors have considerable experience of the thalidomide cases. Dr. Vaughan has been involved in assessing the degree of damage in thalidomide victims since 1968 and has written psychiatric reports on the mothers and their children. Dr. Newman runs the unit that was set up by the Department of Health to look after the problems of thalidomide children some four years after the drug was withdrawn. Its work has now been broadened to include other disabled children, but 120 of the British thalidomide victims had artificial limbs fitted or long-term treatment at Dr. Newman's unit. Both doctors, more than fifteen years after thalidomide was withdrawn, have for the first time made a remarkable public indictment of the way their profession handled the thalidomide disaster.

* See Appendix, pp. 265 ff.

The first major mistakes, they say, were made in the way the mal-formed baby was concealed from its mother after its birth, and then suddenly presented to her—with its little limbs and flippers—when she was leaving the hospital and it could be hidden no longer. Midwives and nurses would give one excuse after another to delay the moment when the mother had to be told. "He's a lovely child—a bonny boy—but he needs a bit of special care," they would say, without mentioning the gross deformities that would be obvious to the mother the moment she saw the baby. Because they realized they were not being told the truth, some mothers built up fantasies about the baby, deciding it was already dead, and were relieved to see it alive, however badly deformed. Others believed the stories about their "lovely child" and were horrified and re-pelled by the creature placed in their arms.

"They didn't allow me to see him, because they said I was too ill," says Florence Evans, whose son Liam is blind and has no arms. "When they gave him to me, his face was split, hanging apart like on a butcher's slab. The doctor was crying and said my baby wouldn't live. But he did, and two weeks later they sent him home with his face stitched up. He was my own flesh and blood and had to be cared for. I didn't cry outwardly, but inside I screamed. I've never left the house on my own from that day since."

One woman did not discover her child had no arms until she had taken him home and went to give him a bath. The hospital staff—and one can sympathize with them—had found it impossible to tell her. An-other describes the birth of her daughter as a trauma beyond anything she had imagined. The baby was brought to her "with feet sticking out from each hip, and absolutely purple in the face." The mother began to scream and had to be kept behind screens and under sedation for days. On the fourth day, she waited until night and then went to the baby's cot with a pillow and began to smother it, but the child wriggled and struggled and the mother kept thinking of the commandment "Thou shalt not kill." Sobbing, she took the pillow away, and fell into an emo-tional depression that lasted for three years.

"When I first saw my baby I thought it was the cruellest thing that could ever happen," another mother, Betty Rastin, remembers. "It's still a living grief every time I see her and always will be. If only she had arms or legs or even hip bones, it would have been wonderful. I thought at first I couldn't cope. I did, but it's changed my life."

Often it was the father who saw the new baby first. Some fathers coped reasonably well. Thomas Diamond, a Philadelphia systems analyst, was at work when the obstetrician telephoned. "Come over right away," he said. "You've had a son but he has no arms." Diamond drove to the hospital in a daze and was told that he would have to break the news to his wife himself. First he went to see the baby. "They held him up for me and he scared me half to death. He had no arms except that on one side he had something. His face was very red and he had a strawberry birthmark down the centre of his face and over the nose. I broke the news to Joanne and we had a good cry. The hospital didn't offer any reason for my son's deformities. They just told us to take him home and love him. Oh, yes. And they did say to have more children immediately because they didn't think our son would survive the first year."

Other fathers could not accept the situation. Several were so appalled they fainted on the spot. One told his wife: "If you bring that monster home, I leave." She did, and he left her. Indeed, fathers tended to be affected more than the mothers. Stanley Jones, a psychiatric nurse, was one of those who fainted when he first saw his deformed son, David. The strain continued to be too great for him: he had a series of breakdowns and became a psychiatric patient himself. "When my baby was born," Mrs. J. Pollock recalled, "I had him at home. My husband fainted. I was kept under doctor's care. I couldn't look at the baby when the nurse was washing him. I was in a terrible state, but I said to myself, 'He is mine.' God gave him to me, and if he had nothing he was still my baby." Her husband was unable to accept the child so philosophically. He became depressed and had to be given drugs and eventually electric shock therapy. But the Pollocks found that their armless child, in addition to distressing them, caused great embarrassment with other people. "We have an old custom in the area where I lived," Mrs. Pollock said. "People would come in, find the baby's hand, and put a silver shilling in it. When they couldn't find his arm or hand to do this, it upset them. When I took him out for a walk, it was like a circus with children following me saying, 'Look at this kid. He's got no arms.' Thank God, I got over that."

Sometimes the father, unable to accept the child's deformities, turned on the mother. "He blamed me for his condition," explained the mother of one badly damaged child. "He wanted to put the baby into a home and never see him again." The woman eventually divorced her husband on the grounds of cruelty and desertion, a not uncommon event in families with a thalidomide child. "If it weren't for you, I wouldn't have the son I have," said the father of an armless boy when he left his wife, never to return.

Sometimes it worked the other way around, and the father was left to cope. Christine Clark, a Liverpool mother of a girl with short arms and legs, broke down under the strain, later spent some time in psychiatric hospitals, and never returned home. Her husband was left to look after the family and bring up their handicapped daughter. In one or two cases, the burden became insupportable. Not long after her deformed baby had been born, one mother went alone to a hotel and committed suicide. "I did try to end my life," another mother said. "I started to take the pills, but all the time I thought of her lying helpless with her awful stunted body, and I kept repeating to myself, 'Who'd look after her?' "

Other children were often upset by the arrival of a thalidomide brother or sister. They felt displaced and threatened, often with good reason. Some had to live through their parents' bitter divorce; almost all had to live with the fact that their mother's time was largely devoted to the thalidomide child. Few accepted the new arrival so philosophically as one little boy: his mother had told him he would have a new sister for Christmas; when he saw her for the first time and noticed that she had no arms, he said, "Santa must've done it when he brought her down the chimney."

The anguish of the parents was aggravated by the fact that many did not know that thalidomide was to blame, that the seemingly innocent pill prescribed months earlier to help them sleep, relieve headaches, or quieten morning sickness was the cause of the tragedy. Until they read about thalidomide in a newspaper or heard the story on television—and this often three years or more after the birth—many parents believed that something must have been wrong with *them,* and they blamed themselves, or each other, for the child's deformities. "It's all your fault," the mother of a severely brain-damaged boy was told. "It's inherited from your family." It was especially hard, when reviewed in this new, sinister light, if one or other parent did have a handicapped relative.

The one obvious person who could have relieved some of this sort of distress was the family doctor. But he was often reluctant to speak out, partly because he felt guilty at having prescribed the drug, partly because he feared that the parents would sue him. Most doctors were advised by their professional groups to say nothing, to avoid incriminating themselves. Some even refused to reveal records of the drugs they had prescribed.

When the truth finally did emerge, many parents were overcome with resentment and guilt, and this put further pressure on family life. Some mothers felt—and still feel—guilty for having taken the drug for a relatively trivial complaint such as morning sickness and regard their child as some sort of punishment for not having put up with their illness. For a time, there were suggestions that the women had taken thalidomide because they were neurotic, that they had dosed themselves indiscriminately, accusations that do not stand up since many of the mothers took only a few pills—in some cases just one. Judith Flawn took only two thalidomide pills during her pregnancy. Lisa Donaldson, born in February 1961, without arms, or even shoulder blades, was damaged by the three to five pills her mother had been prescribed when she thought she was suffering from menopause. "They'll calm you down a bit and lift your depression," her doctor told her. She was actually pregnant. Joanne Diamond took three pills—the only sleeping pills she had ever taken in her life—because when they were on a trip her husband was rushed to the hospital. A doctor in the emergency room noticed how upset Mrs. Diamond was. He arranged for her to have Compazine tranquillizers and thalidomide tablets. "Here," he said. "You look terrible. Take these." Later, she learned that she was pregnant.

What was so terrible about the thalidomide deformities? Why did thalidomide throw the medical profession into a state of shock? What was so horrific about its effects that it took many years before a thalidomide child was publicly acceptable? "In my unit at Guy's Hospital, we have a lot of badly handicapped children," says Dr. Vaughan, "but I have never seen such a reaction among my staff as when they were faced with the thalidomide children. They were horrified. I had great difficulty in getting them to carry out a psychological test or examination. They were repelled in a way I have only witnessed on the faces of people going into a major burns unit for the first time. And these were doctors and nurses!"

Dr. Newman, who arrived later on the thalidomide scene, encountered similar problems. "People said they shouldn't be allowed to live. But that was because they had a basic murderous attitude towards them. Excessive sympathy was mixed with fear and a threat. Faced with the sight of a disintegrated child, passers-by and professionals alike seemed to feel their own mental and physical wholeness at risk. I remember seeing a family with a thalidomide child on the beach. There was always an empty space around them."

The reaction of the families was to shun public places. They lived in great isolation, and when they did venture out, public reaction would send them hurrying home. Terry Wiles, a totally limbless thalidomide child, was visited in hospital by his adoptive parents-to-be, Leonard and Hazel Wiles. They wanted to give him a treat, so they took him to a tea-shop in a local village. But the stares and comments were too much, and it was years before they dared do it again.

But why are children mutilated in car accidents acceptable, while those damaged by thalidomide are so shunned? "It's because we regard the car as essential and accidents a necessary evil," says Dr. Newman. "Taking a drug to make oneself feel better is not essential. Whereas it's strong to have a car, it is weak to need a drug." Parents already coping with this crippling guilt, either self-imposed or inflicted by a bewildered society, then had to face the further trauma of the need to make the children look as normal as possible, so that they appeared more acceptable to people around them. Whereas all the internal operations were necessary, and many orthopaedic operations did help children to use their deformed limbs, many other operations had no purpose other than cosmetic improvement, and often that was minimal. "We doctors had no concept then of the value of those little tendrils of flesh and muscle," says Dr. Newman. "With everything that was extra, not quite right, or sticking out, the tendency was to say: 'Off with it!' No one saw then how these remnants of limbs could be invaluable in later life for operating switches or holding tools, and it was the parents who realized this before the medical people."

Nevertheless, for good reasons or bad, many of the children went through long series of surgical operations. Patrick Pope, who had major internal abnormalities, was operated on forty-two times. "My son keeps asking me, 'Mummy, please don't let me have any more operations,' " his mother, Mrs. Julie Pope, wrote in a letter to *The Sunday Times* in 1973. "He [still] has only one kidney. He had to have a colostomy. He has an abnormality of the penis and may be sterile. His hands are not normal. He has sight only to eye level. . . . There is a possibility of more operations but I keep my fingers crossed and pray that God will be good and the body will have its own capacity for healing."

Patrick Pope's pain and his mother's anguish were necessary for his survival. But other surgery seems to have been much more questionable. Between twenty and thirty of the thalidomide children in Britain were born without ears, and at least four went through a series of seventeen or eighteen operations simply to give them a flap of external flesh that looked something like an ear, although it could never be used to hear. "There was a feeling that the useless but visible outward ear would bring about some magic to make the child hear. It was a kind of collusion between doctors and parents to expiate their guilt," says Dr. Vaughan.

The grafting procedure was long and painful. In a first operation, a flap of skin tissue would be raised from the belly and attached to the child's arm. After the child had spent six or eight weeks with his arm strapped to his belly, the tissue would have attached itself firmly. It was then severed from the belly, and the skin flap was grafted to the side of the head and the arm splinted to hold it in position for a further six to eight weeks. In a third operation, the tissue was cut from the arm, leaving the flap of skin on the head. Further operations then shaped the tissue into something resembling a human ear. The whole procedure was painful, very uncomfortable, and carried a great risk of infection. Dr. Vaughan's verdict is uncompromising: "It was a monument to well-intentioned, but misguided effort, and it left indelible psychological scars on the children."

The mistakes of the ear grafting were made time and time again in other guises. Limbless children were fitted with artificial arms and legs in the hope that modern engineering ingenuity could give them back some of the functions thalidomide had stolen from them. But engineers are no match for Nature. Sometimes all that the metal legs and unwieldy arms could do was to give the wearer some outward appearance of normality. At least he was the right size and shape. Inwardly, the picture was very different. In many cases, tiny deformed bodies had had inelegant but potentially useful limbs amputated so that they could be strapped into the leather harness of the artificial legs.

At Chailey Heritage in Sussex, a home, hospital, and school for disabled children, the thalidomide victims practised standing in their legs, like tin soldiers, wearily clinking from one leg to another or shuffling slowly across the room. "How we envied the boys who could sit in their wheelchairs," says Terry Wiles, who spent the first nine years of his life at Chailey. "We used to get so tired, balancing on our legs and hoping the wheelchair boys wouldn't come and knock us over." Chailey had

special high desks built with semicircular bays in them so that the tin
soldiers could do their lessons standing up. A bar across the small of their
back fastened to the desk at each end kept them from falling out of their
bay.

Artificial arms were almost as much of a torture. The first arms came
from Germany and were called "pat-a-cake" because they could carry
out only a simple clapping motion. They were not much help, and were
exceedingly uncomfortable. The child had to be fitted with a moulded
plaster waistcoat whose two halves were bolted around him; this waistcoat carried the arms and their power supplies. But there was one major
flaw. Small limbless bodies have very little surface area with which to
dissipate body heat. When their bodies were enclosed in a heavy, tight-
fitting plaster waistcoat with all its paraphernalia attached, several of
the children ran very high temperatures and were in danger of being
seriously ill.

The more sophisticated and expensive gas-powered arm was not
much more successful. It was driven by a gas cylinder carried on the
back, had a relatively light jacket to support it, and offered a considerable range of arm and finger movements. But human body and engineering miracle did not prove sympathetic. The arms were far too heavy
for small, frail bodies and left ugly weals where the harness cut into the
children's backs. They were difficult to control, and made hissing noises
on every movement as the propellant gas escaped. Worse still, the gas
cylinder would sometimes run out without warning and leave the poor
wearer with his arms outstretched as though crucified, and with no
means of moving them.

Gradually, as the children grew older, common sense began to prevail.
Leonard and Hazel Wiles showed that their son, Terry, could do better
using his flippers and rolling on the floor than attempting to manoeuvre
limbs that were as large as he was. Leonard Wiles started to develop new
gadgets for Terry that helped him to use what muscles he had instead of
attempting to mimic the limbs of normal people. He quickly persuaded
Terry to put aside his artificial legs and set about designing a special
"car" to give him mobility. Terry was lucky to have an inventor in the
family, but most of the other thalidomide children gradually dispensed
with their artificial limbs and made do with what they had.

"A sorry tale," says Dr. Vaughan. "Thalidomide exposed aspects of
medical technique which were not up to the job. The experience has
benefited many of today's handicapped children, but it has not taken

away from the damage done to the families at that time. Those children had to go through psychological trauma and considerable pain just to satisfy some community conscience that the doctors had tried to do something to put the tragedy right."

There was also considerable reluctance in the medical profession to accept that less obvious but equally incapacitating birth defects could be due to thalidomide. Only in 1976, when many of the children were sixteen years old, did doctors finally agree that thalidomide could cause epilepsy, autism, and mental retardation.

Morag MacCallum, seventeen, but with a mental age of two, totally deaf with no ears, practically blind in one eye, her face and throat paralysed, is one of the more severe of these brain-damaged cases. Often she grunts and screams all night, her mother says, "like a rabbit caught in a snare." According to her parents, one doctor told them: "I have never seen a child with such deformities of the head as I have with this child." Some years ago Glasgow surgeons operated on her. One surgeon said, "A complete mess, with everything missing."

It is likely that there are many more cases of brain damage still not attributed to thalidomide. "It is all forgotten now," says Dr. Newman, "but these more curious effects without limb abnormalities were rarely blamed on thalidomide. The idea was not really accepted until we had shown that a large proportion of thalidomide children cried every time their mouth watered, a phenomenon known as 'crocodile tears,' a well-established symptom of central brain damage."

So it is clear only now that the human consequences of thalidomide have been more tragic and more widespread than anyone ever imagined. Dr. Vaughan says, "There is not one family I have seen that you could say was reasonably adjusted. Relationships were distorted by the experience, and few mothers escaped psychological trauma. The more subtle the damage—autism, epilepsy, mental retardation—the more alienated the families have become, destroying all efforts on their behalf. They are the greatest personal tragedies I have ever seen."

9 Let the Law Decide

It was in Germany that thalidomide had first been sold, and it was in Germany that the law was first asked to decide who was to blame for the disaster that had followed and how the victims should be compensated. The public prosecutor's office in Aachen, North Rhine-Westphalia, started investigations in December 1961, only a matter of days after the drug had been withdrawn, to see whether it could justify criminal action against the executives of Grünenthal. The prosecutor's office was breaking new ground—there was no precedent for such an action in German law, and its outcome would clearly establish a new legal relationship between German drug companies and the consumers of their products—so there was a genuine excuse for the time it took the prosecutor to decide to go ahead. Nowhere else, in any event, did the government itself take such legal action on behalf of the victims.

His investigation took four years, partly because of the peculiar technical nature of the inquiry, partly because of the large amount of documentation to be analysed, and partly because of Grünenthal's obstruction: very few of the company's internal files were surrendered voluntarily and most of the important documents had to be seized in police raids. But on September 2, 1965, the prosecutor drew up a preliminary bill of indictment charging nine Grünenthal executives with intent to commit bodily harm and involuntary manslaughter. The full bill of indictment took another two years to compile and ran to 972 pages. The state investigators had examined 5,000 cases of thalidomide damage and had settled on 60 cases of peripheral neuritis and 50 cases of malformations. They proposed to call 352 witnesses, and evidence they had already collected ran to 70,000 pages. In scale and emotional intensity, the trial promised to rival Nuremberg.

It began on May 27, 1968, in a converted club house belonging to the Eschweiler mining association in the little town of Alsdorf, six miles from Aachen. It was the only building in the area with sufficient space for the six hundred people—judges, jurymen, lawyers, stenographers, witnesses, defendants, co-plaintiffs, press, radio, and television reporters, and spectators—who were expected to attend the trial each day. The Ministry of Justice, which was organizing the trial, decided to plan for every eventuality. There were standby judges and jurymen in case anyone fell ill. There were doctors on call, Red Cross officers present during the trial, and a special traffic scheme for the town. Grünenthal, still convinced that the attitude of the German press had been partly responsible for forcing it to withdraw thalidomide, organized its own news agency, which prepared press releases on the trial and regularly sent reports containing its version of progress in the case.

Two of the accused were dropped from the indictment because of ill health. The case against the other seven, who included one of the founders of Grünenthal, Hermann Wirtz, a seventy-one-year-old father of five, and Heinrich Mueckter, the co-inventor of thalidomide, was that:

1. They put on sale a drug that even when taken according to instruction caused an unacceptable degree of bodily harm.

2. They failed to test it properly.

3. They went out of their way to advertise it as safe when they could give no guarantee that it was.

4. In fact, it caused those who took it to itch, shake, sweat, vomit, and suffer peripheral neuritis.

5. When these reactions were reported to them, they first systematically brushed them aside; some of them lied to doctors who questioned them; and when reports became too insistent to ignore, they did all they could to suppress them.

6. The drug caused an epidemic of malformed babies.

Grünenthal's defence appeared unbelievable. It maintained that it acted promptly and responsibly when the peripheral neuritis damage was first brought to its attention. So far as the malformations were concerned, the company argued, there was absolutely no proof that thalidomide was the cause, and it produced a string of expert witnesses who agreed. It further argued that even if there were such proof, it had still done no wrong because under German law an unborn baby had no legal protection except in connection with criminal abortion. Grünenthal's lawyers contended that unless an abortion was intended—and it was not in this case—then it was not a criminal offence to administer a drug that caused malformations in the unborn child.

The hearing was noisy, angry, and marked by bitter exchanges between the prosecution and the defence and between lawyers and medical experts, and some unusual but effective tactics by Grünenthal. The first medical expert was Professor Lenz, the Hamburg doctor who had first linked thalidomide with foetal malformations in Germany. Eighteen defence lawyers spent twelve days cross-examining Lenz in an effort to make him contradict himself. Lenz remained the model scientific witness, even to the extent of pointing out to the court certain weaknesses in the way he had conducted his investigation, which, however, he did not consider affected his basic conclusions. He was wasting his time in being so objective. At one stage, a defence lawyer asked him if he would not agree that some unknown virus could have caused the epidemic of malformed births. Lenz replied that there had been no cases in East Germany—where thalidomide was never on sale—and "a virus would not stop at the Berlin wall." Lenz then added, "If you make such an absurd claim, then the burden of proof rests with you." The judge immediately reprimanded Lenz for not showing sufficient respect.

Lenz nevertheless made such a strong impression on the court that Grünenthal's lawyers countered by moving that the court should reject Lenz as a medical expert on the grounds that they suspected him of partiality. They charged him with being "an expert obsessed with his position, with an almost religious conviction of his mission." They said, "He has made it his duty to bring to light the causes of the recent deformities by proving the sole responsibility of thalidomide and Grünenthal. He is guilty of slander, treachery, disparaging remarks, implicit and explicit criticism, not to mention other offensive behaviour, and he has personally attacked his scientific opponents with arrogant lectures and insulting insinuations and criticisms." Lenz was further accused of having actively supported civil lawsuits against Grünenthal and of having acted as medical and legal adviser to the parents of thalidomide-damaged children.

The court's decision on this issue was a bewildering one. On October 10, 1969, the judge announced that the court rejected Lenz as an expert witness on the grounds of "non-objectivity." The judge emphasized, however, that the court had deliberately not taken upon itself to rule whether *in reality* Lenz was prejudiced. It had, he said, merely considered whether the defence lawyers had reasonable grounds for *assuming* that Lenz was not so unbiased towards Grünenthal as an expert witness was required to be. This was a blow to the prosecution, exacerbated by the fact that another important expert witness it wanted to call, Dr. Frances Kelsey of the FDA, had been forbidden by the U.S. government to testify. (It was FDA policy not to allow its employees to give evidence in foreign trials.)

The prosecution faced other difficulties. Grünenthal and its lawyers adopted some very questionable tactics. The defence lawyers repeatedly asked medical experts appearing for the prosecution: "If thalidomide causes malformed births, then how do you explain the remarkable increase in 'thalidomide-type' malformations in Czechoslovakia, Hungary, and Poland, where thalidomide has never been on sale?" Grünenthal's lawyers never produced any figures to support this claim of increased malformations, and it turned out to be false. Next, Grünenthal mounted a public relations campaign outside the court to push its view that thalidomide had not been proved to cause malformations, and to suggest other possible causes. Eminent physicists, pharmacologists, and medical embryologists were said to have expressed doubts about thalidomide's blame. Professor Lenz noticed that many of the articles quoted had been written by someone called "Alfred Pullman," and he tried to find him and interview him. When he failed to find anyone with this name, Lenz wrote to the scientists who had been quoted in Pullman's articles and asked them for verification of their published statements. All of them denied categorically that they had ever made such statements. When Karl Schulte-Hillen, the young Hamburg lawyer who had a thalidomide child, accused Grünenthal of manipulating the press, a Grünenthal lawyer replied, " 'Manipulation'? We would call it 'influencing.' Certainly we try to influence the press through our handouts. In our opinion not only is this not dishonourable, it is our duty." How far this "influencing" went was revealed on May 26, 1970, when the prosecution told the court that at least five journalists had contacted the prosecutor's office during the trial to complain that they had been threatened with "reprisals" by representatives of Grünenthal because the company had not liked what they had written.

But Grünenthal's most effective tactic, as the trial went into its second year, was to suggest that the criminal action was holding up an out-of-court settlement of compensation claims from the German thalidomide families. Representatives of the company declared: "If we wait to see where the trial gets us, we shall still be sitting here in ten years' time and the children will have nothing. If we are forced to, we shall fight to the end, and that, of course, will diminish the resources available for any payment by the company." To add to this pressure, on January 26, 1970, Grünenthal put a figure on its offer: it would be prepared to pay DM 100 million (about $27 million) as compensation to the thalidomide children if the parents abstained from civil proceedings. It said, "The company is concerned to avoid the legal wrangles that may possibly follow—and that in the light of the experiences during this trial may prove interminable—so that it and its employees may once again devote themselves without distraction to their proper tasks."

Although German newspapers attacked this offer as "justice for sale," it was true that if the criminal verdict was appealed, a new verdict could take another three years. After that, the civil compensation claims, again if taken to appeal, could take a further five years, making seven to ten years before the thalidomide children would even know how much compensation they would receive, if indeed they were to receive anything at all. So on April 24, the organization representing the parents of German thalidomide children decided to accept Grünenthal's offer of DM 114 million (about $31 million), plus an additional DM 50–100 million (about $13.5–$27 million) from the German government. This settlement took all the vigour out of the criminal trial, and on December 18, 1970, two years and seven months after the case began, the court, with the explicit consent of the prosecution, suspended the hearing.

The court left no doubt that most of the charges originally brought against Grünenthal had been substantiated, but it stressed the mental suffering the accused had already endured and the influence German society had had on Grünenthal: "It was inherently dangerous that a producer of pharmaceuticals would give priority to commercial interests as being of the most immediate importance. There was great temptation to place the interests of the company above objections expressed by junior colleagues. . . . The struggle for a market position demanded the emphatic promotion of commercial goals."

Grünenthal had not been acquitted but neither had it been found guilty. The outcome may have brought some kind of satisfaction to the German thalidomide families, but it had by no means got to the roots of the tragedy and it had failed to provide a clear legal precedent that would establish a drug company's responsibilities to its consumers, especially when the damage the drug caused was to an unborn child. Worse was to come.

In Sweden, the enlightened welfare state that had pioneered many social reforms in health and law, it at first appeared as if the law would quickly resolve the issues raised by thalidomide. The Germans were the first to draw up an indictment, but the Swedes were the first to get a civil case into court, and on December 15, 1965, in the city court of Södertälje, a preliminary hearing began of a personal compensation claim against Astra, the pharmaceutical company that had marketed thalidomide in Sweden. But the case quickly ran into difficulties.

To begin with, the Swedish Medical Board, the highest medical authority in the country, had cleared the drug for sale on the Swedish market and it now announced that the tragedy had been unavoidable and no one was to blame. Further, an inquiry by the ombudsman had cleared the board of any negligence. Astra, while accepting no legal responsibility for the 105 Swedish thalidomide children, had donated 1 million Swedish kronor (about $200,000) before the case began to an association formed by the children's parents. Astra was the largest pharmaceutical company in Scandinavia, known all over the world for its product Xylocain, a local anaesthetic. Its reputation was that of a conscientious company with a big and well-qualified research department. Prominent Swedes sat on its board, including Dr. Lars Werkö, the chairman of the Swedish Medical Association. The feeling in professional circles was that Astra was the victim of an unfortunate, unavoidable accident.

The lawyer for the thalidomide children, Henning Sjöström, a young and successful Swede whose practice was largely in divorce, soon found that Swedish expert witnesses were reluctant to give evidence that could be used against Astra. Internationally, the drug companies appeared to be closing ranks. A simple inquiry to the Swedish branch of the Union Chimie Belge met with refusal to help: all pharmaceutical companies within the Belgian group had agreed to support Astra, because if Astra lost, it would have far-reaching implications for the whole industry. When Sjöström went outside Sweden for expert witnesses, he ran into further difficulty. The obvious place was Germany, but there the problem was that most of the German experts had already been called for the German criminal trial, and the prosecutor's office in Aachen did not want them to appear in a Swedish court and be cross-examined before they appeared in Germany.

Sjöström was more successful in the United States, where he found Dr. Thiersch, of the University of Washington, would give evidence, and in Britain, where Professor Walter Landauer, formerly of the University of Connecticut and then honorary research associate at University College,

London, helped to prepare depositions. He also found a first-class technical adviser in Sweden—Dr. Robert Nilsson, of the Royal University of Stockholm, who resisted strong pressure from his colleagues to dissuade him from working on the case.

Nevertheless, it still took Sjöström nearly four years from the date of the preliminary hearing until his final statement of proof was ready for the court. The proof ran to one thousand pages, much of it highly technical material, and it appears to have made Astra decide that in the long run an out-of-court settlement would be in its best interests. Over the years, not only had the parents showed no signs of weakening, but the administrative costs of the case were becoming a burden for the company: many members of its scientific and medical staff were spending a lot of their time on legal matters instead of their normal work.

So Sjöström and Astra negotiated, and on October 4, 1969, the Association for the Parents of Thalidomide Children accepted the company's offer. Its main advantage was that it included in the 105 children about 20 to 30 cases that were "questionable," in that it would have been difficult to prove either by medical records or by the nature of their deformity that the mother had taken thalidomide. The actual amount of the settlement will not be known for many years, because Astra agreed to pay yearly to each child a sum calculated according to his disabilities. If every child lives for seventy-five years—the average life expectancy in Sweden—and inflation continues throughout this period, then Astra will eventually pay out about 70 million kronor (about $14 million, or a crude average of about $140,000 per child). Astra's own calculation made on insurance and statistical data was that its liability will be only about 28 million kronor (about $5.6 million—$56,000 per child), and a third calculation by the Swedish magazine *Veckans Affärer* (Business Week) was that if Astra were to invest only 10 million kronor (about $2 million) in inflation-proof securities, then the interest from this investment would cover its liability under the settlement.

At the time of the Swedish settlement, there was also one in Britain— we shall go into this later—but the overall picture in Europe at this point was that the thalidomide children were being offered sums of money that could hardly be called generous in out-of-court deals that still left a lot of important legal and social questions unanswered.

In the United States, a very different pattern was emerging. There, although the attitude of Richardson-Merrell towards compensation was no different from that of its European counterparts—if anything it adopted a tougher stance—the lawyers were more aggressive on the children's behalf and the courts more willing to probe the issues.

The first case to come to trial in the United States began before Judge E. Mac Troutman in the U.S. District Court for Eastern Pennsylvania, Philadelphia, on February 17, 1969. Thomas Diamond and his wife, Joanne, on their own behalf and as parents of David, sued the William S. Merrell Company and Richardson-Merrell Inc. for $2 million, alleging that the company had shown negligence and callous disregard for the public in its handling of thalidomide. Diamond was the systems analyst whose wife had been given thalidomide on a trip and whose son, David, had been born without arms and with other injuries.

Three years after David's birth, friends had shown the Diamonds a *Time* magazine article that had photographs of German thalidomide victims. One German child had deformities that looked like David's, but the Diamonds did not make the connection because they thought thalidomide had never been available in the United States. The Sherry Finkbein case enlightened them. Mrs. Finkbein, a television commentator who became pregnant in mid-1962, was convinced her child would be born deformed because she had taken thalidomide during pregnancy. She went to Sweden for an abortion, and the child was indeed malformed. Her case received wide publicity in the United States because of the abortion issue—abortion then being illegal.

The Diamonds now tried to find out precisely what were the two kinds of pills given to Mrs. Diamond on their trip. The packet of Compazine tranquillizers was still in the medicine chest, but there was no trace of the thalidomide pills. Fortunately, on the Compazine envelope was the signature of the doctor who had prescribed both tablets. Through their own doctor, the Diamonds tried to gather proof that Mrs. Diamond had been given thalidomide, but they had no success. The hospital where Thomas Diamond had been treated, the Cleveland Clinic, said it had no records for Mrs. Diamond (this was quite possible, because she was not a patient), that it was "impossible" for her to have been given thalidomide because there was none in the hospital pharmacy at that time.

The Diamonds were convinced that Mrs. Diamond *had* been given thalidomide and they wanted to sue—apart from any other reasons, their son's medical bills in his first three years of life had totalled $20,000. So they went to a Philadelphia law firm specializing in negligence actions, Richter, Lord, Toll, Cavanaugh, McCarty & Raynes, where B. Nathaniel Richter agreed to take the case on a contingency fee basis—the firm would handle the case for nothing but would take a percentage of the damages if the Diamonds won. Arthur G. Raynes, then only in his thirties, took over the case early in 1967 when it was at discovery stage (the point at which each party has the right to examine the other's documentation).

Since the case was the first one Richardson-Merrell was facing over thalidomide, it brought its heaviest fire power into action. Fred Lamb, a vice-president of Richardson-Merrell and an attorney in its legal department, told Raynes that he was too young to take on such an important action against such a large company and that he had no chance whatsoever of winning. He said that Richardson-Merrell's defence would be that David Diamond was not a thalidomide child, thalidomide was not dangerous, the company had relied on Grünenthal's studies, there was no way it could have known about the drug's teratogenic effects, and above all, it was not legally responsible to David under American law. Lamb engaged a top-drawer law firm to act for Richardson-Merrell: the company was represented in court by the establishment firm of Pepper, Hamilton & Sheetz through John B. H. Carter and Edward J. Madeira, Jr. The lines were drawn: Raynes for the child and the family—Merrell for its company image. "There was a lot at stake for everyone," Raynes says, "and as a result it was a very bitter fight."

Raynes went into court reasonably confident. Going through thousands of Richardson-Merrell discovery documents, he had found a letter written by the doctor who had prescribed the sleeping pills for Mrs. Diamond in the Cleveland Clinic. The letter, addressed to the Richardson-Merrell executive who was in charge of distributing thalidomide for the clinical trials, related Mrs. Diamond's inquiry and ended, "If Mrs. Diamond got thalidomide, I wonder where she got it." The file copy of Richardson-Merrell's reply contained a small notation indicating that a copy of the reply had been sent to another doctor at the Cleveland Clinic. Raynes checked on this doctor and was pleased but not surprised to discover that he had been doing the thalidomide clinical trials at the hospital and had been distributing the drug around the hospital before, during, and after the time that the Diamonds were there. The doctor admitted that he had no records as to what he did with his drugs and was unable to account for more than 1,500 thalidomide pills

Richardson-Merrell had shipped to him during this period. Then, just before the trial, Raynes found the nurse who had administered the sleeping pills to Mrs. Diamond. She was able to describe the colour, size, and appearance of the pills, and when shown Richardson-Merrell's thalidomide pills, Kevadon, she made a positive identification.

Raynes felt he had strong proof of ingestion and in addition had medical evidence that David was a thalidomide child from doctors in the United States and Canada. But soon after the trial started, the judge said he would like further medical evidence. Dr. Lenz testified that David's type of upper-limb malformations occurred when thalidomide was taken between the twenty-eighth and thirty-fifth days of pregnancy. Raynes's calculations showed that Mrs. Diamond had taken the sleeping pills during this exact seven-day period.

From then on, everything went Raynes's way. James Knox Smith, a laboratory technician who had once worked for Richardson-Merrell, gave evidence that the company had not reported to the FDA animal test results that were unfavourable to thalidomide. Raynes read into the court record the depositions of Pogge and Nulsen about their "ghosted" paper for the *American Journal of Obstetrics and Gynecology*. The hearing was receiving wide publicity, and on March 12, after a dispute in which Raynes demanded and Richardson-Merrell refused the originals rather than the copies of certain company documents, Richardson-Merrell made the Diamonds an offer for an immediate settlement. The Diamonds accepted and the case was closed. (One of the conditions of the settlement was that the amount of damages remain secret.)

Richardson-Merrell had decided that the Diamond case was not the best one to fight through to a verdict, but realized that sooner or later it would be faced with a damage claim so high that it would have to fight it all the way. The case it chose was in California—a state renowned for its high awards in compensation cases—and in March 1971, in the Los Angeles County Court, there began the only thalidomide trial in the world that went through to a jury verdict.

The action was brought by Shirley McCarrick—the Los Angeles girl who had married and become pregnant while she was still attending high school—both on her own behalf and on that of her daughter, Peggy. Peggy was born on May 26, 1962, with a short right leg that ended in a flipper, malformed hip joints, and bladder and anal abnormalities. In 1966, after reading about the German cases, Shirley McCarrick began to wonder whether the pills her doctor, Edward M. Sullivan, had given her for nausea could have been thalidomide. She went to her family lawyer, Jack A. Rose of Anaheim, and he engaged a high-powered firm to act for her. Four years went by, during which Rose and Shirley McCarrick believed that the partner handling the case was vigorously pressing Richardson-Merrell for a settlement. Unfortunately, he had been seriously ill during this period, and he committed suicide in 1971. His son arranged to meet Shirley McCarrick in Rose's office. There he told her about his father's illness and said that he was sorry but that his father had done nothing to get Richardson-Merrell into court. In a little more than three months, the statute of limitations would apply and that was not sufficient time to mount a proper case. Richardson-Merrell had offered to settle the claim for $6,000. In the circumstances, he recommended that she accept. The lawyer said that if she wanted time to think it over, she could have five minutes or so. When Shirley McCarrick refused, he held out a cardboard box containing the files and resigned the case by tipping the contents into Rose's lap.

Rose now acted swiftly. He approached another attorney, James G. Butler of Butler, Jefferson & Fry, told him the story, and asked him to take the case. Butler, a genial and flamboyant lawyer, at first demurred: three months to prepare an action against a company with the resources of Richardson-Merrell was simply not long enough. Rose persisted, and Butler agreed to meet Shirley McCarrick and Peggy. The meeting clinched matters. Butler, who has nine children of his own, watched Peggy hopping around on one leg, irrepressibly cheerful despite her deformity, and was, he said later, "deeply moved."

Butler took as many short cuts as possible—he flew to Philadelphia and conferred with Raynes—but it was doubtful until the last moment whether he would beat the time limit, especially since it became clear as preparations for the trial progressed that Richardson-Merrell's determination to fight Shirley McCarrick's claim all the way to a verdict meant that it was assembling what seemed like every thalidomide expert in the world to give evidence for the company. The reason soon became clear. When the trial began, Richardson-Merrell's defence was simply that Peggy was not a thalidomide child, and it was to put expert after expert into the witness box to testify that Peggy's defects had been seen in babies before thalidomide had been invented and were seen long after it had been withdrawn. Further, these experts said, even if Shirley McCarrick had taken thalidomide, then it could not have caused

Peggy's malformations, because on the dates in her pregnancy Shirley McCarrick said she had taken the drug, it would not cause malformations such as those seen in Peggy.

Butler was not deterred. Richardson-Merrell's expert witnesses might outnumber his two to one, but he had Peggy, and to stress the human tragedy behind the dry scientific argument, he produced her before the court on her ninth birthday, wearing a pink dress made for her by her grandmother. Butler told Judge Julian A. Beck and a jury of six men and six women that Peggy's deformities were of the type caused by thalidomide. He emphasized that experts could not agree among themselves that a specific pattern of malformations invariably emerged in response to thalidomide taken at a specific stage of development of the foetus. He drew attention to Dr. Lenz's testimony—that Peggy's deformities were *not* due to thalidomide—but pointed out that Lenz had conceded that other competent doctors would disagree with him.

The core of Butler's case was that there was no absolutely typical thalidomide syndrome and that the absence of one or another thalidomide characteristic was not significant. Richardson-Merrell had recklessly scattered millions of thalidomide pills all over the United States and should not escape liability simply because the damage those pills did was difficult to define. The jury agreed with him. After a trial lasting two months and nineteen days, and after retiring for a week to consider its verdict, on June 18, 1971, by a majority of ten to two, it decided that Richardson-Merrell had been negligent, and it found for Peggy and her mother. The amount the jury awarded came as a surprise. Butler had asked for $2 million for Peggy ($1 million general damages and $1 million punitive damages) and for $200,000 for Shirley McCarrick (divided in the same way). Richardson-Merrell had asked that if the jury should find the company liable, damages should not exceed $187,000. The jury gave Peggy $2.5 million, made up of $1.5 million general damages and $1 million punitive damages, and her mother $250,000 divided equally between general and punitive damages.

Shocked, Richardson-Merrell moved for a new trial. Judge Beck denied the application but reduced the damages to $775,000. Richardson-Merrell then went to California's Court of Appeals, where the case would be argued before judges who might be less susceptible to the human side of Peggy's case than the county court jury had been. But the case never came up. Over a two-year period Butler and Richardson-Merrell negotiated a settlement that, in keeping with other settlements, was secret. But we understand that Peggy received about $500,000. The final amount was less important than the principle: a case had been fought to a jury verdict and that verdict had been against the drug company.

In Canada, the case for thalidomide children was very strong because the drug remained on the market there for nearly three months after it had been withdrawn in West Germany, Britain, and the United States. William S. Merrell, part of the Richardson-Merrell group, continued to market it with the approval of the Canadian Food and Drug Directorate until March 2, 1962, when a public outcry led by the Canadian press forced its withdrawal. Because thalidomide had come late to Canada, its effects took longer to reveal themselves, but eventually at least ninety Canadian mothers gave birth to thalidomide-deformed children, and it was obvious that some of them had taken the drug after Richardson-Merrell had been warned about its teratogenic effects. These families had a powerful case, and in May 1968, Donald Traci of the Cleveland law firm of Spangenberg Traci negotiated a settlement for ten Ontario children that gave them a rough average of $200,000 each.

Richardson-Merrell immediately imposed two conditions on this settlement. The first was that it should be kept secret. Craig Spangenberg described the terms: "There should never be any revelation by clients or counsel of the amounts of settlements either privately or publicly, the court proceedings approving the settlements should be sealed, and all principals and attorneys should use their utmost effort to avoid any publicity of the settlements." The second condition was that Spangenberg Traci should agree that its firm would not represent any other Canadian children in claims against Richardson-Merrell. The reason for these conditions soon became clear. During negotiations, Spangenberg had put it to Richardson-Merrell that they had a moral obligation to all thalidomide children in Canada, and that without waiting to be sued, the company should try to locate these children and make a prompt and reasonable settlement with them. Instead, Richardson-Merrell replied that its legal obligations to its shareholders ruled out any such settlement. Obviously the company hoped that by keeping secret those settlements it had been forced to make, it would ensure that other thalidomide children would either not know they could sue or, when they did, would find that they had been barred by the statute of limitations.

This is exactly what happened. The parents of twenty-six thalidomide children born in Quebec found they were unable to sue because the local

Civil Code's statute of limitations required that personal-injury cases had to be started within a year of the injury. No appeal was possible, and the Quebec children had lost hope, when Arthur Raynes, the Philadelphia lawyer who had negotiated the out-of-court settlement with Richardson-Merrell for the Diamond family, and who had been introduced to the Quebec case by Spangenberg Traci, found a way out. Raynes, now with his own firm of Raynes, McCarty & Binder, discovered that Richardson-Merrell had a wholly owned subsidiary in New Jersey, J. T. Baker and Co., which had manufactured large quantities of thalidomide for its parent company. And New Jersey was one of two states (the other is California) that have a doctrine of governmental interest—that is, if Raynes could prove that the Quebec cases concerned the state government of New Jersey, then they could be tried there, irrespective of where the injury took place.

So on June 25, 1973, in the U.S. District Court, Newark, New Jersey, before Judge James A. Coolahan, the test case of Denis Henry, an eleven-year-old Quebec boy whose thalidomide deformities prevented him from laughing or crying, began. His parents sued Richardson-Merrell, alleging that the company was guilty of "negligence and a conscious disregard for the safety of human beings." The first stage was to get a decision from the judge as to whether the case could be heard in New Jersey. Richardson-Merrell argued that if Denis had lost his right to sue in Quebec, then he had lost it everywhere else. Raynes argued, "Richardson-Merrell should not be allowed to escape their legal, moral, and social obligations by using a loophole allowed by Quebec law." Judge Coolahan agreed with him. "This court cannot realistically ignore the fact that the defendant's New Jersey activities played at least some part in the general thalidomide tragedy which occurred in Canada. . . . Infant plaintiff was only one victim of this tragedy. Thus Denis Henry's cause of action is clearly brought in New Jersey as a test case in the hope that this court will apply the state's favorable statute of limitations law. This court will not shatter that hope." Richardson-Merrell appealed. In January 1975, the U.S. Court of Appeals in Philadelphia ruled in the company's favour—suit in New Jersey was dismissed. While an appeal was pending, Richardson-Merrell agreed to a contractual arrangement which in effect waived its reliance on the Quebec statute of limitations if the Henry case and others like it were prosecuted in Quebec. Raynes then announced that he would file suit in state court in New Jersey, but Richardson-Merrell decided that it had had enough.

Raynes and Spangenberg Traci had earlier arranged to attack Richardson-Merrell on two fronts. While Raynes was conducting the Henry action in New Jersey, Spangenberg Traci started in Canada a class-action suit, meant to cover all thalidomide victims, including those who had already had settlements and those who had yet to come forward. (In the interim, Richardson-Merrell had agreed to lift its ban on Spangenberg Traci's acting for other Canadian children.) The action claimed $80 million general damages and $1 million punitive damages. After Raynes's announcement that he would sue in state court in New Jersey, Richardson-Merrell moved to settle all the outstanding Canadian cases. Raynes videotaped most of the Canadian thalidomide children and ran some of the tapes for Richardson-Merrell's lawyers (one of the lawyers was so upset he had to leave the room). Long negotiations finally produced for some of the Canadian children the highest awards in the world: Spangenberg Traci got $999,000 for a child in British Columbia, and in June 1975, Raynes got $15 million for twenty-six Quebec children and two others, one from Saskatchewan and one from Ontario. Individual amounts in this settlement ranged from $100,000 to $999,000 (Richardson-Merrell refused to pay $1 million, on principle).

It is impossible to say exactly how much Richardson-Merrell eventually had to pay thalidomide victims in North America because of the secrecy the company imposed on its settlements. What is certain is that but for Frances Kelsey and the FDA, Richardson-Merrell might well be out of business today. If thalidomide had gone on the American market, then judging from experience elsewhere, an estimated ten thousand deformed children would have survived. Taking those American and Canadian cases where we know the amounts of the settlements, these ten thousand children could have got from Richardson-Merrell damages in excess of $3 billion.

Bitter and protracted though the legal battle in the United States had been, in the end the record there was impressive. No one had been denied the right to go to law because of the expense, the lawyers had been vigorous and resourceful, a case had been fought to a jury verdict, substantial settlements had been achieved, and apart from the secrecy imposed by Richardson-Merrell on publishing the amounts of these settlements, the press had been free to report the thalidomide tragedy in full. The contrast with what was occurring during the same period in Britain could not have been greater.

10   Is This British Justice?

In November 1961, Mrs. Pat Lane, a Bristol schoolteacher who had taken Distaval, gave birth to a daughter with one twisted outer ear and growths over her eyes. Like many of the other mothers, she spent the early months in a state of shock, grieving and depressed. But in July 1962, when Julie was eight months old, Mrs. Lane returned from the hospital where her daughter had undergone an operation—and for the first time she felt overwhelming anger. At one o'clock in the morning she sat down to write a letter to the Ministry of Health in the hope that it would somehow help. She addressed it to the minister, Enoch Powell.

> I am the mother of a malformed baby and I took Distaval tablets when I was five weeks' pregnant. These tablets were prescribed for me by my Doctor after I had an asthma attack. Within a short while (same day) of taking Distaval my hands and legs were affected—they were completely numb. This in itself was negligible against the horror which was in store for me at the birth of my baby, when my Doctor had to tell me that my baby had only one ear and that was very tiny and deformed and yet again two days later when a Child Specialist told me she had growths on each of her eyes—for which she is now a patient at Bristol Eye Hospital. Before you cast this letter aside, just try to imagine how you or your wife would have felt at hearing such news, the heartbreak of talking to a baby when all the time you are afraid to admit to yourself whether she can hear or not. It took us approx. 10–12 weeks to find out that she has very slight hearing from her one ear—these weeks were just spent wondering, hoping and praying. Until recent press reports the public have always been left in the dark, regarding side effects. We pay our National Health contribution in *full* confidence that the treatment we shall receive will help, if not cure our illnesses—NOT CREATE deformities. Why should

my child and the 1,000 others, some much worse affected, have
to spend a lifetime of pain and embarrassment, just because a
company were allowed to market a product which could not
have been properly tested?

I want to know what you intend to do about compensating
these children. If you or your family suffered such circumstances as a result of negligence, I feel sure you would also expect compensation for the unnecessary suffering involved. As I
have watched my seven month old baby girl crying in the hospital cot recovering from an operation on both eyes during the
past week, I have felt compelled to write this letter to you as
my duty to her.

I am sorry if the letter appears at all rude to you, but this is
exactly how I feel in my heart, plus the fact that I am FRIGHT-
ENED to take any tablets or medicine in future, unless we can
be assured that every precaution is taken by pharmaceutical
companies and also inspected by an independent body who do
not benefit from the profit made on these drugs.

Four weeks later, Mrs. Lane had still not heard from Mr. Powell, so
she contacted her local paper, the *Bristol Evening Post,* and in its next
issue it carried a story headed DRUG MOTHER IS PLANNING COURT TEST
CASE. The same day, Mrs. Lane received a letter from the Ministry of
Health, signed by Mr. B. H. Betts, a civil servant in the supplies department, with an apology for the delay. Had it arrived earlier, Mrs. Lane's
determination might well have been crushed, for it asserted with authority that the manufacturers of thalidomide could not be held responsible for the tragedy.

I feel that nothing I can say will help you much in your personal distress but you should know that the emergence of these
horrible side effects from the use of Thalidomide (Distaval) has
caused the Minister deep concern: he is keeping a close watch
on the situation and is at present seeking advice through his
Standing Medical Advisory Committee on the testing of new
drugs generally.

This is not to say that Thalidomide was put on the market
without being properly tested according to the state of knowledge at that time. The Minister is advised that it was subjected
to the usual laboratory trials, that is, on animals followed by
tests on the people developing the drug, and then given to
doctors wholly independent of the firm for controlled clinical
trials on selected patients. In this particular case there was not

the slightest reason to suspect that the drug could have the side effects it has and subsequent experimentation has shown that only in one of the several animal species investigated, the rabbit, was it able to produce congenital deformities in the young. You will see, therefore, that even negative results on animals would still not guarantee absolute safety when a drug comes to be used for humans.

The broad implications of this tragic problem are being examined very closely. There are already available under the National Health Service, part of a comprehensive set of welfare services, free facilities for the treatment of babies born with deformities. Specialist advice can be obtained through the hospital and specialist services from paediatricians, orthopaedic surgeons, and patients may be referred by a hospital doctor of the Ministry's limb-fitting centres for the provision of artificial limbs and other appliances. When a child is being cared for at home, the local authority services, such as health visiting and home nursing, may be made available to the parents as necessary.

The same day Mr. Betts set out the ministry's official view to Mrs. Lane, an even more comprehensive exoneration of Distillers was being written for *The Times* by "A Special Correspondent." It outlined, for the first time, Distillers' legal defence (it was to remain essentially unchanged) and was remarkable for its detailed knowledge of what seemed to be the facts of the case. Headlined THALIDOMIDE TESTS SHOWED NO SIGN OF DANGER, the article began in much the same vein as the ministry's letter:

It seems established beyond doubt that before being put on the British market the drug was subjected in Britain with great thoroughness to all the tests which any pharmacologist would have applied in the circumstances at that time, and was given extensive clinical tests with no sign of danger.

The writer went on to say that the drug was tested "extensively" by Grünenthal, that Distillers had made its own pharmacological investigations and provided quantities of the drug for outside clinical tests so that it was being given "a second independent scrutiny." Distillers had conducted a long series of tests—"which is right and normal with new drugs"—on rats, mice, guinea pigs, cats, and rabbits, all leading to the conclusion that the drug was virtually non-toxic. The Special Correspondent dealt with the question why no tests were made to see if the drug produced birth malformations:

> The answer quite simply is that the need for such tests in such circumstances has never been made evident before. Testing new drugs is an evolving science and grows progressively more complex and more costly. The need to test for teratogenic effects has been irrevocably established . . . but it would be entirely wrong to say it should have been recognized earlier. . . . This is not a matter in which a commercial firm has omitted tests which professional pharmacologists with no commercial interests would infallibly have carried out. . . . There is no reason to suppose that any pharmacologists would, unless by accident, have discovered this form of toxicity.

That very same day *The Guardian*, too, carried an article on thalidomide, written by the paper's medical correspondent, Dr. Alfred Byrne. It took a line similar to that of *The Times*' report. Dr. Byrne began by asserting, "Neither the British manufacturers of the drug thalidomide, nor the doctors who prescribed it for expectant mothers who gave birth to deformed babies, were in any way to blame for the present epidemic of congenital abnormalities." The available evidence suggested, said Dr. Byrne, that the "thalidomide incident . . . was something completely new to therapeutic medicine that could not have been foreseen from the scientific evidence available before the event." He also described the originators of the drug, Chemie Grünenthal, as a "reputable firm"—a statement that was, at the time, debatable. Dr. Byrne then touched on the key issue. He accepted the view that thalidomide was not tested on pregnant animals "because pharmacologists the world over did not consider it necessary to try to find out if any new drugs might have such an effect."

The amazing similarity between the Ministry of Health's letter to Mrs. Lane and the articles in *The Times* and *The Guardian* was no coincidence: the primary source for all three was Distillers itself. Dr. Byrne was at least frank with his readers and stated openly that he reached his conclusions after "inspecting the files of the makers" and interrogating their medical advisers for several hours. The origins of *The Times*' article were more difficult to locate. Strangely, it had been written not by the paper's medical correspondent, but by Duncan Burn, the industrial correspondent until the day before the article appeared, when he left the paper. Burn told us that he, rather than the medical correspondent, wrote the article because his specialty was innovation and innovation was involved in the risk in launching new products. In preparing his article, Burn agrees, not only did he speak with executives of DCBL, "frankly and openly," and with medical men of DCBL, but he had access to what was "relevant" in DCBL's files. (After leaving *The Times,* Burn took a job as an adviser to the Central Electricity Generating Board, and then, some years later, he went to work for Distillers.)

How the Ministry of Health came by the information contained in its letter to Mrs. Lane was related to us by Dr. E. Conybeare, a senior medical officer at the ministry. Dr. Conybeare had succeeded Dr. Walter Kennedy, also a senior medical officer until he went to work for Distillers as its chief medical adviser in 1956. In July 1962, Dr. Conybeare was approached by Dr. D. M. Burley, another Distillers medical adviser, who worked under Dr. Kennedy. Conybeare had a lengthy discussion with Burley on thalidomide and later talked to Enoch Powell before Powell answered questions on television. (He remembers Powell's asking later if he got it right.) It was not, he says, a particularly formal briefing of the minister as Conybeare was not directly concerned with drugs like thalidomide; this was the concern of the supplies division, which had to arrange that the Health Service had drugs and equipment that doctors and hospitals needed. Conybeare says he told Powell that at the time thalidomide was marketed, no one had had any idea of its potency and that no animal tests existed at the time to test for the properties it had. "Distillers had taken thalidomide on trust from Chemie Grünenthal."

Dr. Conybeare had also been impressed with two other points: an acquaintance in the industry—someone not in Distillers—told him that if he had been faced with the drug, he would not have questioned its credentials. Conybeare says he was persuaded that thalidomide had been a valuable drug for old people because it could give them a good night's sleep without any of the dangers of the barbiturates. It was, he thought, "impossible to kill anyone" with an overdose and its main side effect, polyneuritis, was not very serious, particularly when compared with the dangers of the barbiturates. He concedes that—like many others who spoke or wrote on thalidomide—he had never seen any of the research. His information was based "on hearsay . . . I knew nothing directly. But others were satisfied. It was only when used for pregnant women that this phenomenon appeared."

As well as Mrs. Lane, there were others interested in knowing more

about thalidomide and its sale in Britain. Maurice Edelman, Labour
M.P. for Coventry North West, and a group of twenty-seven other
M.P.'s asked Powell to set up a public inquiry. On July 23, 1962, their
Early Day Motion (a parliamentary device that enables M.P.'s to indicate support for a point of view not yet formally up for a vote) was discussed, though not debated, in the House of Commons. Edelman
described the tragedy of the thalidomide babies as "a great national disaster, greater in its ramifications than any single train accident in the
history of this country." He argued that it was premature to draw a veil
over the subject while so many aspects of the disaster had not been
cleared up. Why, for example, during 1960 and 1961, when there was a
sharp increase in the number of abnormal births, did no one notice that
these coincided with an increase in the use of thalidomide?

Edelman made the point more fully in a letter to *The Guardian* following the article by Dr. Byrne. In it he expressed himself as less than satisfied with Dr. Byrne's acquittal of Distillers' own evidence. Surely it was
desirable, he said, "not only to have the evidence of the producers of the
drug and their medical advisers but also the independent evidence of
scientists and pharmacologists." Enoch Powell clearly thought not; he
refused to set up the inquiry. Powell declined to discuss the matter with
us—but some of the parents feel that he had little sympathy with the
whole affair.

A delegation led by Peter Carter, a municipal employee from Reading, near London, went to see Powell in January 1963. Christine Clark, a
member of the delegation, took notes of the meeting. She recalls: "We
called for the setting up of a drug-testing centre to try to ensure that the
tragedy would not be repeated. The minister was quite sharp and said
that anyone who took so much as an aspirin put himself at risk. We then
suggested a publicity campaign to warn against thalidomide that might
still be in medicine cabinets. The minister said that this would be quite
expensive and foolish; he refused to accept that there were any more thalidomide tablets around, and said the scheme was a 'scare-monger stunt'
aimed at drawing publicity for our own purposes. Since the minister had
told us that he had never seen a thalidomide victim, we suggested he
visit a centre or meet a child at home. He rejected the idea. We asked
him to issue a press statement that he had seen us and saying that the
ministry would help wherever possible. He refused; there was no reason
for the press to be brought into the matter, he said. The thing which

struck me was that the minister expressed not one word of compassion or understanding. He astounded us by his coldness."

One reason for Powell's attitude could have been the well-founded fear that his ministry might find itself sued for compensation because thalidomide had been prescribed under the National Health scheme. (Mrs. Clark remembers Powell's telling the delegation: "I hope you're not going to sue for damages. No one can sue the government.") But whatever Powell's motives for refusing a public inquiry, it was a decision that had far-reaching consequences. It meant that unlike other major technological disasters, in this case there would be no official examination of the tragedy. The public was thus denied the right of learning how it was possible that a drug that wrecked more than four hundred lives in Britain came to be sold there.

So in August 1962, the parents were left to the law. It was a disastrous experience, which they had to suffer in secret, because the moment writs were issued, the whole affair was sealed by the laws of contempt of court into a legal cocoon from which it did not emerge until 1977—too late for the law to help the children. (The parents were also enjoined by their legal advisers not to talk to outsiders and especially not to the press.)

In Britain, the laws of contempt of court, which are enforced by imprisonment or fine, are built on the proposition that the outcome of a case should not be influenced by evidence other than that given in a court of law under the court's own rules. There should especially be no prejudgement of the legal issues, and the parties to litigation should not be under any outside pressure or persuasion aimed at making them withdraw their case or settle it on terms they would not otherwise have agreed to. Newspapers customarily refuse to be silenced in libel cases by the mere issue of a writ—a so-called gagging writ—and have been upheld, but numerous court rulings have protected the court's prerogative in other categories, whether in civil cases decided by a judge alone (as thalidomide would have been) or in criminal cases, where there is often a jury.

British judges have always taken the laws of contempt of court very seriously, and the British press was in the habit of observing the silence imposed by these laws. So for nearly ten years the parents of thalidomide children were to have no recourse to one weapon that could have helped them—publicity—when their case began to go sour. In the early days they trusted the law to help them; then when it began to fail them, the law prevented any protest about the legal merits of the case.

The decision to sue Distillers was taken at a meeting held in the Dolphin Hotel, Southampton, on August 19, 1962. The meeting had come about following Pat Lane's letter in the Bristol newspaper. By coincidence, Peter Carter had written to the Sunday national newspaper *The Observer* at about the same time, saying he would like to contact parents of other thalidomide children. The newspaper published his letter, and this prompted Frank Goldsworthy, a reporter on the *Express* who knew Pat Lane, to put four parents in touch. The other two were Michael Carr Jones, the owner of a small London furniture business and father of Graham, who had short arms, and Edward Satherley, a travelling librarian from the Isle of Wight, whose son, Richard, was missing both arms. The main purpose of the meeting was outlined by Carter: "I suggested that we should form some sort of a society to help one another and the many other parents who were as yet unknown to us."

Stories of the meeting appeared in newspapers, and other parents began to write to the group. When they had twenty-two members, they formally established The Society for the Aid of Thalidomide Children and received official status as a charity. Eventually the society had more than four hundred members, but in its early days it had to struggle to survive. To help this fight, the society decided to ask Lady Hoare, wife of the then Lord Mayor of London, Sir Frederick Hoare, a banker, to become president. Lady Hoare later also took on the post of chairman, and to help financially, she set up the Lady Hoare Thalidomide Appeal.

Lady Hoare threw herself into the parents' cause, and gradually she and her aide, Brigadier George Chatterton, took over the parents' problems. But her approach was to try to solve things by charity rather than by launching a legal battle, genuinely believing that the thalidomide families might lose public sympathy by such action. She established an uneasy existence with the parents' lawsuit, and under her influence the Thalidomide Society adopted the position that the parents should be discouraged from discussing the action. It was regarded as a "private matter," and even the early members seemed to come to share Lady Hoare's feelings that the suit was about money when what they should have been concerning themselves with was how to share the emotional burdens of attending to the deformed children.

There was a similar attitude in the Kevin Club, another organization for thalidomide families started in the north of England by Dr. R. W. Smithells, and named after one of the children. Smithells had a rather special involvement with thalidomide. In 1959, he had taken up a post at Alder Hay Hospital, in Liverpool, and as he had the resources and the time, decided to set up a register of all birth deformities. In the summer of 1960, he noticed that five children in the area had been born with limbs missing. They were all, as he later discovered, severely damaged thalidomide children. His curiosity aroused, he set out with a camera and a questionnaire to quiz the mothers in detail about their prenatal histories. "Unfortunately," he says, "three of the five mothers had had severe flu during their pregnancies, and I concluded that some bug or other must be responsible."

When the news broke that thalidomide could cause such deformities, Dr. Smithells took immediate action. Through the registry he was able to contact virtually every family with a deformed child. He visited them all and wrote to their doctors. At the end of the initial study, Smithells had obtained a "positive history" for about half the children—where the doctor either confirmed prescribing thalidomide (and not many did) or where the mother remembered taking the pill and was able to identify it from a selection shown to her.

By 1963, Smithells knew most of the northern thalidomide families through the Kevin Club, and he was wary about the lawsuit: "I was concerned as a doctor at an early stage that some of the parents were devoting their energies to legal action rather than giving the children the enormous amount of help they needed. As far as I could see, Distillers could not have anticipated the damage and that in common justice an action for damages could not succeed." So he urged the parents to spend what financial resources they had on their children and not on any legal action.

So in the only two organizations for thalidomide families, the psychological pressure was heavily against mounting a vigorous, determined, and sustained legal assault on Distillers. The anger that some of the parents felt about the company might have overcome this disadvantage if they had been encouraged by their legal advisers. But early on, the lawyers representing the children became persuaded that the case had little chance of success, and they allowed a consensus view along these lines to develop within the whole legal establishment. This, as we shall see, mattered greatly, particularly as the case was to be funded by legal aid. (Legal aid is a scheme under which the British government pays all or part of the legal costs of anyone who can prove that he is too poor to pay himself.) Since the costs of mounting a case against Distillers could have been as high as half a million dollars, there was certainly no parent rich enough to finance his own case. Thus, although only twenty-six of the first sixty-two parents to issue writs against Distillers were legally aided, all relied on government funds to prepare the actual case. Legal aid in Britain is administered not by a government department, but by the Law Society, the solicitors' professional body, which accounts to the government for the manner in which it has spent these public funds. The Law Society was acutely aware that it was spending large sums of public money, so it decided that one firm of solicitors should handle all the cases, as principal or agent, and that this firm should mount the single test action. (In the end, of course, it cost the public nothing because Distillers paid all the costs.)

This, no doubt, made sound financial sense, but one cannot help speculating to what extent the Law Society was influenced in this by its belief that the parents had little chance of winning. In the words of David Napley, one-time chairman of the Contentious Business Committee and later president of the Law Society: "We have known virtually from the beginning that there was no case." It is laudable, too, that the Law Society should have been careful in spending public money but its criteria for deciding when and how much to allow the parents to fight their action put an additional and probably insuperable obstacle in their path. As Napley explains it: "You have no right because you are poor to be put in the same position as someone who has money. As far as possible the legal aid applies the test of how would a person of reasonable, not excessive, means spend his money."

This would be acceptable when one man of reasonable means litigates against another. But when it was a number of private citizens suing one of the largest corporations in Britain, experienced in litigation and backed by the legal expertise and finance of its insurers, it was no longer a valid proposition.

There was *still* hope for the parents even though at this stage everything seemed stacked against them. They had received little sympathy from the government, the mood of their own two organizations did not encourage their lawsuit, none of them had the money to finance the case himself, they would have to rely on legal aid, which, it was already clear, was going to be handed out with great care and some reluctance, and they were depressed by a great cloud of pessimism from the legal establishment. The remaining hope was that they would be able to find a team of experienced personal injury solicitors to handle their case, lawyers used to the tough cut-and-thrust atmosphere of a very complicated area of British law. There *are* such solicitors, and the Law Society knew of many of them. But it was in the difficult position of wearing two hats. As administrator of legal aid funds, it was in its interests to see that the parents got the best personal injury solicitors possible. But as the professional body for solicitors, it takes the ethical position that it cannot under any circumstances advise a plaintiff which firm of solicitors he should consult. In addition, the society strictly enforces a rule that solicitors should not advertise their experience and expertise. This means that someone in Britain contemplating a lawsuit and seeking a specialist solicitor has to adopt the somewhat random method of asking for advice from friends or taking his chance with the telephone directory. This is what happened to the thalidomide parents. They were forced to take their chances in a legal lucky dip, and their first pick had the far-reaching result of transforming a small firm of London solicitors into the thalidomide lawyers, and of placing on its shoulders sole responsibility for handling what could have been the most important personal injury case of the century.

When the four parents met in Southampton in August 1962 and took the decision to sue, they picked Edward Satherley's son, Richard, to be the test case. Satherley's doctor admitted prescribing the drug to Mrs. Satherley in early pregnancy, and Richard's deformities—both arms missing—were typical of what became known as a "middle bracket" thalidomide case.

Only one of the families, Carr Jones, had regular contact with a solicitor—mainly for the purposes of debt collection and other minor commercial transactions—and the families agreed to contact this firm: Kimber Bull, of Cheapside, London. None of the families seems to have appreciated that the thalidomide case was classically the kind for personal injury specialists. Ironically, such a firm, Thompsons—which handles many personal injury cases for trade unions—was brought into the case by another parent, and not much more than six weeks after Kimber Bull. But it was six weeks too late, and Kimber Bull consolidated its position by becoming solicitors to the society.

In the short time in which Thompsons was actively involved in the case, it had done a good deal of work, which perhaps explains why barrister Desmond Ackner, Q.C., when the firm asked for an Opinion, was then more hopeful than he was to be when he returned to the case four years later. Ackner wrote, "Having regard to the magnitude of information so industrially [sic] obtained by those instructing me I am by no

means unhopeful. . . ." But the problem was that at that very point
Thompsons had to drop out of the case. As Ackner put it, "In view of the
fact that this action and the Satherley action is being financed out of
public funds, it is clearly undesirable that there should be duplication of
research into the experts' aspect of this case." So Thompsons had to give
way to Kimber Bull.

There, one of the four partners, Charles White, moved full time onto
the case, and in November 1962, he obtained an opinion from barrister
Gerald Gardiner. The parents had first to decide, Gardiner said, who
should be sued: the Crown, the doctors, the dispensing druggists, and the
manufacturers were all possible defendants. In the event, when the
Satherley test case writ was issued in November, Distillers and Boots, a
large chain of pharmacies that had dispensed the drug, were named as
defendants; the case against Boots was dropped in 1966. Serious consideration was given to suing Satherley's doctor, but from the outset Gardiner was aware of the difficulties they would meet in obtaining help
and advice from medical experts. He urged an early decision about
whether or not to sue the doctor, because he was "quite sure that a great
deal more help will be available from the medical profession if it is
known that the doctor is not being sued." Even if the doctor was not
sued in the test case, Gardiner still felt that unwillingness of experts to
give evidence against one of their own members was likely to be the biggest single obstacle in preparing a case.

This makes the next development the more puzzling, for if Gardiner
were right, then what the case would clearly need was an expert witness
of impeccable credentials to act as ambassador to the medical profession
and the pharmaceutical industry. The first expert to offer assistance in
the case was Dr. Montagu Phillips, a consulting pharmacologist and
chemical engineer, whose wife had taken thalidomide and suffered from
polyneuritis. He was engaged by Kimber Bull despite two serious shortcomings. First, although no one could question Dr. Phillips's devotion to
the case, his scientific reputation was not high. He was known to be associated with a cut-price drug firm—an association certain to antago-
nize the pharmaceutical industry. Second, he could not give evidence
because the lawyers believed his credibility as an independent witness
was compromised by his wife's lawsuit against Distillers. Yet until the
very last stages prior to settlement, Dr. Phillips remained Kimber Bull's
only scientific adviser.

There were other points raised in Gardiner's Opinion. To succeed in this first action against the drug manufacturer, the parents would have to show that Distillers had been negligent in marketing a drug that maimed unborn children. But there was no authority in English law that a child injured before birth even had a cause of action. And indeed Distillers would certainly have argued that no such cause existed. Gardiner believed, however, that this would be a minor obstacle, particularly given the appalling nature of the children's injuries and the fact that no English legal decision said the child could *not* sue. Success in the suit would also depend on the plaintiffs' ability to prove that when thalidomide was being developed and marketed, the manufacturer *ought* to have known that drugs administered during pregnancy could damage the foetus, and ought, therefore, to have tested the drugs on pregnant animals.

Distillers' defence would be what it had rehearsed in the press—thalidomide was a valuable drug that had been submitted to all "the standard tests"; at the time, tests were not done on pregnant animals because no one thought drugs might be dangerous to the developing foetus; and anyway it was universally believed that if a drug did little or no damage to a mother, it would do correspondingly little or no damage to her embryo. Even if they had done the tests, Distillers would say, they would not have given any indications of thalidomide's potential to damage the unborn child.

Evidence to rebut *every one* of these propositions could have been discovered, much of it from published scientific literature, as we have already shown. But very little of it was ever discovered by Kimber Bull, who, with their various counsel, allowed Distillers' defence, formulated early in 1962, to remain undented.

Gardiner went on to advise that a somewhat more complex second line of attack against Distillers' defences should be constructed. He said that from 1960, Distillers knew that thalidomide caused peripheral neuritis with serious, and in some cases permanent, injury. Yet it failed to withdraw the drug or to give warning as early as it should have. He felt that the strongest hope for what he saw as a difficult case lay here. (He had personal reasons for disquiet. A friend who was a tennis coach had developed peripheral neuritis. When thalidomide was identified as the cause, he was taken off the drug; while his condition did not deteriorate, it did not improve, and in desperation the man eventually committed suicide.) Gardiner believed that Distillers' response to this evidence of thalidomide's toxicity revealed much about the company's general ethics. He said that despite the company's knowledge of the drug's neuritic effects, by—at the latest—September 1960, company salesmen were told only in November 1960. Then Distillers wrote only to a certain number of doctors in December, when, said Gardiner, "they clearly played down the effects." He believed that the crucial point was that the evidence was cumulative. Even if it could not be established that thalidomide should never have been marketed, it might be possible to show that thalidomide should have been withdrawn or restricted in use when evidence of its toxicity became available.

For this reason, Gardiner believed that the Satherley case was not particularly good as the test action. The best case would be one where the mother had proof of having taken thalidomide not only after evidence of peripheral neuritis had emerged, but after Distillers had actually advertised the drug as safe for pregnant women. Gardiner strongly advised finding a later case than the Satherleys'. "Although it may be illogical," he wrote, "I think that if one thalidomide claim fails, others are unlikely to be fought; while if one succeeds, the defendants are not likely to fight another." For reasons we have been unable to discover, Gardiner's advice was not taken, and the Satherley action remained the test case for establishing Distillers' liability.

Gardiner had done his best, but his Opinion was of limited value. Clearly he could not have given any really useful advice on the question of negligence until a lot of scientific detective work had been done. But the legal aid certificates authorizing funds were initially restricted to pay only for advice from a barrister formally to issue a writ against Distillers. The legal aid committee at first refused to sanction any expert consultations and then, when it did so, insisted that contacts with experts should be justified one by one. Judging from our own experience of trying to understand the complexities of the thalidomide affair, no serious progress at all could be possible on such a basis. To prepare a vigorous case, a substantial initial budget and continuous access to counsel were necessary; there were no separate scientific and legal aspects of this case, since throughout, the two were closely intermingled.

Instead, the parents found themselves in the hands of the Law Society. Kimber Bull understandably felt that as a small firm it could not carry even the smallest expense itself and extended this financial caution to its interpretation of what the taxing master—who decides what is a fair bill for legal services—would allow on the legal aid certificates. The Law Society, with its anxiety not to waste public funds on what it believed was a weak case, further restricted progress. For example, it was not until the end of 1966 that the legal aid committee authorized payment of half the sum requested for costs for the pharmacologist, Dr. Phillips, and then it pointed out that the balance would have to stand in abeyance until the conclusion of the case. (True, there were considerable sums involved: by 1970, the lawyers had received £108,000 [about $240,000] from the legal aid fund and this covered only the first sixty-two cases.) The extent to which these financial constraints mattered is perhaps best illustrated by more detailed example.

The Law Society agreed to the appointment of Dr. Phillips in February 1963 and Kimber Bull was authorized to obtain reports from him about further expert witnesses. When Phillips asked to see counsel for a second time, to clarify a point of law, Kimber Bull told him, "You know our difficulty, that we can in fact only pay what is allowed either against the defendants or against the fund." It was only after nearly two years' work on the case that Phillips was allowed to contact the main German expert, and then only when the Law Society had given permission.

Discovery, the process by which a case is built up through evidence found in the opposing party's documents, letters, and internal memoranda, did not begin until 1964. At the end of that year, Dr. Phillips, still the only expert adviser, had not seen anything at all. The whole of 1965 passed with Phillips asking, in rising agitation, when he could examine the documents. Kimber Bull replied to each inquiry that discovery was not yet complete and until it had gone further, the Law Society would not authorize any payments for expert witnesses to scrutinize the documents. It was not until April 1966, when Phillips said he would examine the documents free of charge if necessary, that at last he got to see them. A few days later the Law Society lifted the restrictions on the certificate, thus making money available to prepare the way for trial—nearly three and a half years after the writ had been issued.

What sort of case had Kimber Bull built during this time? In the first year, Dr. Phillips and Charles White made approaches to a number of potential expert witnesses. Following Gardiner's advice, White approached Dr. J. A. Black, a senior lecturer in Child Health at Great Ormond Street Hospital for Sick Children. In July 1962 Dr. Black had written an article that appeared in *The Practitioner,* surveying the literature on drugs which affected the foetus. Almost all of it predated thalidomide. Dr. Black, who was about to leave his London post, was reluctant to get involved in what was likely to be time-consuming litigation. He

also told Kimber Bull that there were others far better qualified to give
evidence. He had only surveyed the literature, not done any of the original research himself, so suggested they contact some of those whose work
he cited. Kimber Bull accepted Dr. Black's initial refusal and never approached him again. Yet Dr. Black recalls the approach to him as being
"exploratory" and says he "didn't get the impression they were trying
very hard." Had he understood Kimber Bull's difficulties, there is no
question in his mind but that he would have been willing to give evidence. What would he have said? "I wrote *The Practitioner* article to bring
people's attention to the problem in general. My feeling was one of general principle. If you are going to market a drug used in pregnancy, you
are morally—even if not legally—obliged to test it on a number of pregnant animals. And not just of one species. Had they done so, it might
have ended up as a nice drug for keeping horses quiet. It would not have
been used on humans." And had Dr. Black been asked if it was common
knowledge that drugs could damage the foetus, he would have replied,
"I wasn't even working in the field but I would certainly have known."
And he would have expected others to do so as well. But he was never
asked.

Another potential witness, Dr. Alexander Speirs, the consultant paediatrician at the Stirling Royal Infirmary, Scotland, who had written
about thalidomide in *Lancet* in 1962, was approached by Kimber Bull in
January 1963. Dr. Speirs replied, three days after receiving the letter, to
say, "I would prefer not to become involved in legal proceedings, *if at all
possible*" (emphasis added). Kimber Bull never approached Dr. Speirs
again.

The most important witness could have been Dr. McBride, the Sydney obstetrician who had reported his suspicion that thalidomide caused
deformed births to the Sydney office of DCBAL in June 1961—five
months before the drug was withdrawn. A substantial number of the
mothers who had thalidomide children in Britain took the drug after
June, so Dr. McBride's evidence could have been vital to their case.
Kimber Bull wrote to Dr. McBride in October 1963 and asked him
about his warning to DCBAL. But when there was no answer, Kimber
Bull dropped the matter for five years—by which time, as we shall see,
an agreement on liability had been reached. So by October 1967, just
four months before the action was due to go to trial, the plaintiffs' side
had no expert witnesses to speak for them. There was worse to come: according to Desmond Ackner, now retained by Kimber Bull to replace

Gerald Gardiner (who had become Lord Chancellor), they had little chance of winning.

(One of the difficulties the parents had to face was that their counsel changed four times—Gardiner, Ackner, James Miskin, and John Stocker—as the lawyers went on to higher appointments. Distillers, in contrast, retained John Wilmers, Q.C., throughout.)

The Opinions on which this view was based were never shown to the parents—indeed those solicitors sent the culminating Opinion were advised *not* to show it to "the lay clients," partly to ensure that the press would not see it. And those parents who asked to receive a copy met with a blunt refusal. We have seen these Opinions. They show why, when Distillers agreed in 1967 to settle—they would accept that they were 40 per cent liable for damages if in return every parent dropped his claim and withdrew all allegations of negligence—the lawyers grasped at this offer so readily and exerted such pressures on the parents to accept it.

The main pressure began at a meeting between solicitors formally representing the families, and Kimber Bull and Ackner, who had mounted the case against Distillers on behalf of all the families. One solicitor has told us that he found the meeting "a distressing business." He said: "Ackner came with the heavy hammer, making it clear that if we did not accept, we would deprive all the others of a settlement. He was insistent that Distillers meant what they said, that it was an all-or-nothing deal, and that if Distillers withdrew their offer, a ghastly tragedy could result." Another solicitor said he found it "intolerable that terms had been agreed without us being involved in the negotiation." One said he had protested in private against accepting Distillers' first offer and, in particular, its insistence that all the parents settle or the offer would be withdrawn. "Distillers' conditions were disgraceful; they should have been told so, and warned that publicity would be sought if such a proposition was put seriously. Ackner, instead of saying to Distillers, 'Get out of here and don't come to me again with such a suggestion,' seemed to become a party to it and took on himself the duty of telling everyone else they had to accept."

But many of the solicitors at the meeting came from outside London, were in the main inexperienced in cases like this, and knew little about negotiating a settlement in the rough and tumble world of personal injury litigation. One of the dissident solicitors* remembers, "They all

* They are unwilling to be identified. Ackner is now a judge, and in the legal world, one does not openly criticize a judge.

thought Ackner was wonderful and told him so. He had performed the miracle of producing a settlement plus costs, even though he thought there was very little of a case." If the majority of the lawyers were so impressed by Ackner's view, how could the parents be expected to resist? Summoned to a meeting in London, they listened in shocked silence as Ackner told them that Distillers had done all that was humanly possible to check thalidomide, that Distillers had not been negligent, and that the 40 per cent settlement was an all-or-nothing deal—that if any one of them refused, they might all end up with nothing, and those who refused would be "robbing the others." Christine Clark, a mother of one of the most severely damaged girls, had gone to the meeting not knowing what it was to be about and, like others, expecting to see her legal advisers alone. Instead there were about eighty others—all Kimber Bull's clients. After the meeting, Mrs. Clark asked to see Ackner alone. Her request was refused; there was no point, she was told, Ackner had said everything there was to say and he was not going to repeat it sixty-two times. Despite Mrs. Clark's distress—"I was left feeling that we were the guilty parties for having taken the drug"—Mrs. Clark firmly told the legal team that "to accept on these terms is to succumb to moral blackmail. I want to see Distillers in court." Ackner replied that if the parents went ahead with the case, there was a possibility of having nothing and of losing their legal aid. There was, of course, some truth in this warning. Had the parents fought the case in February 1968, as scheduled, we believe that they would almost certainly have lost everything. They would have lost because their lawyers believed they could not win and had failed to mount the best case.

Moreover, as the undisclosed Opinions reveal, the lawyers misjudged the strength of the parents' case by saying an expert witness, Dr. Edward Paget, would not give evidence, when, in fact, he was never asked. There was, Ackner wrote, "no evidence" to suggest that prudent drug manufacturers in 1958 tested their drugs on pregnant animals to ascertain the effect of the drugs on the conceptus. No doubt Ackner, basing this view on information supplied to him, genuinely believed it to be so. But, as we have shown earlier, as a general statement it was simply not true. Certainly Hoffmann–La Roche, Lederle, Burroughs-Wellcome (in Britain), Pfizer, Smith, Kline & French, and ICI were companies that in the 1950s did routine reproductive studies. Furthermore a number of the tranquillizers used in direct competition with thalidomide had been tested for their effects on pregnant animals and the results had been published. Yet the atmosphere created by the absence of publicity, the secrecy, Kimber Bull's lack of vigour, and Distillers' efficient dissemination of its defence explained why Ackner was forced to conclude rather confusingly, and without anyone contradicting him, "Our failure to obtain that evidence is, we believe, that the practice in 1958 of manufacturers of sedatives and hypnotics to test these drugs on pregnant animals, due simply to the fact that such practice did not exist."

One man who could have provided evidence to contradict this assertion was Dr. Edward Paget. As we have recounted earlier, when Dr. Paget was director of toxicology at ICI, any ICI drug that might be used by pregnant women was first tested on pregnant animals. Immediately after news of the thalidomide disaster broke, Dr. Paget wrote to George Somers, the DCBL pharmacologist, telling him this. Ackner knew of this letter. In his culminating Opinion—one of those kept from the parents—he cited the letter and then went on (taking his information from Kimber Bull) to say that Paget had been approached to give evidence on these lines but had refused to do so. There is a mystery here, because Dr. Paget's recollection is in contradiction to this allegation. Dr. Paget, director of Inveresk Research Institute, a member of the Medicines Commission, a member of World Health Organization expert committees, senior Honorary Treasurer of the Royal Society of Medicine, Fellow of the Royal Society of Edinburgh, and author or joint author of some forty-eight distinguished publications, has provided us with a statement sworn on oath. Dr. Paget says, "I have no recollection whatsoever of being asked by the plaintiffs' lawyers to give evidence. While the task would have undoubtedly involved a degree of burdensome and time-consuming research, I would have seen it as my duty, if called, to give evidence of matters within my professional knowledge and expertise."

Indeed, Dr. Paget was surprised *not* to be approached by the plaintiffs' lawyers because he was sounded out by the other side. Dr. Paget remembers, "I was informally approached by Dr. Walter Kennedy of Distillers shortly after I joined Smith, Kline & French in 1962. He came to have lunch with me, and I told him that I would have to say that I, as a toxicologist—and others like me world-wide—were testing drugs on pregnant animals. I also told him that I even knew one man, now dead, regularly testing drugs on monkeys and not just rats." (If thalidomide *had* been tested on monkeys, it would certainly have revealed its power to deform the foetus.)

So there is also a mystery as to why Ackner told the parents that even if Paget *had* agreed to give evidence, it would not necessarily have been helpful. Ackner wrote that the effects of Paget's evidence, if given, "would be that ICI were specially cautious in regard to certain drugs which were known in fact to do, and only to operate by doing, certain cell damage—cytostatic drugs such as anti-cancer drugs—and that ICI would not, in 1959, have tested a sedative or hypnotic such as thalidomide on pregnant animals throughout their pregnancy."

Dr. Paget says, "I totally reject this account of what evidence I would have given had I been invited to do so. I would have said that prudent toxicologists who knew a drug might be given to pregnant women would have done experiments on pregnant animals. It was not at all uncommon for pharmaceutical companies to do such tests though it must be understood that the tests were not as sophisticated or as extensive as they are now." His evidence about practices at ICI would, without any doubt whatsoever, have been that *any* drug likely to be used by pregnant women would have been tested for effects on pregnant animals—even, as we have seen, a drug to control anaemia, because anaemia is a frequent ailment in pregnancy. Paget could have given evidence that long before thalidomide was bought by Distillers, he knew that a substance could damage the foetus even when it had no toxic effect on the mother. He had read the Gillman, Gillman, and Gilbert paper and recalled how trypan blue could cause birth deformities in rats even when the dosages were too small to have a toxic effect on the mother.

In support of the lawyers' view that the parents had a poor case, Ackner cited what he said was the view of the professor of pharmacology at Charing Cross Hospital (J. B. E. Baker) that the medical profession in 1958 operated under a false sense of security as to the effects of drugs on the embryo. It is true to say that not all physicians in the mid-1950s realized that drugs might damage a foetus while leaving the mother unharmed. But, as we have said before, a great many doctors *did* observe the ancient precautions that all medicaments should be avoided in pregnancy unless life was endangered.

Perhaps the most remarkable of Ackner's reasons for thinking that the chance of success on the facts of the case was less than 50 per cent was his belief that the marketing of thalidomide in Germany for two years prior to the drug's being sold in Britain was a serious problem:

Tests on animals do not necessarily show what will be the results when the same drugs are used on humans. But for over two years *humans had in fact been testing themselves* [emphasis added] in Germany. It must follow from the nature of the drug and the circumstances in which it would be taken and in particular that it would be obtained over the counter, that a very large number of pregnant women in Germany must have taken the drug in the two-year period prior to the defendants' marketing it. The defendants were therefore in a position to say, even if the animal testing was a wise procedure, in fact better and more reliable "tests" had been carried out. They were able to say, "the proof of the pudding is in the eating." . . . We are firmly of the opinion that the proposals showing that the drug should have been used on pregnant animals before it was marketed merely by reason of the fact that it was likely to be taken by pregnant women is a proposition which has little if any prospect of success. We would not therefore rate the prospects as even approaching forty per cent.

The fact is that humans in Germany were *not* testing themselves—or not willingly—and to be of any use, a test has to have better controls than those allowed by a drug's random use in the population, with little or no monitoring of its effects. Had Dr. Paget been asked about the scientific validity of this part of the Opinion, he would have told Ackner, as he told us: "It's absolutely nonsense. Completely meaningless. There is nothing more illusory than claiming knowledge from the fact that a drug has been given to a large part of the population. Unless a test is monitored, unless specific questions are asked, you cannot draw any conclusions from widespread use in a population." (Dr. Kelsey was also unimpressed by the claim that the drug had been on the market in Germany for two years.)

In this case, of course, the situation was exacerbated by Grünenthal's deliberate suppression of important information about the effects of the drug, which underlines a point not touched on in the Opinions—exactly what kind of firm was Grünenthal? And was it Distillers responsibility to investigate Grünenthal's record and claims about thalidomide? Who should have pursued this point? Thompsons appears to have tried. In

1963, they sent Ackner German technical publications they considere
relevant, but they sent them in the original German. In his Opinio
Ackner wrote that his knowledge of German was "not sufficient to e
able me to ascertain whether they would be of assistance."

Why did no one consider the relatively straightforward scheme
commissioning an independent laboratory to check the British pate
specification for thalidomide, which Grünenthal published in 195'
When we did this, the laboratory reported that three of the four met
ods given by Grünenthal for making thalidomide derivatives failed
function (see appendix, pp. 281 ff.). This result could have suggested th
scientific sloppiness of Grünenthal's work.

Yet another point that might have been used to the parents' advar
tage, but through a curious twist of logic was not, concerned the ev
dence about peripheral neuritis. Ackner posed the question of wheth
or not thalidomide ought to have been withdrawn after evidence of i
neuritic effects had accumulated. He accepted that there would be litt
difficulty in establishing that Distillers took peripheral neuritis to
lightly, and that a strong case could be made out for the wisdom
withdrawing thalidomide from the market once neuritis had becom
apparent. However, he concluded that "if it should have been apparer
in 1960 . . . that the withdrawal of the drug was the only prudent ac
tion that should have been taken, then *a fortiori* this should have bee
apparent to the experts who became aware of the peripheral neuriti
which the drug was causing. No expert so advised." Nor, one might add
would one have expected him to do so, and again Dr. Paget could hav
confirmed this. Only the company could have fully understood the ex
tent of the damage, and it was the company's judgement that was i
question. "No individual doctor could have enough of an overall view t
make that decision," Dr. Paget says. "The fact that doctors did not sug
gest the drug's withdrawal is not evidence one way or another."

It is our conviction that a powerful and scientifically sound case coul
have been mounted against Distillers and that the lawyers failed t
mount it. We would, in fairness, have liked to argue this with Ackne
whose Opinion was vital in the early stages, but this has not been possi
ble because of a dispute between *The Sunday Times* and Ackner that re
quires explanation.

When *The Sunday Times* campaign about thalidomide began, in Sep
tember 1972, we wanted to publish an article based mainly on Distillers
documents. When this was blocked, on threat of contempt of court, w

continued inquiries and interviews with specialists and with parents. These inquiries were stimulated still further by the subsequent ban on the use of Distillers' documents, so that by the time the contempt injunction was lifted, we were forming conclusions independent of the documents about the strength of the parents' case and the conduct of their litigation.

The editor asked Ackner if he would meet the authors to discuss their material. He demurred but later agreed with a suggestion by the editor that he would consider commenting if he had a copy of the article we intended to publish once we were freed of legal inhibition.

In the event, that release from legal inhibition came, in June 1976, at a moment when the article existed in rough outline only, in the process of being written up from scores of thousands of words of notes of interviews, transcripts of articles, and the like. Not until Friday evening of the week of publication was the early part of the article set in type and not until late on the Saturday before Sunday publication did the article exist in its complete form. Ackner was not therefore sent a copy of the article as had been suggested; when the editor wrote to him to explain and to invite him, nonetheless, to consider the criticisms in it so that he could reply for this book, he said he would not in any circumstances meet the authors. The newspaper was willing to let him see the nature of the criticisms contained in this book, but Ackner felt that he had been let down by the failure of the paper to show him the article of June 27, 1976, in advance. He did not accept that it had been physically impossible to get the article to him in time, and he was highly critical of it, saying that the arguments and interpretations of his Opinions were inaccurate and unfair, that this inaccuracy and unfairness "could hardly be said to have been inadvertent," and that we had attributed to his Opinions the very opposite meaning to what was actually there.

Whatever Ackner might have had to say if he had availed himself of the opportunity, the fact remains that at the end of five years of preparation, the main plank of the parents' case was the unsound aminopterin argument. This argument went: both aminopterin and thalidomide were derivatives of glutamic acid. It had been shown in a paper published in 1951 that aminopterin caused deformities in the foetus. Dr. Phillips maintained that when Distillers did its literature search, part of the procedure in marketing a new drug, it should have checked all derivatives of glutamic acid and should have come across this paper. This should, Dr. Phillips argued, have alerted Distillers to the teratogenic

dangers of thalidomide. However, the weight of biochemical opinion i
that since there are thousands of glutamic acid derivatives, the vast bul
of which are not teratogenic, there was no real value in the relationship
between aminopterin and thalidomide as a way of predicting thalido
mide's danger. The seductive simplicity of the aminopterin argument
first mooted by Phillips before Gardiner had even delivered his Opinion
was all too understandable. (We were initially attracted to it ourselves.)
But why did it take five years for the legal team to realize that it was no
valid?

When this became obvious, it was too late. To justify rejecting Distillers' offer, Ackner said, the prospect of success on the facts of the case
would have to be better than 50-50. He had shown that, in his view, they
did not even approach 40 per cent. Depressed by this view and deterred
by the threat of not a penny for anyone, all sixty-two families capitu-
lated and signed an agreement to accept 40 per cent of what they might
have got if they had gone to court and won. It was a humiliating surren-
der that was to have wide repercussions.

11 Sign Here, or Else . . . !

The problems began immediately. The first one was that the two sides could not agree on what the hypothetical figure for the thalidomide compensation might have been, and until a sum representing 100 per cent was fixed, it was not possible to calculate what 40 per cent of it was. This issue of "quantum" went to the High Court before the late Mr. Justice Hinchcliffe in July 1969, and two representative cases—one very bad, without any limbs (David Jones), and one less bad, without arms (Richard Satherley)—were presented for the court to hear evidence and assess damages.

For anyone not accustomed to the strange ways of the law, the proceedings would appear to have bordered on farce. The learned judge was being asked to hear evidence about the lifetime of incomes the children would lose through being handicapped, what they might need to maintain their living standards and provide special care, and then to calculate carefully a lump-sum award—all the time knowing, but not being able to take into consideration, that the children would receive only 40 per cent of the figure he decided was necessary.

Ackner tried to use actuarial evidence about the lost incomes and economic evidence about the effects of inflation on lump-sum awards. John Wilmers, counsel for Distillers, resisted this approach with vigour and success. Actuarial estimates, he pointed out, referred to average incomes and not to the two children actually under discussion—who might for all the court knew, be the sort of people who, even if they had been born normal, would never have tried to earn an average living. As for inflation, he pointed out that the government had undertaken to control it, so that to allow for its effects would be to ignore government policy! Most remarkably, Wilmers argued that the effects of income tax should be regarded as reducing the notional income which Distillers was being asked to replace. But no allowance should be made for the inroads of taxation on investment income from the compensation, because, Wilmers argued, the children might spend it all at once, thus escaping tax altogether.

The result for the parents and their children was disastrous. Their actuary, John Prevett, had calculated that the sum required to meet the lifetime needs of a totally limbless child was £106,000 (about $240,000). Under the Hinchcliffe award, reduced to 40 per cent, such a child was entitled to a lump sum of £9,600 (about $21,700). Clearly awards at these levels would not seriously help even those few thalidomide children whose parents had actually managed to issue writs in time. However, the lawyers remained convinced that the deal that they had made, and had urged so relentlessly upon the families, had been the very best available.

Many families had been waiting for the conclusion of the test case to put in their own claims, and the publicity surrounding the 1968 agreement to settle had brought to light many more thalidomide children. The courts granted leave to the London art dealer David Mason—and eventually one hundred twenty-six other families—to proceed "out of time": to take action three years or more after the event. Finally more than three hundred families joined the suit. Most of them went to Kimber Bull, "the thalidomide experts," either because they had heard of the company through the test case, or because Kimber Bull, with the consent of the Law Society, placed an advertisement in the *Law Society Gazette* suggesting that its services were available to thalidomide cases. It could be argued that in accepting these new cases, Kimber Bull left itself open to the charge of conflicting interests.

For the interests of the first sixty-two families almost certainly lay in vigorous pursuit of an appeal against Hinchcliffe's judgement. However, this would have been against the interests of the "out of time" cases, in that it would further delay settlement and would intensify Distillers' vigour in contesting applications to proceed "out of time." Additionally, interests amongst these plaintiffs varied sharply according to the strength of their cases. Some, for example, had prescription evidence that the mother had taken thalidomide, or the child's deformities were "typical" and the medical consensus was· that the child was thalidomide-damaged; others had much less certain evidence; and some might not have been thalidomide-damaged at all. The best interest for a client with a weak case was to accept virtually any offer, for one with a strong case to continue the fight. For the latter, Kimber Bull was clearly the wrong firm because it was deep into the settlement negotiations with Distillers and could hardly begin a new fight for one client while settling for another. In fact, the legal team never intended to renew the battle. When the test actions were before Mr. Justice Hinchcliffe, Distillers had promised to provide a sum for all the outstanding cases and from then on settlement was the only course the legal team pursued.

During 1971, the details of the settlement Distillers had outlined before Mr. Justice Hinchcliffe were worked out in a series of meetings between the two groups of lawyers. What they came up with was, basically, a charitable trust of £3.25 (about $7.8) million from which the remaining three hundred seventy or so children would draw according to need.

How was this figure arrived at? It was not a figure calculated, as one would imagine, by Distillers, but by the children's own lawyers. Immediately after the Hinchcliffe hearing in 1968, James Miskin, Q.C. (who replaced Ackner when Ackner became a judge), tried to get Distillers to "tell us how much they would put into the trust." But Distillers knew that it would take a long while to work out exactly how much it would have to pay the sixty-two children compensated as a result of the Satherley test case, and until this was known, it was not prepared to discuss how much it would put into a trust for the remaining children.

Not until September 1971 was Distillers ready to talk about a figure, and then it held the trump card. As Miskin reported, "They insisted that *we* say what we wanted so we had to decide what a reasonable figure was. We took the view and strongly advised that if we could get paid into the trust for the children about *half* of what was paid to the sixty-two children in the old forty percent cases, *we would be doing well.*" The three lawyers who determined what this "reasonable total" might be felt that they had to reduce the 1968 settlement levels because these cases were "out of time," an additional legal impediment that stood in the way of their establishing a claim against Distillers, and the chances of success compared with the old sixty-two cases were much lower. The three lawyers' figures for the total were close to each other. Miskin reported: "We thought that about £2.25 (about $5.4) million paid now would be fair. Later we raised it to £2.35 (about $5.6) million."

Distillers, no doubt experienced bargainers, felt it could not accept the first suggestion made and countered with the proposal that it pay the money in instalments over ten years. This, of course, would greatly reduce the cost of settlement but would diminish the worth of the trust.

A little further negotiation produced in November 1971 the sum of
£3.25 million to be paid over ten years.

The simple truth is that if the settlement for the first sixty-two families
was 60 per cent short of what would be sufficient to provide for the lifetime needs of the children, the offer for the second batch of families was
only half as adequate. This did not seem to disturb the children's legal
team, and they now set out to convince the parents that this was the best
offer that could be negotiated and that they should hurry up and accept
lest Distillers have second thoughts. Late in 1971, they began by calling
a series of mass meetings of parents all around the country. At these
meetings, they set out the general terms of Distillers' offer and asked the
parents to vote to accept it.

The parents were in an unenviable position. Distillers had made two
important stipulations in its offer. First, it was an "all-in-or-none-in"
deal; if just one family rejected the offer, then none of the children would
get anything. This effectively committed the children's legal team to
persuading *everyone* to sign, even though the interests of some of the children might have been better served by continuing the legal fight against
Distillers. Second, Distillers stipulated, "It is a condition of all these proposals that all the children and all the parents act through Kimber Bull
& Co. concerning these proposals and their implementation." This effectively confined the families to solicitors who were committed to the settlement. The eventual outcome was astonishing, a dark chapter in British legal history.

At each meeting, the vote on Distillers' offer was taken after a powerful plea for acceptance made by James Miskin. Miskin, with the advantage of speaking from a platform, usually with a microphone, was in a
position of some strength in pressing for a yes vote. At one meeting, he
even suggested that if any parent did not raise his hand, his neighbours
should ask him to explain why. David Mason, a man of forceful personality himself, has said he did not feel equal to raising his hand against
the offer at the meeting he attended. The atmosphere, he said, "resembled a factory gate meeting on a pay dispute," rather than a legal consultation on the future of handicapped children.

Parents were not urged to think the offer over but, rather, encouraged
to sign on the spot at the end of the meeting. Miskin warned that any
person who refused to sign, and who insisted on continuing with the litigation, would lose his certificate entitling him to legal aid from government funds. A number of parents have told us that on several occasions

Miskin said that he would personally take steps to ensure that legal aid certificates would be revoked where parents refused the offer. The parents say these remarks appeared to them as a threat: many had legal aid certificates restricting the amount of legal help they could get, and it would have been hard, if not impossible, to get full legal aid for a new action when counsel had already recommended settlement.

It was also at these meetings that the lawyers announced the establishment of an "X list" and a "Y list," to enable them to settle cases more rapidly once agreement had been reached. Those on the X list—and few of the parents knew which list they were on when Miskin was urging them to settle—were accepted by Distillers as thalidomide-damaged. Those on the Y list were said to have more uncertain claims, and had not yet established their credentials with Distillers. There were, as it turned out, a number of anomalies, and parents who might have expected to be on the X list—who, for example, had prescription evidence of having taken thalidomide—found themselves on the Y list. But the important point about the X and Y lists is that they exacerbated the conflicting interests among the parents. Although these had always existed, they now became formalized.

To point out the danger of a conflict of interests is not to suggest that the parents should have dissolved into a series of mutually hostile groups. Co-operation is quite possible between groups with certain conflicts—provided that in the first place the areas of conflict and co-operation are clearly mapped out. But in urging the parents to settle, the legal team articulated the conflicts *and* chose to ignore them. Miskin, underlining the point that if *one* single parent refused, then the whole deal would fall through, said, "In that event, *a few will gain and the vast majority will lose.*" Protecting the weak cases was a laudable enough sentiment, but a better approach would have been to have arranged separate legal representation for those who stood to gain.

Despite the size of this second group—those who stood to gain—in the end only six refused to settle. (Published accounts have always said there were five; the sixth was a rather elusive travelling family.) They were an improbable collection. In addition to the travelling man there was an art dealer, a plumber, a self-employed electrical engineer, a free-lance construction worker, and a merchant seaman's wife. They were a group in name only and before the court action that brought them together, they had never met. The one thing they had in common was the strength to withstand the enormous pressure to accept the offer; many other parents—and even solicitors—who had wanted to refuse in the end felt unable to do so.

David Mason, the art dealer, was the youngest of the group and the only one who could be described as well off. He runs a fashionable and successful gallery in London's West End and has a large house in North London. He did not actually need financial help for his limbless daughter, Louise, but he was driven by bitter resentment over a promise he said Distillers had made to his father to compensate Louise, and he was determined that the company should pay this compensation "as a matter of right, not as a charitable gesture."

The closeknit family of Bayman, the plumber, was adamant that their son Keith—who had no arms—should be brought up to care for himself. This desire for his independence overrode all other fears and considerations: a charitable trust in any guise would not do.

Mrs. Florence Ogilvie is the mother of a daughter born without arms. Mr. Ogilvie is tubercular, and only irregularly employed as a construction worker in Buckinghamshire, so Mrs. Ogilvie went out to work herself to earn enough money to pay her legal aid contributions. Pride more than anything else gave the Ogilvies courage to refuse the offer—as well as an unpleasant exchange with the lawyers that produced sufficient rage to keep them going. After they refused to sign at a mass meeting, they were asked to see Miskin at his chambers. Mrs. Ogilvie's account of this meeting, sworn on oath, is a disturbing one. "I asked Mr. Miskin . . . if he could guarantee that our daughter would get an annual income. He said no. I then asked if he could guarantee that she would get a lump sum so that when she is older, we could if necessary buy her a business or something like that. Once again he said no." Miskin's description of how the trust would work concluded the matter. He told the Ogilvies that a welfare worker would go and see the family and decide the child's need. "What mother capable of working would allow her child to be in need?" Mrs. Ogilvie said. "I wouldn't want a social worker to think that I allowed my child to go without anything. So she might as well get nothing." The meeting ended abruptly. "Mr. Miskin would not let me talk, and at one point he got up and hammered the table and said, 'Will you listen to me, woman?' I replied, 'You won't listen to me, why should I listen to you?' and I walked out."

Mrs. Margaret Hayler is a seaman's wife, now living in Australia, who used to live in Lancashire. Her daughter, Wendy, was born with short arms. When she attended the mass meeting in Liverpool—the first time she had met any of her legal advisers—she could not sign as her husband was away at sea. About a month after the meeting, Mrs. Hayler started getting telephone calls from Charles White of Kimber Bull. In a statement sworn on oath, Mrs. Hayler said that White telephoned two or three times a week for about three weeks, trying to persuade her to settle. "He told me that one advantage of the trust as opposed to an individual cash award was that my daughter would not be exposed to the wrong sort of person who would want to marry her just for the money." Things got so bad that Mr. Hayler, away for fourteen months on that trip, wrote to White asking him to deal with his wife more kindly, especially as she was on her own. Eventually the pressure became too great, and Mrs. Hayler signed, feeling she could not deprive the others of a settlement. But after a sleepless night and after discussing it with her injured daughter, she changed her mind and withdrew her consent. Above all other considerations, she did not want her daughter to feel in later life that her mother had not done everything possible to secure her future. Kimber Bull then sent for Mr. Hayler, who was in Germany. He knew very little about what had been going on, and decided to sign to accept the trust, but according to Mrs. Hayler, he inadvertently put the signed form in his pocket and returned with it to Germany. Later, Mrs. Hayler signed again but again was racked by doubt and for the final time withdrew her consent.

The motives of Mr. and Mrs. Joseph Hourie were rather more complex. They found it difficult to believe that Distillers had not been negligent. Mr. Hourie, an electrical engineer from Chester, felt that common sense must dictate that the manufacturer of a dangerous drug was responsible for the damage his drug did. He also knew that his child's injuries were different from the others and feared they would not be taken into account. Rosemary Hourie is completely deaf, largely dumb, and has severely shortened arms. Her eyesight is affected, and she has an impaired heart. The Houries attended a small meeting in Miskin's chambers and from their account were exposed to much the same sorts of pressures as other parents. Mr. Hourie is a cautious and deliberate man who insisted on taking the offer document away and thinking about it. "I decided it was unsatisfactory" was his simple conclusion, and some days after the meeting, he wrote to Charles White setting out his reasons for refusing to settle.

In reply, Kimber Bull reminded the Houries that there were no reasonable prospects of their overcoming the problem imposed by the limitation law—the Houries had not issued their writ against Distillers in time—and even if there were, there were no reasonable prospects of establishing negligence against Distillers. The offer was final and would not be increased, said Kimber Bull, and he was warned against disclosing the information to anyone else, particularly the press. Later Kimber Bull informed the Houries it was no longer prepared to act for them, so they approached a solicitor in Nottingham. This solicitor told Hourie that as Kimber Bull had ceased to act for him, his legal aid would have been stopped automatically. And if he wished to get it restored, he should contact the Law Society with the name of his new solicitor. The Nottingham solicitor was not prepared to act for Hourie and advised him that if he decided to represent himself in court proceedings, he would not be allowed legal aid.

The sixth family were Mr. and Mrs. Robert Knowles, who roam Britain with two caravans, a brightly painted yellow truck, a shabby blue mini-van, and eleven children, rarely stopping at any one place for more than a few weeks at a time. Their daughter, Mary, has malformations in all her limbs. A confrontation between a travelling man and the law has its own special problems. Ignorance of the "rules" and a total lack of information about the progress of the settlement provided the Knowleses with the strength and independence needed to refuse the offer. While other parents were attending mass meetings up and down the country and were being vigorously urged to sign for the charitable trust, no one knew where the Knowleses were. Finally, at the end of January 1972, long after the majority of parents had been persuaded to sign for settlement, the Knowleses turned up in Banbury. Knowles read the documents sent by Kimber Bull and replied that he could not accept an offer which "did not guarantee my child an income." Distillers' offer, he said, was not worth "a cup full of snow." He was also unhappy about the charitable nature of the trust. Knowles was asked to come to London and meet Miskin in his chambers. The meeting between the Queen's counsel and the travelling man took place on February 17, 1972, and was over virtually before it began. "Mr. Miskin asked me if I could read and write, I told him, 'I can read and I can write. I can even *understand* what I have read and I don't like it.' " And that was that.

Now a remarkable legal battle ensued. The legal team tried to force the six dissident families to sign by taking them to the High Court to have the judge remove them as "next friends" to their children. This stratagem takes away from the parents the right to decide in legal matters what is best for their children and instead gives this right to a government employee, the official solicitor. The team apparently believed that the official solicitor would see the wisdom of accepting Distillers' offer, would override the parents' refusal, and sign acceptance himself on behalf of the children. The six parents could hardly believe what was happening. David Mason says, "I was being taken to court by the solicitors originally engaged to act for *me,* to have my right to decide my daughter's future taken away from me. I thought, Can this really be British justice?" On March 22, 1972, the case went before Mr. Justice Hinchcliffe, the same judge who had heard the "quantum" side of the Satherley test case. Since Mr. Justice Hinchcliffe had said that the 1968 agreement to settle "reflected credit on all concerned," it was perhaps not very surprising that he now held that anyone who resisted it was unreasonable. He ordered that the six dissenting families should be removed from the position of "next friend" to their children, and the official solicitor be appointed in their place. Miskin, who until a month earlier had been counsel to the six families, at first appeared generous in victory: he announced that his clients would not press for costs. (The costs were ultimately to be borne by Distillers.) But when barrister Michael Eastham, Q.C., who had been engaged by David Mason to act for the six families, rose to give notice of appeal, Miskin leaped up to say that he could not guarantee that his clients' generosity on costs would be continued in the event of an appeal. He added that he did not of course mean this as a threat. Mr. Justice Hinchcliffe said that if it was not a threat, he did not know what it was, and that if Miskin's clients felt that way, they should keep the fact to themselves until it could no longer influence a decision about the appeal.

These proceedings were for all six families a frightening experience, particularly to a parent with no financial security, as was the case with Hourie: "I was told in court by Miskin that the hearing was costing £200 a day. I was most disturbed by this advice as I was not legally aided and had been previously told that I would have to bear the costs of the hearing." Given permission to appeal, Hourie went back to the Nottingham solicitor, hoping to name him on his legal aid application form as the lawyer he wanted to act for him. But this solicitor told Hourie he could not help "because he would not have time to prepare the case. This meant that I would not be able to have legal aid for the appeal."

Mr. Knowles, the words of Mr. Justice Hinchcliffe and Miskin still ringing in his ears, decided he no longer had any option. "When I slipped the letter of acceptance through the letterbox, I felt like cutting my throat." To ease his conscience, he sent a signed note to a few of the parents, saying, "I Robert Knowles have decided to accept but I am disgusted with the terms of settlement and I will not be against any parent or parents who may fight this case to the end, even if the firm decides to withdraw its offer."

But all was not lost. David Mason had the money to finance an appeal, and on his own behalf and for the other dissident parents he went ahead. The hearing was on April 11 and 12, 1972, in the Court of Appeal before Lord Denning, as master of the rolls (senior judge), and Lord Justices Frederick Lawton and Edmund Davies. They found unanimously for the parents. It had not been established, Lord Denning said, that Distillers' settlement was so clearly beneficial that Mason was being unreasonable in refusing it. Each parent had to consider the interests of his own child. None of the parents was being so unreasonable that he or she should be displaced from his position and responsibilities as "next friend." Lord Justice Davies went further. He said the attitude of the dissident parents was completely reasonable. "Any other would be an abdication of their legal and moral duty to their children."

Mason's success threw the whole settlement back to the legal team and Distillers. Distillers would not go ahead with the charitable trust unless the legal team could produce consent from every last one of the thalidomide families. The team had failed to do so, so the settlement was in limbo. A situation of stalemate existed, with no apparent way out. But little of this was known publicly. The legal team had always insisted on secrecy, both in its negotiations with Distillers and in its relations with the parents. Was there no way of bringing the whole incredible mess out into the open?

12   A Cause for National Shame

Back in 1967, Dr. Montagu Phillips, pharmacological adviser to the thalidomide parents, had been to see the editor of *The Sunday Times,* Harold
Evans. Phillips had watched the parents' case against Distillers go stead-
ily wrong, and he was by then already a frustrated and bitter man. He
had told his story to a *Sunday Times* reporter, John Fielding, and on
Fielding's introduction, Phillips was in Evans's office. His proposition
was brief: he was prepared to let the paper have 10,000 internal documents Distillers had been obliged to disclose to the parents' solicitors,
Kimber Bull, so that it could prepare its case against the company. In
return, *The Sunday Times* would finance a book, to be written jointly by
Fielding and himself, that would tell the whole story of how Distillers
bought thalidomide from Grünenthal and marketed it in Britain.

Evans was attracted to the idea. Like Dr. Phillips, *The Sunday Times*
then expected that there would eventually be a satisfactory settlement
out of court of the case between the parents and Distillers. If this happened, it could mean that there would be no examination of the way the
tragedy occurred, and that seemed to Evans to be both a good story and
one the public interest required to be told. The thalidomide disaster had
been unusual in that it had been followed by no official commission of
inquiry, public or private, into the causes of the disaster. Road deaths,
air crashes, major fires, and other disasters are all customarily followed
by searching public inquiries, but the biggest drug disaster of its kind
had been left to the law, and the law, it seemed, was working in a way
that would mean the background would never be explored.

What the paper did not know at the time was that shortly before
meeting Evans, Dr. Phillips had been asked by Distillers to give an undertaking that he would neither use any of the documents for publication of any kind nor dispose of the material. So in January 1968, *The
Sunday Times* went ahead and concluded an agreement with Dr. Phillips

by which it paid him £8,000 (then about $20,000) for technical advice and for sight of the Distillers documents. It copied and returned these to Dr. Phillips. Ten thousand documents occupy a lot of space. They built up into a small mountain in a room set aside at *The Sunday Times,* and *The Sunday Times* Insight team was assigned to catalogue and analyse them. The team was in the middle of this when the paper was approached by a London literary agent representing a Swedish lawyer, Henning Sjöström. Sjöström had been deeply affected by the struggle of the Swedish victims to gain compensation against apparently overwhelming official inertia and a confident stand by the Astra Drug Company. In his battles (finally settled out of court in October 1969) he had acquired from German lawyers access to the documents that Grünenthal had been forced under German law to disclose to the German authorities and documents that had been seized in police raids.

Sjöström believed that the German trial (which began in May 1968) would not lay bare, in reasonable time, how Grünenthal had produced its terrible drug. Grünenthal in Germany did face tougher legal action after the tragedy than Distillers in England or Richardson-Merrell in the United States. A public prosecution had been launched against the company and seven executives on charges that included the German equivalent of manslaughter, causing grievous bodily harm, and selling drugs by misleading statements. But the trial, which had taken seven years to mount, looked as if it would take just as long to conclude, and Sjöström's agent offered the documents to *The Sunday Times.* (He later published his own book, with Robert Nilsson, entitled *Thalidomide and the Power of the Drug Companies.*) The paper bought the documents for £2500 (about $6,000) very promptly indeed when it learned they had been "bought" some months before by the *Sunday Telegraph* newspaper, which had then failed to follow through and complete the transaction, having apparently lost interest. *The Sunday Times'* resident correspondent in Germany, Antony Terry, brought the documents over in three suitcases, and the Insight team now concentrated on the huge task of translating the material and cataloguing it. They wanted to see what light it would shed on how thalidomide came to be made, tested, marketed, and sold for export.

As this work proceeded, Evans asked the paper's News Department to keep a special watch on what was happening to the thalidomide children in Britain, and in February 1968, when an out-of-court settlement was envisaged, but not concluded, for the first sixty-two children, a reporter, Michael Moynihan, produced the first of a series of major feature stories. He revealed that the parents of more than four hundred children had not gone to court and that others had failed to take legal advice in time. "Many parents speak bitterly of indifference, red tape, or even callousness," he went on. "Some tragic cases have come to light. A father of impeccable character who took to drink and recently went to prison for fraud; the mother under psychiatric treatment who slashed her wrists after a teacher had hinted that her son was mentally handicapped, as well as deformed by thalidomide. There is the mother who cannot bear even to touch her daughter on infrequent visits to the home caring for her."

The analysis of the Distillers documents was not complete by this stage, but in any event, the advice of the paper's lawyer, James Evans, was unequivocal: nothing could be published until every single one of the children's actions had been finished. The law of contempt of court would not countenance publication of any material that might prejudice proceedings. (The paper did not need reminding of the seriousness of this offence. By accident, only a few months before, it had broken the contempt law by publishing the previous convictions of Michael X, a black propagandist executed some years later in Trinidad for his part in a murder. The attorney general had sought to commit Harold Evans to jail, and the paper had been fined £5,000 [about $12,000] in the High Court.)

Harold Evans came back on another tack. *The Sunday Times* would tell what it was learning from the German documents. It looked to be an astonishing tale. Could there be any objection to that, since the revelations would be about a German and not a British company? James Evans was not sure it was safe, so the advice of a leading counsel, David Hirst, Q.C., a specialist in libel and contempt, was sought. He was emphatic: he gave first a verbal and then a written opinion that to publish anything at all from the German documents would have a bearing on the British cases and would be flagrantly in contempt of court.

Harold Evans felt that this was a very restrictive view and, if true, would lead to an absurd situation: that when the German trial started, it would be in contempt of court to report it in British newspapers because it might influence the trial of later British cases. Soon after this the *Sunday Telegraph* carried two articles reporting on some of the background to the impending German case, and since they seemed to cover the same area, admittedly without the damning details, Harold Evans asked

James Evans to go back to counsel. Again the answer was no, but despite the undoubted authority of the opinion, Harold Evans remained unconvinced, certainly in logic and possibly in law. A second opinion was sought, and on May 8, 1968, Peter Bristow, Q.C. (now a judge), wrote a somewhat more encouraging opinion, and Harold Evans decided to go ahead.

On May 19, 1968, *The Sunday Times* devoted four pages of the newspaper to a detailed critical article about Grünenthal and thalidomide (of which this book gives of course a much fuller account). At once there was a complaint by telegram from Grünenthal that it had been libelled and that it was contempt of court to publish in advance of the German trial. The paper replied vigorously and waited to see whether the attorney general in Britain or Distillers itself would follow up with legal action. Nothing happened. Grünenthal did not persist, and the paper concentrated its Insight team's energies again on Distillers' documents. There was no great haste. The principle of the settlement agreed to by the judge in February 1968 was that the parents would receive 40 per cent of the 100 per cent damages they would have won in a successful action, but the out-of-court talks to fix a money figure to the 100 per cent were proceeding slowly. The paper accepted, for the moment at least, that if its article on the German company had risked a brush with the law of contempt, then an article on Distillers in mid-negotiation would be foolhardy.

It was mid-1969—nearly seven years from the first writ—before it seemed that at last publication could be planned. The paper learned that Distillers and the parents, having failed to agree on what 100 per cent was in money, were going before Mr. Justice Hinchcliffe to ask him to fix a sum in the two test cases of David Jones and Richard Satherley. The judge's decision came in July—that the 100 per cent for the armless and legless David would have been £52,000 (about $125,000), of which he would receive 40 per cent, and the armless Richard's award would have been £30,000 (about $72,000), of which he also would receive 40 per cent. The publicity for the awards, like the publicity for the earlier settlement in principle, galvanized scores of other parents of deformed children, who came forward to seek legal remedies they either had not realized existed or had been unwilling to attempt. The original sixty-two parents who had begun actions in 1962–63 were soon outnumbered by the new ones, who had first to establish the legal right to sue because they had allowed so long to elapse from the date of the injuries. Since the peripheral-neuritis cases still remained to be settled and all the sixty-two original families had to go before the courts for approval of individual money settlements, the thalidomide story now fell under three separate strands of restraint by the law of contempt. There were the actions to establish a right to sue out of time: eventually two hundred and sixty-six got leave to issue writ. Each new writ against Distillers began a new period when the law required silence until the writ had run its course in settlement. In the aftermath of the awards to Satherley and Jones, there was not even a space of one week's time when *The Sunday Times* might publish.

We have often debated, with hindsight, whether this would have been the proper moment to have begun our campaign for better compensation for the thalidomide children, to have allied a challenge to the law of contempt with the publication of an article on the background to the manufacture of the drug. But the idea of making such a challenge was never seriously considered at that time because everyone thought that the new cases would soon be settled, freeing the paper for publication of Distillers' documents. As it happened, these told only part of the story; some of the most telling evidence against Distillers had yet to be discovered. Nor did the paper then fully appreciate the gap between the compensation awarded and the children's needs. *The Sunday Times*, exceptionally among the press, did demur at the generally warm reception for the compensation sums, but it did not demur with sufficient force, nor with sufficient knowledge. The paper had assigned Nicholas Harman to discuss the settlements, and he wrote an article on the editorial page that was headlined, strongly enough, WHAT PRICE A POUND OF FLESH? It raised the first doubts about what was going on, and pointed out that by definition the settlements would be 60 per cent insufficient. Harman argued that the law on personal injuries needed changing and he suggested that Distillers should become the strongest supporter of the Lady Hoare fund. "All private persons can do is to support still the Lady Hoare Thalidomide Appeal. When the litigation is over, Distillers, without any admission of negligence, might, and should, become the Appeal's chief supporter." This article gave the paper's lawyers some anxieties, though in the light of later events it was an anodyne conclusion. The truth in it—that the settlements were inadequate and the law was making a mess of things—was said only once and not vigorously enough.

The article and the paper, like everyone else, missed what later became the central point, that even 100 per cent damages would have been inadequate by any civilized standards. An important piece of evidence in the court action was overlooked, and it was not to have its proper effect until four years later. But if an opportunity was missed, then it has also to be said that when the campaign did develop later, it gained momentum from the extra legal delays; and the accumulating evidence that the misery caused by the drug was more widespread than anyone had realized.

What was happening in Germany at this time served to reinforce inclinations to be patient and to regard settlements out of court as the norm. So time slipped by, one by one the individual sixty-two settlements were made, and then in great secrecy Distillers began negotiations with the new two hundred and sixty-six litigants plus another one hundred and twenty-three parents who did not sue at all. James Evans kept writing to Distillers' solicitors, asking them when there would be a settlement, and anticipated date succeeded anticipated date. Phillip Knightley, who had replaced John Fielding in responsibility for work on the subject, could report by April 1971 that a rough 12,000-word article on Distillers was ready and that a number of Distillers executives had been identified as candidates for interview, but the paper's lawyers were insistent that there was no way in which *The Sunday Times* could publish a word while a single case was outstanding. It would be risky even to approach potential interviewees. Questions might be asked that would be themselves dangerous and that might certainly provoke Distillers to seek an injunction restraining publication or inquiry. The lawyers also reminded Harold Evans that there were severe problems in proving the contents of the article against any possible libel actions.

By the autumn of 1971, conscious that four years had elapsed since Dr. Phillips first came into his office, and increasingly uneasy about the progress of the cases, Harold Evans wrote to James Evans, saying that the delay was intolerable and that some legal way must be found to publish the article about thalidomide despite the risks of contempt of court. Contempt of court could surely not cast its blanket for so many years over an issue of such public importance.

Within a few weeks, the resolve to publish was strengthened and the risks were underlined by the David Mason case. Nothing emerged from the lawyers or the parents about the progress of the money talks until David Mason made his decisive break. Angered by the sums offered and by Distillers' condition that if one parent objected the money would be withdrawn, he decided to go public. At first he did not know how to begin, but a friend of his knew the editor of the *Daily Mail,* David English, so Mason went there with his story. The *Mail* printed three articles on Mason's theme that he was being legally blackmailed into accepting compensation he thought inadequate: MY FIGHT FOR JUSTICE, BY THE FATHER OF HEARTBREAK GIRL, LOUISE, said the headline. Then the articles stopped abruptly. Kimber Bull had complained to the Attorney General that they constituted contempt and might prejudice the out-of-court settlement. The attorney general agreed and warned the *Daily Mail;* the *Mail* ceased publication of the story.

Unfortunately, Mason's story did not have the effect it ought to have had. The rest of the press and television, which had interviewed Mason and confirmed his account, then carried nothing. There was no ripple effect, largely because of worry about contempt of court. Later in the month, the BBC television programme "Twenty-Four Hours" planned to interview parents of thalidomide children. Distillers threatened action for contempt of court, and this programme was cancelled, too. Again, when Mason won his right to refuse the proposed settlement, there was a brief flurry of headlines about that alone and then silence once more.

At *The Sunday Times,* James Evans was still puzzling how to respond to his editor's request for a path through the legal minefield. Finally he came up with a plan: Knightley's article on how the drug came to be made should be put into page proof and sent around to Distillers the week of proposed publication, asking if it would like to comment. If it commented without seeking a court injunction, the paper could publish with the apparent acquiescence of the company. If it sought an injunction against publication, *The Sunday Times* could fight it. This way the law could be tested, with the hope that the court would declare the right to publish, and without the risk of the editor's going to jail for contempt. It was an inspired scheme, but James Evans remained, he wrote, "not very optimistic about the possible success of this manoeuvre."

James Evans and Knightley began long sessions of checking the draft article for libel, while the paper intensified its monitoring of what was happening to the thalidomide children and their families. "Many mothers," reported Michael Moynihan, "are relying on tranquillisers to keep going, some have reached the stage of almost suicidal desperation, and already strained marriages are reaching breaking point, according to reports from home visitors throughout the country employed by the Lady Hoare Trust for Thalidomide Children." Moynihan quoted parents, such as G. J. Piller, a medical research administrator: "After ten or more years of struggling along and trying to plan ahead, many parents now feel in a limbo of frustration, anger and helplessness." A strong statement about Distillers by Lady Hoare in a remark to Moynihan was included in the report: "It is a tragic and deplorable situation. Many parents feel ground down by prolonged litigation, degraded by the detailed form-filling they have had to undergo, and deeper resentment of being made to feel they were going cap in hand for charity, rather than moral justice from the wealthy Distillers." The remarks gave the paper's legal readers some pause, but the paper published it; and James Evans, reading it, was struck by the phrase "moral justice" and made a mental note to consider its implications.

The rewriting, checking, and double-checking of the article was still going ahead for the manoeuvre James Evans had suggested, but the editor was having second thoughts on two fronts, legal and editorial. He felt that the editorial side of the operation needed strengthening. Knightley was obviously going to take too long by himself, if he were to continue alone. There was simply too much to do.

The paper had recently set up a Special Projects unit headed by Bruce Page, a former Insight editor with a remarkable talent for investigation; Page was assisted by Elaine Potter. The Special Projects unit was trying to decide what it would look into first, but Evans asked Page to take over leadership of the thalidomide project. With Knightley, three experienced journalists were now engaged full time on it.

In addition, he asked James Evans to try to come up with a better legal plan of attack: "We might end up with your first proposed line of action with a formal gag and we ought therefore to plan so that we have a much higher chance, indeed a certainty, of publication." James Evans was not very hopeful. Distillers' solicitors met every request for information with warnings that they would take proceedings if there was any breach of the contempt rules. But by the end of August, Page had produced information that put the whole affair in a new perspective.

Page had read two long and complex articles in the *Modern Law Review* that spring. The editor of the *Review* had wanted to discuss the attitude of the English courts to actuarial evidence, a politely murmuring controversy between the legal and actuarial professions. He had invited a contribution from John Prevett, a forty-year-old actuary with the London firm of Bacon and Woodrow, who had given evidence in the 1969 hearings before Mr. Justice Hinchcliffe to fix the compensation for the tha-

lidomide children. Prevett's evidence in court had barely been reported
at the time, and its significance had not been appreciated by anyone,
least of all by the judge, who had pronounced that the time for actuarial
assistance for judges setting damages had not yet arrived. Prevett in his
two articles used the thalidomide awards to demonstrate the need for
the courts to accept such actuarial evidence. He argued that compensation could be fixed fairly only on the basis of recognized calculations
about the rates of mortality, the interest that would be earned by lump
sums invested, and the effects of future levels of inflation on income and
on the cost of care. His arithmetic showed Mr. Justice Hinchliffe's unwillingness to accept expert evidence, and in particular to allow for inflation, had led the judge to make awards that were *in each case only half of
what they should have been.*

Page talked to Prevett, enlisted his assistance, and wrote a long memorandum to the editor that was a devastating indictment of the awards.
"It is quite a thought," wrote Page, "that the thalidomide children were
offered charity amounting to 40 per cent of something that is less than
half the amount actuarially necessary to make up for their difficulties."

The shock that realization of this produced in *The Sunday Times* had
barely been absorbed before Knightley, who had been trying to keep an
eye on the secret negotiations between Distillers and the three hundred
and eighty-nine families, reported something equally disturbing. Despite Mason's defiant example in challenging the levels of compensation
and his Court of Appeal victory in establishing a parent's right to reject
an offer, the majority of parents were rapidly being signed up for deals
no better than the one Mason had rejected. The charitable trust they
were being offered, said Knightley, would give the children only half the
level of the 1969 settlement. If the Page-Prevett memorandum exposed
an injustice, the Knightley news was a scandal—all the more so since the
parents had been warned yet again not to mention the proposed sums of
damages to anyone on pain of losing every penny.

The original *Sunday Times* judgement—that the major issue was how
thalidomide had been made in the first place—was now regarded as incomplete. Willingness to wait to publish that story had always been
based on the assumption that the legal settlements would be fair. But
that assumption, questionable in 1969, was patently false in 1972. The
editor and his colleagues on the thalidomide story realized in dismay
that they were about to be silent witnesses to an outrage. It could not be
allowed to happen. The complex but normal journalistic objective of an-

alysing the roots of a tragedy had to be accompanied by a simpler but unique objective—winning more money for the children than the lawyers were going to obtain.

The central dilemma of all the years of silence, however, remained like an impenetrable rock. It had been demonstrated that heartbreak stories of the kind *The Sunday Times* had been publishing, and criticism of Distillers' compensatory awards in the tenor of the Harman article and the remarks of Lady Hoare, had no noticeable effect on the company. On the contrary, Distillers was secretly offering half what it had offered in 1969. Nor had any of the articles created a flicker of response in public opinion. No other newspaper followed up. Nobody wrote letters. Nobody made a speech. No Member of Parliament raised a question. No lawyer demurred. A sustained and powerful campaign was required, but how could the paper undertake that if the very first article would invite a court action for contempt? The rest would be silence, just as the *Daily Mail* and the Mason court case had been followed by silence. Some way had to be found not just of challenging the proposed settlements in one week, but of doing it the next week and the week after that and month after month—for making it a national issue that would not go away. It was here that James Evans, pondering on the remark of Lady Hoare about "moral justice," made a contribution that was to be as decisive as Prevett's financial analysis.

The campaign, James Evans suggested, should be divided into two parts. The first part should consist of stories based on the new work by the Special Projects unit and address itself to the *moral* arguments about the delays and the amount of money being offered. It would, as Bruce Page suggested, attack the whole idea that the law was ever going to find a satisfactory settlement by means of a contest between unequal parties. The whole area of personal injury litigation was open to discussion.

Harold Evans told his chairman, Denis Hamilton, his predecessor as editor of *The Sunday Times,* that he was convinced the risks had to be run. Hamilton backed his editor's judgement, and on September 24, 1972, the paper took the plunge. Page, who had been called in from holiday, converted his original memorandum into an analysis of the arithmetic of deprivation, and three pages of *The Sunday Times* were devoted to arguing, with statistics and photographs of thalidomide victims, that the law was failing to produce justice for the thalidomide children. The main long article was coolly written, but the opening headline and an accompanying editorial made it clear that this was not a normal feature presentation. "Our Thalidomide Children: A Cause for National Shame" was the emotional slogan that became a campaign theme. The editorial, headlined CHILDREN ON OUR CONSCIENCE, said the plight of the children shamed society, shamed the law, and shamed Distillers.

> It is appreciated [said the editorial] that Distillers have always denied negligence and that if the cases were pursued, the children might end up with nothing. It is appreciated that Distillers' lawyers have a professional duty to secure the best for their clients, but at the end of the day, what is paid in settlement is the decision of Distillers and they should offer much, much more. . . . The law is not always the same as justice.
>
> There are times when insistence on the letter of the law is as exposed to criticism as infringement of another's legal right. The figure in the proposed settlement of £3.25 million spread over ten years does not shine as a beacon against pre-tax profits last year of £64 million and company assets worth £421 million. Without in any way surrendering on negligence, Distillers could and should think again. And the Government must act. The adversary system will not do. Compassion after disaster requires a state insurance scheme for compensation, something long advocated for personal injuries cases, but even the wisest reform will be a sham if society does not now insist on justice for the victims of an enduring tragedy.

At the end of the three-page report, the paper said that "in a future article" it would trace how the tragedy occurred. This was a reference to the draft, still in rough stage, which was based in part on Distillers' own documents. But the reference carefully did not commit the paper to publish the following week. It was an attempt to test the water.

13 Facts Are Not Allowed

Jack Ashley, Labour M.P. for the Midlands potteries town of Stoke, sat in his Epsom, Surrey, garden in the autumn sunshine and read *The Sunday Times* with increasing anger. Ashley is a remarkable man—a labourer and crane driver from Widnes, in a sprawling industrial area of Lancashire, who became a shop steward for the Chemical Workers Union and then won scholarships to Ruskin College, Oxford, and Caius College, Cambridge. He became a BBC radio producer and television producer and, in 1966, entered Parliament, where he rapidly made a mark. When it seemed likely that he would be offered a ministerial post, he decided it would be a good idea to clear up a minor handicap, a slight deafness in one ear that he thought might limit his ability to respond for the ministry in the House of Commons. The operation was a disaster: Ashley ended up stone deaf. His first instinct was to give up his seat. There was an uprush of support for him so spontaneous and moving that it encouraged him to stay—and to do what he could in Parliament for all handicapped people.

When Ashley read the article, he was chairman in the House of Commons of the All-Party Committee on the Disabled. He was also writing his autobiography. But he put that aside to concentrate on the thalidomide children. Immediately after reading the article, he telephoned Harold Evans at his home. (Ashley has not allowed his deafness to deprive him of the telephone. The person at the other end is unaware of any problem, but Ashley is "hearing" what is being said by lip-reading the words of the other party silently enunciated by his wife, Pauline, who is listening on an extension.) On the following Tuesday, Ashley met the editor and the Special Projects team and in a series of penetrating questions tested the assertions and arguments of the article.

At the end, he promised his full support. It was a crucial commitment. *The Sunday Times* might face legal suppression, but Ashley could transfer the campaign to Parliament. He called a meeting of his committee, wrote to the prime minister, and began a round of parliamentary activity. *The Sunday Times* backed him up by reprinting the September 24 article and circulating it to every M.P., newspaper editor, and television producer in Britain. The rest of the press and television, wary of the courts, did not respond at this stage. But the law soon made itself felt. The editor received a letter at *The Sunday Times* from the legal secretary to the attorney general, T. C. Hetherington:

> The Solicitor General, in the absence of the Attorney General at Strasbourg [it said], has asked me to inform you that a formal complaint had been made to him concerning the article published in *The Sunday Times*. Some parts of the article could perhaps be described as no more than a commentary on matters of general interest, and as such might not, taken in isolation, constitute contempt; but since other passages in the article are related to the negotiations for the settlement currently in progress, there may be grounds for claiming that the article as a whole constitutes contempt.

The letter was polite enough. The solicitor general, it said, would be grateful for the editor's observations, but it concluded with a warning: "You will no doubt wish to consider your position in the light of the complaint that has been made, particularly in view of the reference already made to a future article on this subject." *The Sunday Times* replied defending its action, emphasizing that it had argued on moral and not on legal grounds. It made clear that the paper intended to go on with the campaign. The legal secretary responded by saying that he could not comment on the justification advanced by the paper. The attorney general would have the file on his return. The complaint, he confirmed in response to a *Sunday Times* question, had come from the legal advisers to Distillers. *The Sunday Times* decided to continue its campaign, though it felt obliged to notify the attorney general's office of the scope of its intended coverage.

On Sunday, October 1, in the face of the strong prospect of contempt proceedings, *The Sunday Times* published a further major attack, and gave prominent space to letters from parents of thalidomide-damaged children. One particularly moving letter came from the mother of Patrick Pope, the boy who had had forty-two operations. Mrs. Pope's claim for Patrick had been decided in 1968, but the family was still waiting for money because the lawyers had been unable to agree what the 100 per cent figure should be. The letters and reports were accompanied by an article on the editorial page by Harry Street, professor of English law at the University of Manchester, arguing that the thalidomide case imposed on the victims of disaster the hit-and-miss of damages fixed by judges without reference to actuarial evidence.

The Sunday after this there were more letters, case histories, and reports of Jack Ashley's efforts in the Commons. And on this Sunday morning, there was the first expression of interest by other media: the television programme "Weekend World," whose staff included John Fielding, formerly of *The Sunday Times,* reported a poll among Distillers' shareholders on what they thought of Distillers' offer: it was only a small poll of several hundred (70 per cent thought the offer inadequate), but a welcome sign of initiative and heartening for the paper.

There was even better news next day. The campaign became legitimate. The attorney general wrote to the editor to say that he had considered what had been published and did not propose to take any action over it. This meant the newspaper was free to go on arguing for an improvement in the offer and raising the question of personal injury damages. But there was obviously going to be a battle if *The Sunday Times* wanted to widen the attack. The attorney general said he wanted Distillers to see the draft article based on its documents, so on October 10, Evans sent it to the chairman of Distillers, Sir Alexander McDonald. He emphasized that it was only a draft and asked Sir Alex to comment. Distillers' response was to complain again to the attorney general, and this time he agreed to act. He told *The Sunday Times* that he would apply to the High Court for an injunction restraining publication of the article, and *The Sunday Times,* relieved to have the moral campaign removed from threat for the moment, agreed to delay the article until the case on that could be argued before the Lord Chief Justice in the High Court.

Jack Ashley was also running into difficulties in Parliament at this time—a cause for worry, because it was an essential platform. There was, for a start, very little encouragement from the government. Questions were brushed off by the prime minister, Edward Heath, and by the responsible minister, Sir Keith Joseph. "There is a case before the courts," said Sir Keith, "and the issue raised must be left to them." The prime minister told Tory M.P.'s: "Legal matters are not a matter for this or for a Labour government." The difficulty was the fundamental one that Parliament by tradition does not interfere with any subject being decided by a court of law. If the minister had not foresworn comment,

the Speaker (or chairman) of the House of Commons would have ruled
that the cases were *sub judice*. Ashley tried to table an Early Day Motion,
saying that Distillers' settlement was inadequate and calling for moral
justice. He was told by the Commons clerks that it would be disallowed
because the terms of the settlement were before the courts. It looked as if
the parliamentary campaign might be stillborn.

A way had to be found around the traditional rules of Parliament or it
would be useless as a sounding board of national opinion. Ashley, not
one to give up easily, sought a private appointment with the Speaker,
and two hours before trying to raise the issue on the floor of the Commons called Harold Evans away from a lunch for one of his extraordinary telephone conversations. It was a happy manoeuvre since Evans
was able to tell Ashley that the attorney general had just accepted *The
Sunday Times* article of September 24 and with it must go acceptance of
the distinction between the moral and the legal arguments. Surely
M.P.'s could be extended the same freedom? Ashley was that afternoon
(it was October 19) allowed by the Speaker to put his case as other
M.P.'s listened.

It would be a parody of democracy, Ashley said, if elected members
were denied the right of expressing their views about something that was
already being commented on in a newspaper. He emphasized: "Moral
justice is not a question of the law and therefore cannot be *sub judice*."
The Speaker promised to consider the idea and rule on it the next day.
Ashley went to him in his room, and they discussed the terms that the
motion might take if it was to follow the new distinction between moral
and legal obligations. The next day the Speaker ruled that he would accept an Early Day Motion that M.P.'s could sign if it placed emphasis
on the question of moral justice.

This was a big breakthrough, for it legitimized a whole range of parliamentary activity. Members of Parliament were able to lend their support to the campaign simply by signing Ashley's motion. There was no
need to try to gain a majority of the 635 members of the House; 60 or 70
signatures of both parties is a respectable total to signify concern, especially if quickly acquired, since it suggests that there is a cross section of
opinion behind the move that can be mobilized still further. Within
days, Ashley had no fewer than 265 M.P.'s of all parties signing his motion. It gave him the backing to exploit his new opportunity, and he did
it with pugnacious flair, with press and television reporting. In a short
"adjournment" debate, he was scathing about secrecy: Distillers had

tried to gag the press, he said, and it had tried to suppress television. "But the truth must be ventilated and that is one of the purposes of this all-party campaign."

Ashley had considerable allies, Labour and Tory. Alfred Morris, M.P., later minister for the disabled in a Labour government, knew a medical administrator who, with one of his own children stricken, had helped to organize a group called the Parents of Thalidomide Children. They had collected details of individual cases, and Morris sent these to the Lord Chancellor (Britain's chief legal officer) and the attorney general, asking them to receive a deputation. Ashley's all-party committee also asked the chairman of Distillers to let his executives meet them to discuss compensation. (Sir Alex refused, saying that counsel on both sides had urged the need for confidentiality.) Luck smiled on Ashley and his allies. There is very little chance for an individual M.P. to introduce a new law unless he wins a high place in an annual ballot that determines the amount of time and priority his measure can have. The M.P. who came first that autumn, Ray Carter, was sympathetic to the campaign and decided to introduce a bill redefining the legal liabilities of drug companies—and to give legal rights to the foetus. Eventually it failed, but not before it had enabled still further debate to take place. Another push came from Lewis Carter-Jones, who introduced a bill aimed at speeding up research and development for thalidomide children. Tories like Sir Robert Cary and Norman Fowler joined Labour M.P.'s like Michael Meacher and Barbara Castle in pressing the government to lean on Distillers.

Ashley used every chance to embarrass Distillers, which was saying nothing in public. But when it leaked out that privately its management was letting it be known that it might respond to *The Sunday Times* by breaking off negotiations for a settlement and stand on the legal issue, Ashley produced a savage image: "For the three hundred and seventy children," he told Parliament, "the sword of Damocles has been replaced by the jagged edge of a broken whisky bottle." This rich stuff was duly reported, but in modest measure as yet. The real awakening of press interest in the campaign waited on two events—the High Court hearing against *The Sunday Times'* draft article, which was to take place November 7-9, and a full-scale parliamentary debate.

When the case for an injunction to ban *The Sunday Times'* draft article was heard in the High Court, three of the country's most senior judges were present: the Lord Chief Justice, Lord Widgery; Mr. Justice Melford

Stevenson; and Mr. Justice Brabin. (*The Sunday Times'* case was coupled with contempt proceedings against London Weekend Television for an incidental error in its "Weekend World" programme.) The attorney general, Sir Peter Rawlinson, appeared for the government, with John Wilmers, Q.C., to "observe" for Distillers. The courtroom was packed.

Sir Peter said that the article, which the judges had read overnight and was not read out in court, was "a conscious attempt to use the platform provided by the newspaper to pressurize the conduct and prejudice the position of Distillers." It would be seriously in contempt of court to publish it. Although in one sense the actual trial could be said to lie a long time ahead, there was an attempt to reach a compromise out of court, and the article might affect a resolution of issues that were imminent. The case was of very considerable principle because an unscrupulous newspaper—there was no suggestion that *The Sunday Times* was unscrupulous—could use the right to abuse a party in a suit and abuse a plaintiff as being dishonourable and greedy.

Brian Neill, Q.C., for *The Sunday Times,* argued that in cases like this there were two competing public interests—the administration of justice and the right of the public to be informed. The balance should favour publication in this instance, a civil trial before a judge—if it ever got to trial. The case was not simply whether there was pressure or influence but whether there was *improper* pressure, and supplying of information could not be improper. Neill quoted the remark of Lord Justice Lawton at a preliminary hearing that he wondered if the *Venetian Times* would have been sued for contempt if it had said, "A case is coming up before the doge's court in which a Mr. Shylock is claiming a pound of flesh; he may have a legal case—it is not for us to say—but we are surprised that he brought the action." Neill said that surely it was perfectly proper to make such a comment; the article here was not intended to be any more than that, not a discussion of the legal issue. Neill put Harold Evans into the witness box to emphasize "great public dismay that after ten years the law has not produced justice." Lord Widgery remarked dryly that the judges had not overlooked the fact that a long time had elapsed.

In their decision, given on November 17, all three judges rejected *The Sunday Times'* submission and banned the article. There could be no balance of competing interests, they said. English authorities did not require the court to make such a balance, only to ensure that any comment which raised a serious risk of interference with legal proceedings should be withheld until the proceedings had been determined.

"We think that this is a matter of substantive law and that these authorities bind us. We see no distinction in this case between persuasion directed to a legal obligation and persuasion directed to a moral obligation." London Weekend Television was let off because in contrast to *The Sunday Times* it had tried to avoid contempt and "the spoken words in his programme did not have the impact which the producer might have hoped they would have on the viewers."

The judgement was a reverse but only a partial one. *The Sunday Times* could continue its moral campaign—it was now featuring a thalidomide family every week—and if the judges rejected the moral-legal distinction, it was too late to influence Parliament, which was about to stage a full-scale debate. The government had refused to allow the Commons any time for a thalidomide debate, but by tradition there are a few days in the parliamentary calendar when the opposition has the right to choose which subject will be debated. The leader of the opposition, Harold Wilson, used one of these days to nominate thalidomide as the subject. Wilson called a meeting in his room in the Commons; there were Labour M.P.'s Jack Ashley and Alfred Morris; the opposition spokesman on legal matters, Sir Elwyn Jones; and the editor of *The Sunday Times*. They approved a motion drafted by Ashley. It called on Distillers to face up to its moral responsibilities and asked for a government trust fund to provide for the children. The government amendment, reflecting a softening in its attitude, declared that the House of Commons was disturbed by the plight of the children and the delay in reaching a settlement, but recognized the initiative already taken by the government. It welcomed government undertakings to investigate any case where the children's needs were not thought to be met by state services. It offered to consider whether a trust fund would be needed as soon as the present cases were finished.

As the M.P.'s met for the debate, Distillers made its first positive response to the campaign—an increase in the offer from £3.25 million to £5 million ($7.8 million to $12 million). This offer was lost, as a massive emotional indignation swept through both sides of the House concerning the delays in the case and the attempts at legal suppression. (The one or two apologists for the company were subdued. "I welcome the fact that the company has been able to increase the value of the offer," said John Astor, "but whether it is fair is a matter of opinion. . . .")

Jack Ashley opened with a speech that was heard in silence by a packed chamber. He set the tone at once. They were debating a great national tragedy, none the less poignant because it happened ten years ago. It was one tragedy in which the passage of time instead of healing the suffering had heightened it.

> Adolescence is a time for living and laughing, for learning and loving. But what kind of adolescence will a ten-year-old boy look forward to when he has no arms, no legs, one eye, no pelvic girdle, and is only three feet tall? How can an eleven-year-old girl look forward to laughing and loving when she has no hand to be held and legs to dance on? I ask the House to look at the photographs I have in my hand of these two children. . . . Yet the powerful Distillers Company has had no compunction in fighting these children for the last ten years.

Ashley said the children needed £20 million on any realistic assessment. The new offer was palpably a gimmick. "The children's living standard is falling as the profits of the company are rising. We are witnessing not only a shabby spectacle but a grave national scandal, a display of national irresponsibility which has seldom or ever been surpassed."

The debate was vivid with personal testimony. One M.P., M. S. Miller, recalled the blandishments that were made to him by the pharmaceutical industry when he was in practice as a family doctor. "I was pushed by Distillers in respect of Distaval. . . . I do not think this is an occasion for a balanced argument. There is an outcry in the country, and if the House of Commons is not a place we can shout about it when something is to be hidden behind a smokescreen of legal procedure, God help the ordinary people when it comes to claiming redress of their grievance."

There was new testimony about the nature of the pressures on the parents. Health Minister Barbara Castle told of Christine Clark, who accepted the 1968 settlement and who had written to Mrs. Castle saying, "We tried to get to the press with the evidence that certain matters were being withheld. We were told by our Q.C. that if we persisted we could have our legal aid certificates withdrawn, which obviously meant no case. Who could afford to fight?" Mrs. Castle secured from the prime minister, quoting the lord chancellor, an assurance that legal aid could be withdrawn only by an independent committee and not at the whim of a single lawyer. Dr. Vaughan, the Guy's Hospital paediatrician and a Conservative M.P., said that he had examined all sixty-two cases that had so far been before the courts, and he again emphasized the strain on the parents. "We should all recognize that there is a manifest injustice here."

Harold Wilson was critical of the government's attempt to stay aloof. He gave instances of other occasions when governments had taken independent action despite the existence of legal proceedings. Liberal member David Steel joined the attack. The National Health Service had been involved: "It is no longer good enough in 1972 that we stand aside and say this is a private matter between the person who takes the drug and the company who manufactures it. This is no way to diminish their responsibility but society and the NHS have a right, and therefore the government have a duty, to intervene." Very often justice delayed was justice denied. The government should take over the battle.

This the government was determined not to do. There had been private approaches to Sir Keith Joseph, but the government maintained its position: that it was sympathetic, that the state's own services for helping the children were reasonable, and that it could not interfere in a private dispute. But the parliamentary pressure from all sides was intense, and the government did thaw. Sir Keith, replying, announced that £3 million ($7.5 million) would be set aside for improving services for the congenitally disabled, and he committed the government to considering a trust fund for the thalidomide children at the end of the litigation. And on December 19, the prime minister, impressed by the criticisms of the personal-injury damages, announced a royal commission to examine the subject.

The debate had been a compelling experience, producing new points and a new impetus for the campaign. But it was also remarkable that the House of Commons might debate such a complex issue without the possibility of knowing the background to the tragedy: David Crouch, an M.P. from Canterbury, declaring an interest in the pharmaceutical industry, was able to repeat and have acceptance for the false statement that "at the time that thalidomide was put on the market no tests were being carried out in the drug industry on the effect of drugs on the foetus."

By now the debate and the High Court suppression of *The Sunday Times'* article had turned the thalidomide campaign into a national issue, transferring it from the newspaper's inside pages to the front. It had been slow beginning, but by November–December, it had gained momentum. An engine of public opinion had started that was self-sustaining in the face of the apparent obduracy of the company and the law's apparent insistence on suppressing facts.

The American experience became particularly valuable at this point, reinforcing the campaigners in their determination to win sums comparable to those awarded in California. David Mason had been in touch with the Los Angeles firm of Butler, Jefferson and Fry, which had won $2.5 million (eventually reduced to about $500,000) from Richardson-Merrell for a child victim with one leg and a deformed hip. Butler and his partner, Dr. Robert Fry, had offered to come to England with information on an expenses-only basis. *The Sunday Times* had liked the idea and had flown in both men in time for the parliamentary debate. The American lawyers had sat in the public gallery and later, with telling first-hand authority, they briefed the British press on the superiority of the American system of strict liability. People from universities, from industries, and from the trade unions began to write to Ashley offering support. Student organizations passed resolutions. The *Law Society Gazette* attacked the attorney general for seeking an injunction on the grounds of unfair pressure on Distillers. There was, it said, a large air of unreality about shielding litigants from pressures that might lead them to settle. *The Guardian* seized the point of pressure on the parents: "The wrangles go on and the financial hardship grows. . . . The Government is being remarkably insensitive." *Community Medicine* attacked what it described as "a squalid wrangle." *The Daily Telegraph* picked up Steel's point: "Justice delayed is justice denied."

There was one mysterious and sensational development in the campaign that worried *The Sunday Times* and Jack Ashley. Posters began to appear making savage attacks on Distillers and calling for a boycott of their products, which were named. Thousands of these posters were plastered all over the country, including the door, windows, and railings of Distillers' elegant London headquarters in St. James's Square. The message was rammed home with brilliant brutality in a series of different slogan images:

THEY SAID IT WAS SAFE FOR PREGNANT WOMEN.
LIKE HELL IT WAS.
(Illustration: A bottle of Distaval.)

MOTHER'S RUIN . . . CHILDREN'S POISON.
(Bottle of gin, thalidomide baby.)

HAVE A THALIDOMIDE OLD BOY.

DON'T MIND IF I DO.

(Two men in a bar with whisky labelled thalidomide.)

Fleet Street newspapers got copies of these posters with the information that they were a private campaign aimed at hitting Distillers where it hurt—in its pockets. The venture, it was said, was not connected with any newspaper or thalidomide organization, and there was no name or telephone number given, nor any indication of the printer for the authorities to proceed against.

The attorney general announced that the posters were illegal. Police ripped them down and Scotland Yard began a search for the originators. They were not reproduced in *The Sunday Times* and they had nothing to do with the paper, which feared lest the posters, well meant though they were, undermine the argument on which it and Jack Ashley had based the justification of their campaign: that a debate on the moral aspects of litigation would not amount to unfair pressure. (The attorney general showed himself well aware of the loophole the posters and the boycott call had provided, and so was John Wilmers, for Distillers, when the hearing began for an injunction against *The Sunday Times*. The attorney general tried to put the posters before the court as an example of unfair pressure, and to show what terrible things would happen if *The Sunday Times*' article was allowed. Brian Neill for *The Sunday Times* had been ready for such an attempt and immediately objected. The judges upheld him and the danger passed.)

Nobody at the time identified the originators of the poster campaign—but they did bear the authentic stamp of aggressive flamboyance that one journalist brought to all his products. This was Rupert Murdoch, the Australian newspaperman who had arrived in Britain to capture the *News of the World* and transform the fortunes of the *Sun*. Murdoch went to elaborate lengths to keep his poster operation secret so that it could not be stopped by court order or imperil his papers. A senior *News of the World* executive, Graham King, organized it. King resigned from the *News of the World* so that he would be acting as a private individual, and a few days after the posters appeared (stuck up at night by small volunteer groups), he left for a convenient appointment in Australia. (He later returned to the *News of the World*.)

The posters had direct and popular appeal, whatever the risks they ran for *The Sunday Times.* But one of the thoughts behind them did not work. The intention was that newspapers would reproduce the posters in their own pages and do that without fear of contempt, since they would be merely reporting the news. But this transparent device would not have stood the test of trial, and no newspaper, including the *Sun* or the *News of the World,* attempted it.

Immense pressure had now built up in Parliament and in the press against Distillers, but it seemed to be having not the slightest effect. The company kept its head down, and nothing, it seemed, was getting through to it. There were moments in early December when the campaigners began to feel that they were up against rock. But there was a third element to the campaign, which was only slowly beginning to reveal its full potential.

14 Shareholders into Battle

Sir Alexander McDonald, the chairman of Distillers, was a good representation of Scottish granite, a man of stern principle, who had been at the centre of things in the company for nearly thirty years. He was born in Glasgow, studied law and accountancy at Glasgow University, and joined Distillers in 1946 to help sort out its tax problems. His rise had been steady and assured: company secretary in 1947, director in 1954, deputy chairman ten years later, and chairman in 1967. Over the years he had gathered a reputation for a single-minded, hard-headed approach to business affairs which suited the Distillers image. (Its headquarters in Edinburgh is known to many as the Kremlin because it is formidable and cold.) Married, with two sons and two daughters, Sir Alex was knighted in 1972 for services to exports, and at the time of the thalidomide campaign, he was earning £37,000 (about $90,000) a year.

But Sir Alex and his board did not own Distillers; it is owned by 250,000 shareholders with 300 million shares. This provided, it seemed initially, the company's most powerful defence. As directors, they were required by law to protect the interests of the shareholders. This meant that they should seek the best legal advice on the extent of their liability and then follow that advice. And they had a duty also to their staff, who had, they must believe, carried out their duties conscientiously. As commercial policy and company policy, it was impeccable. In the thalidomide campaign, it raised in a sharp and uncomfortable way the moral responsibility of shareholders for deeds done in their name. The weapon turned. Enough of the shareholders did not like what was being done.

That is, however, to anticipate a relatively slow-moving development. If the campaign in the tightly knit financial community of London's "City" provided the *coup de grâce*, it was most dependent at first on isolated individuals who not only had to put aside their own immediate self-interest but had to be undeterred by the apparent futility of raising one voice among 250,000. Three shareholders—Roger and Sarah Broad and Tony Lynes—had been stirred at once by *The Sunday Times'* article on September 24. The first to contact the paper was Lynes, an experienced writer and journalist and one of the leaders of the Child Poverty Action Group, who had inherited 600 shares in 1969. Lynes wrote to the chairman of Distillers and gave a copy of his letter to *The Sunday Times.* In it he argued that even if the company were completely blameless, it had a clear moral obligation to compensate fully and generously. Even from a narrow commercial point of view, it was essential that the company should be doing what was morally right. The cost of preserving the company's good name might be £20 million. "This is a large sum. The market value of our shares, however, stands at about £600,000,000. The payment of £20,000,000 therefore would be the equivalent of 6p for every pound's worth of shares [sic]. I don't think many of my fellow shareholders would begrudge the thalidomide children this sum."

Sir Alex replied at length two weeks later. It was the first exposition of Distillers' case, and it was an emphatic rejection of the appeal. "The views of Mr. Lynes," said Sir Alex, "were quite impracticable." Legally the parents were probably entitled to nothing at all from Distillers, he wrote. But the company had not been rigid, and the long-negotiated settlement had only failed to achieve finality because of the dissent of a tiny minority of parents. Sir Alex then deployed the corporate case against the moral case set out by Lynes.

> Even if the directors had agreed with you (which they do not) that there were overwhelming moral reasons for giving away £20,000,000 as you suggest, you must realise that directors of a public company who acted in such a way and on such a scale might at once become subject to legal proceedings at the hands of those shareholders who disagreed. And in view of the rights, differences, and liabilities involved in the legal structure of companies, it is quite unrealistic to think that directors of a public company, whatever its financial position, could give away £20,000,000 with impunity.

It was all very well for a shareholder or group to take a moral stand that involved him in little responsibility towards others—"and I would observe in passing that it is even easier for a newspaper editor." There was, however, a great difference between individual shareholders or other private persons giving away funds to a charity and the directors of a company giving away funds for moral reasons which did not have the unanimous approval of shareholders and when legal reasons did not justify it. Sir Alex made something of a plea for understanding. The directors had continually had all aspects of the thalidomide problem under review for many years. They had tried conscientiously within the framework of their powers and duties to steer the company between two extremes and it was not easy for them now, observing the *sub judice* rule, when they were subjected to a campaign going far beyond the purely moral arguments.

But Sir Alex also gave a warning: "If the campaign now being conducted by *The Sunday Times* should result in the breakdown of the present negotiations," the company might have no alternative but to consider in the light of advice whether it should take its stand on the legal issues. The Lynes-McDonald exchanges might have been the beginnings of a public debate between Distillers and its critics, but it was cut short. Sir Alex wrote that he was not going to be drawn into public discussion, and he was, in particular, angry with Lynes for telling anyone about the apparent threat to refuse any money at all if *The Sunday Times* continued its campaign: "You have chosen to publicise the matter by passing to *The Guardian* a copy of my letter to you of 11th October with an ensuing misinterpretation of the company's attitude of such a kind as might well have caused unfounded anxiety to the families with whom we are negotiating. In the circumstances I am sure you will not expect me to continue the correspondence."

The reply did not satisfy Lynes. He wrote again making three points. First, whether the company was liable or not, the children needed an income to live and charitable donations from individual shareholders could not provide the sums needed. "In the absence of a state disablement income scheme either Distillers pay adequate compensation or nobody does." Second, a possible solution would be for the company to guarantee an adequate income for life to each of the victims with annual adjustments in line with current wage increases from which any benefits they might eventually receive from a disablement scheme would be deducted. Third, if the payment of £20 million without legal liability would lay the directors open to legal action by shareholders the same could be said of the proposed payment of £3.25 million. But any such danger could be avoided by asking shareholders to agree or disagree to forego part of their dividends over the period of the years.

Lynes was by now busy writing to other shareholders. Some of them had written to him direct, others had been passed on by *The Sunday Times*, and the result was a meeting at the home of Sarah Broad and her husband, Roger, November 15, 1972. The Broads knew Phillip Knightley of *The Sunday Times* socially and had contacted him. Fourteen people were invited to attend; ten came, and they formed a small shareholders' committee with three officers—Sarah Broad, chairman; Lynes, secretary; and George Roberts (who had also written to McDonald). On the advice of Roberts, who had experience in the City (London's financial center), they decided that their best policy was to argue that Distillers' attitude "was not in the best interests of the company": the shareholders' financial interest was more badly served by the unfavourable publicity for the company than by a generous moral settlement. They were somewhat divided about the amount of publicity they should seek. Lynes and Roberts were shy people, and after some initial confusion, Sarah Broad emerged as the spokeswoman. (David Mason, who was also a shareholder, had, at one stage, appeared to speak for the committee, but he had upset other members by claiming they already had 10 per cent of shareholders with them—"one of the few deliberate lies I told in the whole campaign," he confessed later.)

The Broad group had a number of objectives: gathering together all the shareholders who agreed with them and seeking to negotiate with the company; seeking legal advice on the rights of minority shareholders; and exploring the possibility of calling an extraordinary general meeting of the company. But what could a handful of shareholders do about that? They needed the signatures of holders of 10 per cent of the ordinary shares; that meant 36 million shares. It seemed an impossible task, certainly without the support of the major institutional shareholders, who seemed unlikely allies. They would, they decided, have to circularize all the shareholders. Right away, they realized that they were only in the foothills of the Everest they had set out to scale.

The British system of registration has the advantage that it enables a diligent inquirer, give or take a nominee holding or two, to discover who does hold the shares of a public company (unlike, for example, France or Germany, where the task is impossible). But a search of a company as big as Distillers needed time and money. The lists of shareholders ran to thirty-two volumes. Even when they had raised £1,400 to buy them from the company, which was in no mood to supply them free, they had to sift them for key holdings or holdings by people especially sensitive to public opinion, such as trade unions, churches, and local councils.

The money to buy the shareholders' lists came from a private charity, The Rowntree Trust, via *The Sunday Times*, which approached them on behalf of the committee. Another £8,000 was needed for postage to circularize the names on the list. The overwhelming bulk were very small shareholdings, with many of 100–200 shares. Whether the committee would have got anywhere by this approach is anyone's guess. It was heartened by spontaneous support from perhaps 100 shareholders, including the classic stereotype of an old lady now living in India. But there was no need for this laborious pop-gun approach. The committee soon discovered that the identities of the real owners of Distillers was fissionable material.

The committee dipped into the "L–P" volumes and came up with some names of Distillers shareholders which they gave to John Windsor, a reporter on *The Guardian*. They included big insurance companies, and also a number of city and town authorities. Windsor asked these latter for their views on the uproar over Distillers. Lewisham (23,700 shares) responded at once. It would support the move for an emergency general meeting and was prepared to agree to a reasonable increase in compensation for the thalidomide parents. Others were a bit guarded. They would wait to hear from the shareholders' committee. They never did hear: the committee, from this point, was far too busy coping with the huge interest in the names in the thirty-two volumes.

Newsmen from all over the country wanted to know whether their local town authority or any local big companies were involved. The shareholders' committee found itself running a hectic information service, one delving in the volumes, one answering the phone, and one running the names between them. The telephone started ringing at seven in the morning, with reporters from the evening papers, and went on late into the night. *The Sunday Times* detached half a dozen researchers under Knightley to help the committee and to publish its own huge list.

But it was one of the very first questions from *The Guardian* that proved decisive. In the first list of L–P names, *The Guardian* had alighted on the Legal and General Assurance Society, the second largest life-insurance company in Britain in terms of funds (£1.2 billion), which had no fewer than 3.5 million shares in Distillers worth £6 million. Charles Raw, city editor, asked his colleague Stewart Fleming to canvass the views of Legal and General, and Fleming rang the head of public affairs, Patrick Sullivan-Tailyour, at his home. "At that time we had no viewpoint," Sullivan-Tailyour recalls. He went to the chief executive, Ron Peet, and said he felt they had to make some response. Peet agreed. A draft statement was produced. Peet revised it and passed it back to Sullivan-Tailyour, who rang Fleming. "You asked me for our views," said Sullivan-Tailyour. "Well, here is the answer." He then read out a press release. It was dynamite:

> The Legal and General . . . is sympathetic to the efforts of the thalidomide committee of shareholders. Mr. Ron Peet, Chief Executive Officer, said: "The moral claim of the thalidomide parents makes a strong appeal to our sympathies and we, as shareholders, would support a more generous settlement. Apart from this we feel that the continued failure to reach a settlement must be prejudicial to the interests of the company and its shareholders." Like other investors, the Society . . . is awaiting the circular and cannot say what line it will take at the meeting until it has had an opportunity of studying the committee's detailed proposals.

The Guardian led the paper with this scoop, which created, in the words of one observer, "a fair old stir in the City." Never before had an institutional investor taken a public line on such a controversial matter. "It was a very courageous thing for Peet to do," says Sullivan-Tailyour. Peet himself plays down his own role: "My object was to run an insurance company. On the other hand, when the society was specifically asked for its views, we were put on the spot. This was clearly not a question we could evade. As an individual, I felt personally that Distillers were behaving irresponsibly. They were treating the whole thing in an entirely legalistic manner—probably correctly on that score—but the main issue revolved on the question of the company's responsibility.

"Our view was based essentially on two points. First, whatever the legal rights of Distillers were, the children had a strong moral claim. Here we had a public company involved in a disaster; they were not in a position to wash their hands of the matter, and leave the lawyers to sort it out. Second, Distillers were behaving in such a manner that they were beginning to prejudice their own commercial interests. People were starting to boycott Distillers' products; we heard stories of visitors to the duty-free shop at London airport buying whisky, and stipulating that they weren't concerned whose brand it was so long as it wasn't one of Distillers'. Our own self-interest entitled us to make our view known. It was of course extremely unusual for a society such as ours to make a statement of this kind. We had no plans to do anything further—indeed, as later events showed, there was no need."

Where Legal and General had led, others followed. The Britannia Assurance Company and the Prudential were two more major institutional investors who now expressed disquiet, and a whole crop of shareholder town authorities responded to press inquiries with support for the shareholders' committee and for calling an emergency general meeting of Distillers—Chelsea, Birmingham, Hounslow, Westminster, Stockport, Bristol, Hammersmith, Nottingham, Staffordshire, Blackburn, and the Greater London Council (with the largest local authority holding of 350,000 shares).

The chairman of the Federation of Insurance Brokers, R. D. Worswick, representing 1,400 practising brokers, went on television with a powerful statement on the moral responsibility of corporations: "It is time that boards of directors of large insurance companies and other near-public concerns recognised that they are caretakers of a lot of public money. In this role they must have an overriding social conscience. . . . We pledge the services of our facilities, offices and such pressures as we can make."

The Eagle Star did not agree. It was, it said, improper for insurance companies to get involved, but the Norwich Union and the Pearl said they were considering Worswick's appeal, and the directors of Equity and Law declared they wanted to see a speedy and just settlement.

Distillers had been showing signs of movement but did not have a happy touch. After the parliamentary debate, where £5 million had been mentioned and derided, it put out a new scheme for compensation that reaped rapturous headlines about "Distillers' £11 million offer." This was no doubt partly the fault of the press—who throughout the thalidomide affair showed a tendency to project multi-million–pound headlines without much analysis of what it all added up to. But when the offer was looked at, it was clear that Distillers was still putting up only £5 million (about $12 million). It would amount to £11.85 million (about $28 million) over ten years, but only if the government undertook legislation to enable the trust fund to enjoy tax advantages. Jack Ashley in Parliament denounced the offer as fobbing off Distillers' responsibilities onto the taxpayer.

The bad impression created by this rebounded on Distillers. But there was worse to come—and again of its own making. The idea itself of tax relief was not outrageous: Germany and Sweden had made tax changes, and after all, National Health doctors had prescribed the drug in the first place. But the phrasing in the statement suggested that Distillers had been encouraged by the government: "There is reason to hope," it said, "that the Government will be favourably disposed to a request for the assistance needed." Whatever reason Distillers had for hope when it prepared the statement, it had none on January 2. The chancellor of the exchequer himself, Antony Barber, rebuked them for their presumption. He was, he announced, "astonished that they had made such a claim."

The City was more than irritated. It might have been able to tolerate or even support a clear if cold defence of Distillers' position; what it could not countenance was its clumsiness. Far from showing the smooth discretion expected of a major company, "Distillers," said one City man, "were blundering round like a Glaswegian drunk." Everything now happened at once. Lord Airlie, speaking for the merchant banks of N. M. Rothschild and Schroder Wagg, announced that they intended to arrange a meeting between major shareholders and Distillers; both companies were said to think the compensation offer too low. Distillers' financial advisers, Robert Fleming and Co., whose other clients between them owned about 5 million shares, said they were disturbed and would be co-operating in arranging a meeting.

Harsh commercial pressure was also building up. The Wrenson chain of shops and supermarkets, with 260 outlets, announced a total boycott of Distillers' products until it had offered something like £20 million in settlement. A potentially more formidable warning, if eloquently expressed, came just before Christmas from Ralph Nader, scourge of the big corporations. Nader, who had been following the campaign in *The Sunday Times,* wrote a Christmas letter to the chairman of Distillers which even included a draft of a public statement he suggested Sir Alex should make. Nader did not actually say he would be calling for a boycott of Distillers' liquor in America, but there was a hint of the importance of the United States market in the opening paragraph, and Nader went on to say that Distillers' attitude to the campaign for compensation was "singularly offensive to the free expression of conscience and duty by your world-wide constituency of consumers." Distillers, said Nader, should settle at least $500,000 for each child. It was necessary for Distillers to develop "creative responses." With annual profits exceeding $150 million and a very substantial advertising budget, the company, said Nader laconically, could bring "impressive resources to bear on a new approach." He suggested that the chairman secure adequate television and radio time to communicate a message to the public that Nader had drafted for him and that in part went like this:

> My friends in all the nations of the world whose citizens we, the Distillers Company, serve with our products, I take this extraordinary opportunity to propose a new form of corporate responsibility for the injurious consequences of thalidomide. The path we have chosen we believe will express the basic Christian ethic of love towards the children and families who have and will continue to suffer due to the unintended effects of that drug. With the advancement of this ethic through the partial accommodation of grievous tragedy with which we have been associated, it is hoped that an example will be set for other economic institutions whose impacts harm or deprive innocent human beings of their God-given rights and opportunities. . . .

Nader then had the chairman proposing to contribute for the next twenty years $10 million a year in trust for the victims, inviting them and their families to the United States, and acting as an employer of last resort for the children upon their attaining adulthood. The words Nader drafted for the Distillers chairman concluded:

> You may by this time be puzzled, unbelieving or startled by these remarks. You may wonder how we arrived at these proposals after a decade of bitter struggle and litigation with the plaintiffs. Our explanation is simple and earnest. We, too, have been reading the letters, the editorials and the observations reported in the media. We have been approached by our clergy, our neighbors and our families. Our feeling began emerging to the frontiers of our consciences: what a Christian would have done, a corporation of Christians should do. And we propose to so do. Thank you.

The restless David Mason, on reading of Nader's intervention, telephoned Washington and, having survived scrutiny by Nader's aides, arranged to fly there in January to meet Nader himself. Mason wanted Nader to launch an international boycott. (He had a practice run in the Pan American jumbo jet on the way over. The captain would not let him use the public address system so he followed the drink trolley down the aisles and whenever anyone ordered a Johnnie Walker whisky or a Gordon's gin—Distillers products—he told them his story and offered to pay half the cost if they would accept an alternative brand. "Nobody," Mason said later, "bought a Distillers drink.") In Washington, he and Nader laid down an anti-Distillers barrage at a press conference. Nader said he had had no response to his Christmas appeal to Distillers. He warned that he would consult consumer and union organizations and within a month expected to announce a U.S. boycott of Distillers' products. It would be called off if Distillers gave compensation comparable to that paid in the United States. The boycott—never, in the end, required—made headlines back in Britain, and nervous dealers in the shares knocked £11 million ($26 million) off the group's value in a day. In the next nine days, the shares fell £35 million ($80 million).

In the middle of all this, there was a fissure in the legal platform on which Distillers had stood with such rectitude for fifteen years. An Australian court, in *Watt* v. *Rama*, permitted a right of action in negligence for an unborn child who had suffered brain damage when its mother was injured in a car crash.

Confronted with all this, and with Barber's rebuff still stinging, McDonald flew from Edinburgh to London on January 3 and met all day with legal advisers. The £5 million offer was withdrawn. Two days later the war was over, and only the terms of the peace treaty, awkward enough, remained to be thrashed out. Distillers said that it was going to offer ten annual payments of £2 million a year into a charitable trust. It was the £20 million that had begun to assume significance as the major target of the campaigners.

Later in the month, there was a two-hour meeting between Distillers and major institutional shareholders. After it, McDonald, exceptionally, issued a statement saying that it was the urgent desire of his board to find a speedy and satisfactory solution: "We are fully aware of the intense public interest in the current position of the thalidomide children." He was true to his word. The company that had done so much stonewalling at last showed signs of spontaneity and generosity.

Not everyone immediately recognized that peace had broken out. In the light of all that had gone before, this was hardly surprising, and there was considerable uncertainty about just how generous the Distillers offer was. Ralph Nader thought at first it was not enough, and talked of going ahead with his boycott unless each child received $500,000. But Jack Ashley did not back that idea; David Mason said from America he would like to take advice in the light of the £20 million offer; and several stores that had stopped buying Distillers' products started to sell them again. *The Sunday Times* and the shareholders' committee agreed on a careful welcome to the £20 million, subject to expert scrutiny, and the paper set up a liaison committee chaired by Jack Ashley. It included five members of the Council for the Thalidomide Parents Society, and distinguished advisers from the City, law, and medicine—including the well-known solicitor Lord Goodman; Sir Gordon Newton, retiring editor of *The Financial Times*; and Gerard Vaughan, the Conservative M.P. and medical man who had made such a stunning speech in the Commons on his personal experiences of thalidomide children. The suspiciousness that had inevitably opened up between parents and lawyers did not help, nor did the removal of the parents' chief counsel (he became a judge), nor the discovery by the new Ashley committee that— nearly fourteen years after their birth—most of the children had still to be examined in a systematic way that would ensure equal compensation for equal degree of disability. There were several months of acute anxiety. Lawyers met lawyers. Actuary consulted actuary. An expert on the taxation of charities was brought in. Finally, however, by July there was something that the liaison committee, *The Sunday Times,* Jack Ashley, and David Mason all felt they could commend to the families. It was an imaginative scheme, agreed on by Distillers, and representing, in the opinion of John Prevett, the original questioning actuary, a better deal than any 100 per cent award the children might have won in court for negligence. This scheme, approved by the High Court on July 30, 1973, stipulated cash payments of £6 million to compensate the 340 outstanding cases at the same rate as the families who settled in 1968, and then payments of £2 million a year for seven years to a charitable trust for the benefit of both groups. There was £20,000 a year for ten years to help operate the trust. Inflation—that nonexistent phenomenon dismissed by Mr. Justice Hinchcliffe and John Wilmers, Q.C.—was now accorded the recognition of a clause entitling the children to more money up to an extra 10 per cent if prices went on rising. (They did, of course, and well beyond the 10 per cent, creating its own problems for the trust.) In the end, the liability for Distillers worked out to at least £28.4 million instead of the original £20 million that had marked the end of the full campaign;* and when Jack Ashley discovered that the

---

* Distillers recovered only £3 million from their insurers, Lloyds of London. They had claimed at least £10 million, but Lloyds refused to pay, claiming that Distillers had failed to carry out adequate tests and research on thalidomide. The claim was settled out of court in September 1976.

Treasury was going to tax as income the money the children received, the prime minister, Harold Wilson, topped up the charitable trust with £5 million from government funds to offset the income tax.

The contrast in the children's state between 1972 and 1973 could hardly be more striking. The average cash settlement in 1973 had been about £54,000. Only a year before, in its decision to replace five parents with the official solicitor, the High Court had pronounced that £7,500 was all right.

Money could not of course solve anything for the thalidomide children themselves. As David Mason said frequently during the campaign: "Nobody is getting any glory out of this; at the end of the day, my daughter Louise still has no legs." But the money did make an enormous difference to the lives of the families—and the prospects for the children in Britain, America, Germany, and Sweden were at least more hopeful than for the children in Ireland, Brazil, Argentina, and Japan (four countries where government inertia, the complications of international drug production, Byzantine judicial procedures, and the absence of a campaigning investigative newspaper effort meant the children had still to receive compensation at all). Three years after the settlement in Britain, Alec Purkis, chairman of the Thalidomide Society and one of the original leading critics, could sum up positively: "It's a story of achievement."

15 How Much for a Ruined Life?

During the thalidomide campaign, the authors—and other *Sunday Times* reporters—visited many children in Britain, the United States, Canada, Australia, and New Zealand. Marjorie Wallace saw more than one hundred cases. We have kept in touch with many of them. Most are now in their late teens, trying to start a career and form relationships, difficult enough challenges for normal teen-agers, more so for thalidomide-damaged ones. Some are managing very well. Linda Turner, a nineteen-year-old girl with short arms, is to study law at Glasgow University, one of five to gain a place at a university. Fifteen or twenty others in Britain have places in special colleges for the disabled, most of them to take business or secretarial courses. One of the boys has arranged to study electronic engineering. Thirty are already in full-time employment. One is a shop assistant, another a paths and gardens supervisor. Others, like Marion Ryan, have passed their driving tests and have had cars specially adapted for them and paid for by the Thalidomide Trust. One boy in New Zealand is a swimming champion, an American girl does charity work for the blind, an American boy runs a small newspaper, an Australian is studying accountancy. Elaine Hurton has married and is expecting her first baby.

But problems remain. As their friends become more independent, the thalidomide teen-agers, still tied by physical dependence to their families and embarrassed by the humiliation of needing to ask help from strangers, often find themselves left out. "Many are turning inwards again towards their family," says Group Captain Ronald Gardiner, who administers the Thalidomide Trust in England. "The family strains are becoming worse, especially if the children have left school and cannot find a job."

So the families have found no respite. The years of living with the consequences of thalidomide have left a trail of wrecked families and broken marriages. The backache and exhaustion of lifting overweight limbless children, or changing diapers on a sixteen-year-old, and the stress of dealing with a handicapped child have depleted the emotional and physical resources of many parents. Even those who stayed together have found that the years have brought increasing demands on their endurance and courage. While in some cases association with a thalidomide child has brought out the best in human nature, it has sometimes brought out the worst. People in cars who catch a glimpse of a limbless thalidomide girl slam on the brakes and then reverse to get a better look. One limbless British boy was attending a special school for handicapped children with seven other less severely damaged thalidomide victims; when the seven learned how much money the boy was to receive from Distillers, they attacked him, kicking him with their artificial legs as he rolled across the playground. To balance this side of the tragedy, we start our account of how some of the thalidomide children are coping by describing the case of Terry Wiles.

Terry was born without arms or legs: in their place, two flippers or rudimentary feet—one with four and the other with three digits—extended directly from his tiny torso. One eye hung halfway down his cheek and had to be surgically removed. His body was supported by a pad of muscle where his pelvis should have been. In addition to his gross deformities, Terry was illegitimate, born of a white mother and a black father. His mother, thinking that he would not survive, abandoned him at the East Anglian hospital where she had been confined.

As Terry grew up, it became apparent that he was not only without limbs but that he was a dwarf. Even today, at the age of sixteen, he measures just over two feet high and weighs no more than an infant. But Terry has never allowed his physical shortcomings to eclipse the sharpness of his mind and his vivid personality. He goes to a local technical college where he keeps pace with boys and girls of his own age, and his accomplishments would be the envy of many an able-bodied teen-ager. He reads extensively and writes short shories, typing with his flippers on an adapted electric typewriter. He plays the electric organ, takes singing lessons, and makes and flies model aircraft. With the aid of gadgets, he has learned considerable independence. He can fish, swim, ride a pony, and even challenge his friends to a game of darts; he throws them with his mouth while lying on his side.

Terry's achievements did not happen overnight. They were the culmination of Terry's own courage and the efforts of the two people who adopted him. The splicing of their three unhappy lives came about in the most unlikely way.

For the first year of his life, Terry grew up in Chailey Heritage Craft School and Hospital, a sprawling institution for severely handicapped children set in rural Sussex. He saw no family, and social workers would visit once but seldom returned. Terry grew withdrawn and bitter. Then, when he was nearly five years old, he had a surprise visitor, Leonard Wiles, a sixty-year-old van driver who had been asked by one of Terry's ageing relatives to act as guardian to the boy. Leonard came to the hospital expecting that all the job would require would be the formality of signing papers for a helpless vegetable. Instead, he found a bright, cheeky little boy who had one hunger: to find a home and escape from the prison the hospital had become to his imaginative, rebellious mind.

At first, Leonard's wife, Hazel, a large, tempestuous woman eighteen years his junior, refused to have anything to do with Terry. She had lived through rough times: born in a caravan, brought up in a workhouse, illiterate until the age of eighteen, twice divorced, once widowed, and with two babies already taken away by social workers, she did not want anything to upset the security she had finally found. But over the next two years, Terry came home for visits and holidays, and the Wileses found their lives revolving more and more around this "scrap of humanity," as they used to describe him.

They had a hard life. Leonard, a clever but untrained man, always obstinate in the face of authority, earned only $30 a week as a driver for a plant nursery. They lived in a ramshackle cottage belonging to Leonard's employers, isolated in flat countryside. They often went without heat or sufficient food, and were always negotiating with bailiffs and bankruptcy courts. They appeared the most unstable, unsuitable people to have children, let alone a difficult boy without arms or legs. It took them two years to decide to adopt Terry and a further two years to persuade the medical and social services to agree to it.

Terry legally became their son when he was nine years old. The Wileses then started their second battle—to get Terry out of hospital, into a local school, and accepted into the local community. To achieve all this, Terry needed far more independence, and Leonard, falling back on his latent engineering talents, turned inventor. "Just looking at a child like Terry," he said, "turns you into a kind of visionary." He designed many gadgets, but the most remarkable was his Supercar, a chair that, working on the principle of a fork-lift truck, could raise Terry from ground level until he could stand "six feet high." Terry would shuffle into the seat at floor level, press a knob with his shoulders, and within seconds, not only raise himself to any level but drive himself through the narrow doors of the cottage, using his feet on a joy-stick control. He could reach books on any shelf, turn switches and knobs, serve tea, and, most important of all, talk to people face to face. (The chair was featured in 1977 in an "Exhibition of British Genius" held in London.)

When we first met Terry, in the autumn of 1973, Supercar was in its pioneering days. Terry was ebullient. Once in Supercar, he was like the frog who became a prince. Zooming up in the chair so that he could conduct us above our heads, the little boy without arms or legs regaled our tea party with his favourite boy scout song:

"If you're happy and you know it, clap your hands,
If you're happy and you know it, stamp your feet. . . ."

Today, five years later, Terry is still unembarrassed by his deformities, but he is having to face new problems. He is fast approaching adolescence, his voice has broken, and his face and body are thickening. He plans to work from his adapted bungalow, doing something in the field of writing or music, and to help other disabled people. The security of his home with the Wileses will never leave him. Nor will the scars of his early, forlorn childhood.

Terry sums it up in the preface of Marjorie Wallace's book, *On Giant's Shoulders*—the book that tells his story:

I would describe my life as a never-ending road with its bumps and smoothness. Sometimes I would be travelling on smoothly and then suddenly I would hit a bump of sadness in my life, but that bump would die away into nothing. Then I came to a hole when I thought life was not worth living. But as usual I carried on. Then suddenly I met two loving parents who ended my journey and who protected me from life's hardships. My father is a pioneer in his way because he invents machines to enable me and other physically handicapped children to lead a normal life.

When Terry left Chailey Heritage Hospital, he said good-bye to more than twenty less fortunate thalidomide children, some of whom have still had no chance to experience anything outside a protected institutional life. One of them is Graham Tindale, born with short arms and legs, and two fingers missing on each hand. His father, who now works in a security firm, was then in the navy. His mother is a nurse. Both parents felt that they could not cope with him at home and that he would receive better care in hospital. So at the age of six months, Graham joined the sad troupe of deformed children who had no family or whose families decided not to keep them.

Graham grew up in Chailey, seeing his parents and two younger brothers once or twice a term and during the holidays. He does not recall much of his early life. On weekdays (except on Fridays when they went swimming or those who could joined in games) the thalidomide children had lessons. He remembers how hot and sore he was in his artificial legs, and last year he was allowed to discard them for good. He gets about more quickly by hopping or shuffling on his bottom and has acquired considerable agility manoeuvering his eighty-four-lb. weight.

During the last year, Graham has been given independence training: for two days at a time, he and another handicapped boy were taught to fend for themselves in an adapted bungalow. They were given £5 ($10) a week and expected to buy and cook their own food (Graham cannot yet manage to cook), make their beds, and do the housework. An occupational therapist was there but only as a guest. They were also encouraged to go out alone and learn to use public transport.

"I can get myself on and off a single-decker bus by crawling up the step," Graham says. "I have to ask someone to fold my wheelchair up. If I go by train, I ask the ticket collector to find a ramp. It's not easy but I manage."

Graham hopes that one day he will be able to live in a flat and get a job, but the transition from sixteen years under supervision to living alone will be difficult. He is due to leave the hospital soon, so his future is his foremost concern. "I want to be an engineer," he said, looking for approval at the occupational therapist who was present at our interview. "The headmaster at the school here thinks it is a good idea. I won't ever be able to live at home. It's too difficult, and Mum and Dad think I should go into a permanent home for the disabled and work in the workshop there."

David Diamond, the Philadelphia boy whose case was the first against Richardson-Merrell, is now sixteen. He graduated from his private preparatory school at thirteen, second in his class and winner of the headmaster's award for academic excellence. He now attends Germantown

Academy, Philadelphia, a private school from which he will be graduated in two years' time. He is editor of the school newspaper and wants to be a journalist or a publicity agent.

The birthmark that covered his face for several years and that so horrified his father when he saw him as a newborn child has now faded. His body is small for his age, but he makes good use of the three fingers attached to his short right arm. He can type, write, drive an adapted car, play table tennis, and ski. His mother, Joanne, says, "David has never once complained to me about himself. He has always regarded himself as a normal person with short arms. I think he feels independent and secure. He has always been comfortable with girls, and although he has dated, he doesn't have a steady girl, and I think he would like one."

David is determined not to identify as a handicapped child. "Everyone at school treats me normally. They think of me as an equal and so do I. I don't think about the drug company and what it did to me. I'm too busy. I want to be a normal person."

Dominic Galvin, nineteen years old, is one of the oldest and most tragic of the thalidomide victims. He was born with crooked hands and clubbed ankles, but there was no sign then of the central brain damage that has since destroyed his mind and distorted his behaviour. "He was a great little boy," says his mother, Sadie Galvin, a remarkable fortyseven-year-old Irish woman who has devoted her life to him. "Flash Harry we used to call him. He was walking and talking very early and was extraordinarily perceptive. Then one day when he was three years old and standing beside me in the kitchen, his speech suddenly became slurred, he made a gurgling sound, and he fell unconscious at my feet, frothing at the mouth." From then on, Dominic has suffered from recurring major epileptic seizures, or *grands mals*. On the day Marjorie Wallace of *The Sunday Times* saw him, Dominic had undergone four *grand mal* seizures the previous night and at least a hundred *petits mals*.

Dominic's speech has deteriorated into grunts and sounds that only Sadie Galvin can interpret, and what once appeared to be childish playfulness has darkened into savage outbursts. (Left alone with Wallace for a few minutes, Dominic suddenly attacked her and grabbed her throat.) He staggers about the small semi-detached house in Weybridge, Surrey, where he lives with his mother, two brothers, and a sister, clumsily knocking over anything or anyone in his way. He is a pathetic sight: 5 feet 9 inches tall, heavily built, often violent, and between seizures and outbursts sufficiently aware of his condition to become frustrated, which only precipitates further attacks.

"He gets into a kind of claustrophobic panic," says Sadie Galvin. "He is not too bad if he is alone with me in the house, but the slightest disturbance—a knock at the door, people in the room, even the noise of an aeroplane overhead—will trigger him off. He screams and tries to break away. If he can't get out of the door quickly enough, he will throw himself through a window. When I went away last year for a few days, I had only been gone a few hours when he went through the upstairs window. He is so used to pain he didn't cry, but he had to have a hundred and five stitches. When he came out of hospital, he looked so odd, like a giant teddy bear sewn together."

On another occasion, Dominic was offered a seaside holiday at a home for mentally handicapped people at Hastings, Sussex. Dominic cannot walk in crowds or travel by public transport, so he went with his mother in a taxi arranged by the Thalidomide Trust. "He resents being classed with the mentally subnormal," says Sadie Galvin. "He is very fussy about his surroundings. When we arrived at the home and saw all those people sitting in a miserable room, Dominic went crazy. He pushed everyone aside and dashed for the door. It took the taxi driver and all the nurses to bring him back and hold him down until we could get him to a doctor for an injection. He sobbed on and off the whole of the next week. 'I'm not mad, Mummy,' he told me again and again."

Sadie Galvin is sure these assaults are not deliberate. "Part of his problem is his intelligence," she says. "He can't read and can only just write his name, but he can't tolerate silly questions and patronizing behaviour. I can have marvellous conversations with him on his own. I always tell him what is happening and I never suggest he is stupid or doesn't understand. He longs to communicate, so I must carry out what his brain wants. My brain must belong to him."

As Dominic's behaviour grew more bizarre, the Galvins' family life fell apart. When Dominic was nine years old, his father was dismissed from his job as manager of a clothes shop and they had to move from the flat above the shop. Joe Galvin began to suffer from depression and could not work. Sadie Galvin, a trained nurse, had to get a job three nights a week at the local mental hospital. "I was spending all my days looking after Dominic and all my nights either working or lying on the floor holding him down. I was always ill and exhausted." The marriage foundered and Joe Galvin left home.

At that time, during the 1960s, the doctors were reluctant to diagnose epilepsy in relation to thalidomide. They were also hesitant about the Galvins' claim that thalidomide was involved at all, but after a long struggle, Dominic was accepted as a definite case. Alongside the fight for compensation, Sadie Galvin conducted a fifteen-year battle with the medical profession and local authorities. "They said he could not be educated: even the home tutors had to give up. At one time, we had someone from the social welfare department knocking at the door almost every day trying to persuade me to put Dominic in an institution. I work in one of these, and I would never let him go. He'd die of drugs or a broken heart."

But the physical and emotional price of keeping Dominic at home is high. "Every week we have to find money to pay for breakages. Last week it was $160 for damage to the washing machine. A window costs $200. It upsets him to see the debris he leaves behind, so I always mend things as quickly as possible and clear up after he is in bed. If there is anything untidy, Dominic gets in a dreadful state. I always put some flowers on the table and try to keep the place looking like a normal home. It's a twenty-four-hour-a-day job watching him and clearing up after him."

Sadie Galvin does not look on her life with Dominic as a sacrifice. As a devout Catholic, she feels that Dominic, rather than wrecking their lives, has given the family a purpose and even happiness. His two younger brothers and thirteen-year-old sister take pride in looking after their damaged brother and are equally determined to keep Dominic at home. "I don't think he will live long," Sadie Galvin says sadly. "His epilepsy is uncontrolled despite all those drugs. His muscles are wasting and he looks gaunt, but if anything happens to him, I will have enjoyed him and everything he gave me, and I'll have no regrets."

Peggy McCarrick, the only thalidomide-damaged child whose case went to a jury decision, is now an attractive sixteen-year-old student at Ball Junior High School, in Anaheim, near Los Angeles. Her mother's first marriage broke up, so Peggy now lives with her brother, two stepsisters, a stepbrother, a stepfather, and her mother in a ranch-style house about five minutes from Disneyland. Two major hip operations, a foot reconstruction, and a stump revision have enabled her to get about very well on her artificial leg. Financially, she is well off. Her trust account at the First National City Bank of Orange holds $338,000 and she receives

$400 a month from her trust fund. In two years' time, she will be legally entitled to look after this money herself. Peggy leads an active social life. She is a member of the school Pet Club, which leads the cheering for the school football team. Out of school, she and a group of friends wash cars and bake and sell cakes to raise funds to provide Seeing Eye dogs for the blind. Her only complaint about her life is that she is only 4 feet 8 inches tall, but even that is not a serious worry. "I've got faith I'm going to get taller," she says.

Patrick Pope, one of the few thalidomide children with extensive internal abnormalities to survive, is fifteen. His father is an ex-navy man who lectures at a school near their pleasant home in the southern county of Hampshire, England. Julie Pope, his mother, gave up a singing career when Patrick was born. Today the more than forty operations Patrick endured have corrected most of his deformities. His digestive system works almost normally, he is of average height and weight, and as far as the doctors can tell, the only operation he will still need will be one to correct his vision. He swims, rides a bicycle, goes to a boys' boarding school, and wants to be a veterinarian. But like many of the thalidomide youngsters who have spent so much of their childhood in a world of isolation and pain, he is behind in his schoolwork and is apprehensive about mixing with boys of his own age.

"He's a lonely boy," says his mother. "He's difficult and grumpy and not always lovable. He went through so much suffering, this round-shouldered, skinny son of mine. He's frightened to death of hospitals. He sometimes rings me from his boarding school in tears because the other boys have taunted him, because he still wets the bed. He's not a very happy teen-ager."

Patrick says: "It's a bit hard. The other boys don't like me going to the matron, and they call me a 'spastic.' They always get the wrong end of the stick. They think it's all trying to get attention. I have only two friends and I keep to them. I get on quite well with babies and young children. I got used to looking after them in hospital."

During the holidays, Patrick also avoids his own age group. Instead he has got to know any neighbour with dogs and regularly takes nine of these dogs for long walks in the nearby forest. He collects stones, cycles for hours in the countryside, and raises money for the Heart Foundation by persuading people to donate a sum for each length of the local pool he manages to swim—thirty lengths is his record. "I wish to be normal, terribly normal," he says. "But I can't help getting depressed and angry about it all."

Catherine Purkis, a pretty, intelligent fifteen-year-old girl, has used her disabilities as a spur to her creative talents and her outgoing personality. She was born with deficient arms: her left shoulder is missing, so that her short arm just hangs. The hand is clubbed with two fingers and thumb missing. Her right arm is two-thirds the normal length. But she can grip a pencil between two of her four stiff fingers and write. She has started a book and plans to set out her own experiences as a thalidomide child.

Her father, Alec Purkis, who became chairman of the Thalidomide Parents Association (the new name for the old Thalidomide Society) and devoted a year of his life to the campaign, works as a manager of the branch of an insurance company in Southampton. They live in a comfortable home in near-by New Forest. An intelligent man, sheltered by his stable home life with his wife, Margaret, and their four healthy children, he was shocked by the birth of his daughter. "We had a strong sense of guilt. Margaret had been worried about our son, who was in hospital, and she took three pills to make her sleep. For a year after Catherine was born, Margaret shunned all contact with people, but Catherine grew and decided her own personality; she just became part of our large family."

During her early years, Catherine had a series of unsuccessful operations to straighten her clubbed hands. She was backward in sitting up and walking, and like many thalidomide children, because she was not able to break her fall, she was afraid of walking. But she was determined. "We got her a doll's pram when she was a little girl," says Alec Purkis. "She couldn't reach the handles, so she just stood there swinging and stretching her short arms for days on end until she succeeded. From then on she began to overcome her disability."

Catherine taught herself to tie her own shoelaces, ride a bicycle, and openly to accept her deficiency. She recalls with delight the day when the class was being taught decimals using their fingers and thumbs. "What about me?" she asked the teacher. Now she is a boarder at a girls' school, taking her college entrance examinations. She has decided that her first ambition to nurse was unrealistic and instead she has chosen to become a speech therapist.

Christopher Lingard has never come to terms with his handicap. He resents any reference to his short arms and has refused any aids. He would rather have help in undressing than have his trousers fitted with a special fastener that he could manage himself. He is hostile to offers of help, yet, according to his mother, Joyce, he uses thalidomide to gain sympathy and advantage. "He used to tell people that it was his house, and once when we were on holiday he turned round and said to me: 'It's my money which is paying for us, you know.' Yet he won't go away without me. He's a very complex person."

Christopher and his mother are victims of the kind of claustrophobic relationship brought about by her self-imposed sacrifice and his conflict between dependence and rejection. Christopher was her *second* thalidomide child. Her first, a daughter, born in the autumn of 1961, died at birth. Mrs. Lingard's doctor had given her samples of Distaval for morning sickness during this pregnancy, and then, finding herself pregnant again, she took one of these left-over tablets. Christopher was born with three-inch arms fixed to his chest. "I didn't want to keep him," she says. "I was a dancer, used to moving my arms and hands, and I couldn't accept his deformed stumps."

Unfortunately, it was not her first experience of handicap. Before either of her thalidomide children, she had a *spina bifida* son, who died at three months, and her eldest son, now attending university, was born with a stomach complaint which meant that as a baby he had to be fed by teaspoon every hour. To revive the failing morale of the family, she was advised to adopt a healthy daughter, Susan, who is now twelve years old.

When Christopher was three years old, his father left home. He has not contacted his family since. "He tried so hard at first," says Joyce Lingard, "he became involved in all the groups of parents and did everything to help the children, but it was too much for him. He hated anything imperfect, especially his own son." Mrs. Lingard's second marriage was a disaster, and she has since divorced on the grounds of cruelty and desertion. She has had three nervous breakdowns and is still taking heavy doses of tranquillizers. She says she feels hatred towards Distillers. "I can accept the death of my *spina bifida* son, but I can't accept what thalidomide did nor can I forgive the manufacturers."

Joyce Lingard is also bitter about the way the financial settlement could work out now that Christopher has access to the Thalidomide Trust money and will soon inherit his own. "In three years' time, this house will be his, and if he wants to, he can leave me and his younger sister homeless. We mothers gave up everything for these children. We kept them when so many people suggested we put them away, and now we risk being discarded. Soon my own son could turn round and say to me: 'Thank you very much. I've had enough of you.' "

Andrew McRoberts is an articulate, reasonably contented young man of seventeen who has accepted the limitations of his body and his life. He is taking his college entrance examinations in English, French, and mathematics next year, and he hopes he will gain a place in a business-studies course at a college for the disabled. His ultimate ambition is to manage his own business, and his hopes are set on the drapery shop his father runs in the small Ayrshire village where they now live.

"I decide my own timetable," says Andrew. "Every morning I do my essays and then a teacher comes in several afternoons a week. The rest of the time I watch television or play records. I'm really quite happy. My dad helps me in the bathroom, and if he couldn't do it, the Thalidomide Trust would probably pay for someone to come in and help. They quite often advise me on the things I need and on what I should do."

Andrew's optimism is remarkable in the face of his cruel deformities. He was born without arms. Three digits hang loosely from each shoulder. On his left side his leg is tiny, with a small inward-turning foot. His right leg is also deformed, with a club foot. He suffers from fluctuating deafness, and to replace his useless bladder, he has tubes that drip into a bag. His father has to change this bag several times a day. He needs a wheelchair, and because he weighs 135 lbs., he is becoming increasingly difficult to lift.

With help from money from the trust, the family has moved from its cramped house on the outskirts of Edinburgh to a roomy old manse surrounded by acres of land. "We adapted it for Andrew," says Mr. McRoberts. "It has wide doors, a special bathroom, and he has his own flat downstairs."

Before the settlement, in 1973, the tightness of their budget and the problem of coping with so damaged a child in a small town house had put almost intolerable stresses on the McRobertses. "Colin, our second son, suffered the most," says Mrs. McRoberts. "*He* was the one who felt the odd one out. Andrew would use him vicariously, making him do all the things he couldn't do. 'Run, Colin, jump, Colin,' he would say until the poor boy was exhausted."

Now Andrew feels more secure, and although he does not make much effort to go out with people of his own age, he finds satisfaction within his family. "We've all accepted it now," he says. "I had an operation to make my leg stronger last year, but apart from that I am fine and healthy. I don't think about being thalidomide now. I have never known what it is to feel anything different."

For Liam Evans, now fifteen, life is an endless, dark confusion, lightened only by the commands of his father or vague flickers of a match held close to his remaining eye. For he is almost totally blind. His right eye has grown an unsightly white tumour and his other eye, with its discharging red eyelids, has only a tiny eyeball. He has no arms, his legs are thin and distorted, and he cannot walk. He has an artificial palate and cannot speak, and he has severe brain damage.

Liam is taken to a special school in Worcester during the day, but at home he needs constant care. Since Liam is doubly incontinent, his father has to change his diapers every few hours day and night. He has to be turned in bed, lifted, dressed, bathed, and fed. He sits for hours on a plastic sheet in front of a large television screen that he cannot see, but he nods happily to any sounds he can understand.

Liam is the third damaged child in the family. Paul, the eldest, is in a hospital for the mentally subnormal. He is violent and epileptic, and his weekends at home are a trial to the whole family. "He has taken a knife to me several times," says his father, Sydney Evans, an ex-truck driver, "so we deliberately keep a row of knives in the kitchen, just to try and show that we trust him." The next eldest child, June, a pretty girl of sixteen, is also a problem. "She lives in her own world and it's not ours," says Sydney Evans. "She can't stop lying—she's way off beam." Then there is Liam, and after him a precocious six-year-old.

Florence Evans, an ex-waitress, has collapsed under the strains of her awkward children, and she will never leave her house to go out alone. The family lives under the care of Sydney Evans, who looks after the house, does the shopping, cooking, cleaning, and caring for Liam. "I'm the guv'nor," he says. "It's a scream, my lot. I've forgotten what a normal child is like. We had all the tests and they couldn't find anything wrong with our genes—I don't know what happened."

But Sydney Evans takes positive rewards from his twenty-four-hour-a-day domestic and nursery routine. He has the insight to know that he is using his sacrifice for Liam for his own good. "If it weren't for thalidomide and Liam, I would have been back in prison by now," he says. "I was never much good at anything before. I tried the lot—art school, studying medicine at university, lorry driving, then I took to crime, stealing cars, burglary—anything and everything. Now with Liam to look after and the house to run, I can't afford to go back to prison."

For Morag McCallum no sum of money could give her the world she will never know. She is blind, deaf, and dumb. One side of her body is paralysed so that she cannot smile. She is severely retarded, and there is little hope of breaking through to her dark, silent mind. She boards at a special school for the deaf, fifty miles from where she lives in Stirlingshire, Scotland, but she will soon be sixteen. Then the educational authorities will no longer be responsible for her, and her mother has not been able to find a place willing to accept her. Mrs. McCallum says, "Somebody has to be with her all the time. You never know what will happen. She's just a wild animal. There is no communication with her at all."

Morag's savage, disturbing presence disrupts all family life and demands great endurance from her parents, brother, and two sisters. Morag was born as a non-identical twin. (Her brother suffered no damage.) "For the first three years no one came to help us," says Mrs. McCallum. "Then when a doctor did come, he had a piece of paper which I could sign to put Morag away into a mental hospital. I refused."

Alexander McCallum, an accident-repair mechanic for buses, has been even more upset by his daughter's fate. After her birth, he became a psychiatric outpatient and now, after further health problems, is an invalid and never likely to work again. The McCallums are both angry for having agreed to the low settlement in 1968. "Morag got only £16,000 and yet a boy with short arms but normal intelligence and likely to be able to earn his living got £2,000 more. It's an unfair world," Mrs. McCallum says. "When I took her down to London for assessment, they said, 'You're lucky, she's got arms and legs.' But what are they, when you have no brain?

"We bought her a rocking chair for her fourteenth birthday. Can you imagine buying your teen-age daughter such a present? Every time I look at her, I say it was my fault, and I feel so sad. If no school will have

her when she's sixteen, she will have to stay at home. What can I do? I
can't put her to sleep, nor can I live her life for her. I can only do my
best."

The money Heather Bird received from the settlement has done much
to relieve the physical stress on her and her family. The Birds have built
a five-bedroom house outside Lanark, Scotland, specially adapted for
Heather's wheelchair. They have a hoist in the bathroom, and they can
afford home help for two hours every day. The help is essential because
Heather, sixteen years old and with rudimentary arms and no legs,
weighs nearly 125 lbs. and needs to be lifted on and off her wheelchair
and into the taxi that takes her to and from her special school.

There are times, Heather says, when she feels a little bitter. She finds
it difficult to go out except with one other thalidomide girl friend, or to
social evenings with her mother, but she does not feel embarrassed and is
proud of her achievements: she writes, sews, types with an electric typewriter, and puts on her own make-up. "I get into bad moods," she says,
"but I am not unhappy, and things are a lot easier now."

When we first met the Birds, they were living under intolerable stress.
Heather was a late child, born when Mrs. Bird was over forty. Mr. Bird
had given up his job in an engineering firm to nurse his wife, a tired
woman who had developed a slipped disk from lifting Heather and who
was suffering from frequent ill health and depression. All three shared
one small bedroom and living room in the lodge of a lonely country
house. They had no aids to help Heather except a standard wheelchair
and a pedal car given by the Lady Hoare Thalidomide Appeal. The
constant lifting, feeding, washing of clothes and diapers—Heather is still
incontinent—had worn her mother down, and relations between the
three were tense.

"She does say hurtful things now," says Mrs. Bird. "They are mainly
about the money—about *her* house and *her* clothes—but on the whole
she is quite well adjusted. I've brought her up to be pretty tough and not
to feel sorry for herself."

Alexander is the now sixteen-year-old son of the former export manager for Distillers, John Flawn. The breakthrough in Alexander's life
came when he was fourteen, in 1976, when his parents gave him a large
red scribbling diary. At first they used it to write messages—Alexander is
totally deaf, dumb, and severely brain-damaged. Before he had the

diary, he was never able to realize where he was going or what was happening. With the diary, he began to take an acute interest in dates and times. "He began to recognize words and then he was able to copy messages," says Judith Flawn. "Instead of living in bewilderment, he began to understand something about the world around him." With encouragement from the teacher at Roffey House, the special school that he will attend as a boarder, until he is sixteen, Alexander has learned to copy out long entries and give shape to the feelings and activities of his day.

> 2:45 Thursday Dec. 7th
> At 2 o'clock it stopped raining. We went for a little walk. Poor Alex (me) I got very wet because a lorry splashed lots of water from the puddle all over me.

Wherever he does not understand a word or what it means—the word "Alex" could also mean "me"—the teacher has given him a shorter word that he can understand. The next step is for him to write his own entries. He is making the first steps. When Marjorie Wallace, of *The Sunday Times,* arrived to see him half an hour late, he had already gone to the diary, and crossed out the time his mother had given him and changed it from 3:30 P.M. to 4:00 P.M. "He thinks writing is magic," says Mrs. Flawn. "If we are not doing anything and he is bored, he will keep putting a pencil into my hand as though by writing it down something will happen. I never dared dream he would reach this stage. I am very proud of him."

But there is another side of Alex that his parents have had to accept with a sad humour. He is crafty, devious, and has to be watched day and night. "He makes ghastly noises and can be very embarrassing," says Judith Flawn. "He'll strip naked, overbreathing like mad, and come into my bed whenever he knows his father has gone. He'll strip anywhere. When we were on holiday in Greece last year, he stripped, and he's not a pretty sight. The Greeks didn't like it."

Most of the time he behaves like an overgrown toddler. "He has locked me in the cellar several times and run away chuckling," says his mother. "He hides things. We found his sister's teddy bear with its head split open stuffed under the floorboards. It had been missing for a year. Nothing is safe. He'll take food from our plates and spit it out again over us. He'll throw towels down the lavatory. The last television set we had was filled with metal rods, pennies, and all the odd things he had collected. When he was ten years old and in nappies, he would take them off and fling them anywhere. We had a dog that was always fishing them out of the garden pool."

The Flawns live in a country house in Surrey surrounded by horses and fields. They have three other children, Simon, an adopted Nigerian who is sixteen; Michael, aged fourteen; and eight-year-old Victoria. The boys find their ungainly brother an embarrassment, but Victoria takes it in her stride. "I think it's quite funny," she says. "I just tell my friends that he is handicapped and they don't worry."

Because he is so handicapped, Alex's financial future is more secure than that of many other thalidomide children. His compensation money will pay for him to live in a special community in Surrey, where, provided he is not found too difficult to control, he can spend the rest of his life. Along with twenty-four other mentally retarded adults and adolescents, he will learn to do limited tasks.

But John and Judith Flawn, while accepting the odd looks and behaviour of their son, still dream of what he could have been if Mrs. Flawn had not taken those two or three thalidomide pills.

Denis Henry, the Canadian boy who was the test case for the Quebec families who could not sue in Canada, is now sixteen. He is tall and strong, but he is totally deaf and speaks in a slurred voice using disjointed words that no one but his family understands; a nerve damaged by thalidomide has left him with a face so twisted that it is incapable of expression. He cannot laugh or cry, and by some quirk the only time he sheds tears is when he eats sweets. He can smile, but with only half his face. "When I first saw him he was trying to cry," says Lorraine Henry, "but the sound was more like an animal which has been hurt. This is not so important now. We can talk to each other using sign-language, and although he can only write some words, we can leave messages for each other."

Like many thalidomide children born without ears, Denis suffered many painful operations in which bones and skin from other parts of his body were grafted to shape artificial ears. "The ears are not a success," says Mrs. Henry. "They took cartilage from his ribs and skin from both legs. They even tried to bore a canal in his head in which he wears a hearing aid, but he cannot hear anything—only a few vibrations. The ears were made too low, where the hair line is, and now hair is beginning to grow through them."

Until he was fourteen Denis went to a special school for deaf children. Now he is too old for special school and goes to a local school in Montreal, fifteen miles from his home in suburban Laval, where he tries but fails to keep pace with seventeen hundred normal children. "He is at least three years behind his age group," says his mother. "It's very hard on him. He struggles to lip-read, but he really needs special tuition, and these special teachers are very rare in Canada. When he doesn't understand, he can't cry so he gets mad and fights with his brother and sister. He reads, but there are a lot of words he cannot understand and he writes everything like a telegram. If he has gone out he writes: 'Denis gone Jonathan,' but he is very intelligent and is always asking questions."

Gaston Henry is a fireman and the family lives in a comfortable detached house. They have two other children—an eighteen-year-old daughter and a son who is twenty. "We have been here seven years and Denis has not made a single friend," says Mrs. Henry. "They are very isolated, these deaf children. They can only talk to each other, and they never mix. We don't know what his future will be. He works hard—sometimes he'll stay up until late in the evening doing his homework—but he depends on us too much. We just hope that we will find someone in the world who will operate on his ears and face. At least if they replace the missing nerve, he might be able to smile."

Compensation and government help seem to have taken care of the thalidomide children's financial problems in most countries. But of course, it did not make up for their ruined lives, help them to accept their deformities, ease the bitterness of being an outsider, or offer their parents any simple answer to how to live with a daughter who is virtually a vegetable, a violent, deformed son, or a boy who cannot laugh or cry. The truth of the matter is that no amount of money can ever compensate these families for what the thalidomide experiment did to them.

16 Victory at Last—Or Is It?

The future of the thalidomide children was always the emotional heart of the thalidomide campaign, but there was another side to it: the desire to gain some lasting benefit for society from the sufferings of the families. The decade between the disaster and the final settlement with Distillers had dramatized the case for reform of the laws relating to personal injury, which had permitted the uneven match of isolated parents against a powerful corporation, and the law of contempt of court, which had silenced discussion: for ten years, Distillers had pursued a course in secret that, when publicized, turned out to be something society would not accept.

But the wall of secrecy that had concealed a major disaster had only been breached. Money had been won but not reform. There was a royal commission on civil liability for personal injuries and there was renewed debate on contempt, but these were proceeding without the benefit of publicly accessible information on how the disaster had occurred. The original *Sunday Times* article was still banned by contempt, and a legal injunction was soon granted to prohibit publication of any material derived from Distillers' documents on the grounds that these were protected, confidential documents.

The immediate aftermath of the settlement of the money in 1973 was a backlash against *The Sunday Times'* campaign at two levels, the reasoned and the rhetorical. The *Law Society Gazette* said it was a seedy campaign that had "all the subtlety and legal justification of Robin Hood's activities in Sherwood Forest." Peregrine Worsthorne in the *Sunday Telegraph* thought it nauseating to focus on a company that had only done what the country willed. The Oxford historian A. J. P. Taylor, writing in the *Sunday Express,* described the campaign as "a witch hunt, an exploitation of popular feeling such as the late Dr. Goebbels would have rejoiced to direct, a demagogic clamour, far beyond the bounds of reason." (That the Goebbels technique was to tell lies and *The Sunday Times* had been attempting to print facts was a nicety Mr. Taylor and others could ignore.)

There had certainly been public clamour and emotion. But it was a public response that the law itself provoked. The law's position came to be that *only* an emotional discussion would be allowed. Factual discussion of negligence was banned by the law of contempt and eventually enforced by the highest court in the land. So anyone with misgivings about the law's delays and the possibility of witnessing a massive injustice was forced to focus on sympathy for the children and the families rather than on the rights of the issue. (And even discussion of levels of compensation had become possible only at considerable risk to *The Sunday Times* of imprisonment for its editor, and fines for the company.)

Critics of the thalidomide campaign, especially in the legal profession, assumed that there had been two equal parties to a rational contest and that the legal processes would see that the truth came out and justice was done. This was palpably false. The parents of the damaged children were capable neither emotionally nor financially, after all those years, of fighting Distillers. Time put pressure on *them,* not on a corporation that had no handicapped children to worry about. The unreality of the legal fiction was matched by a certain selectivity in the application of legal restraint. The High Court ruling of November 1972 prevented *The Sunday Times* from publishing critical information on the marketing and testing of thalidomide. But it did not prevent or punish an earlier series of statements on the same subject—all on the side of the company. The burden of them all was that Distillers had been made a scapegoat for a community responsibility. Distillers had done everything it possibly could have done when it manufactured the drug. Professor Leonard Strang maintained in a letter to *The Times* that the company was no more to blame than mothers who took the drug and suffered malformed babies. It had no special liability. Sir James Marjoribanks, a Distillers director, succinctly prejudging the whole trial, declared, "We were not negligent over the distribution of this drug. We went through all the necessary tests at the time. We could not have done more." Kenneth Fleet, then city editor of *The Daily Telegraph,* declared that Distillers was not negligent because "at the time it was standard medical dogma that the foetus was effectively isolated. We now know better, but one cannot attribute negligence in the light of this later knowledge." *The Economist* went further: there was not even a moral responsibility on the company, since "no serious evidence has been led to suggest the Distillers board was negligent, according to the standard of the times, when thalidomide was manufactured and sold in this country. The German tests had not been controverted, the British Standards were adhered to, and the providential hesitation about the drug in the United States was concerned with some quite different, and far less damaging, side effects. There is no apparent moral responsibility on the shoulders of the Distillers directors." (The editor of *The Sunday Times* wrote to *The Economist* to suggest that these assertions might be tempered by the knowledge that the Lord Chief Justice, in banning *The Sunday Times'* draft article, had said that no one reading it could fail to gain the impression that there was a substantial case against Distillers. The response from Distillers was an unsuccessful protest in the Court of Appeal by its counsel, John Wilmers, Q.C., that with this letter the editor had committed contempt of court.)

The campaign against the campaign was inevitably short-lived since the most public issue, that of compensation to the victims, had been settled. What remained to be resolved was the right of the public to know what *The Sunday Times* had known for years—what was in the documents Dr. Phillips had passed to the paper in 1967. Distillers had taken two defensive measures, both of which were supremely successful. On the first—the argument that it was in contempt of court to publish—it had been upheld by the High Court. The second was a claim that the documents were confidential. Distillers learned of *The Sunday Times'* possession of the documents for the first time when it read the draft article in October 1972. On November 2, 1972, the company served a writ, claiming that the use by *The Sunday Times* of Distillers' documents breached confidentiality, but the case was put on ice (pending the trial of the contempt hearings) by *The Sunday Times'* agreeing that it would not use the documents without first informing Distillers. *The Sunday Times* did this because its main battle at that stage was on contempt: until it won that, nothing about the manufacture of thalidomide, whether obtained from the documents or not, could be published by anybody. Nor did it want to risk losing the documents at this stage.

The paper contested Distillers' first victory by asking the Court of Appeal to set aside the High Court's ban, and a four-day hearing began on January 30, 1973, before Lord Denning, Lord Justice Phillimore, and Lord Justice Scarman. It was an appeal on wider grounds than were originally set out in the first hearing. The compensation to the victims now looked as if it was going to be all right, but other developments, said the paper, emphasized the unfairness and unwisdom of prohibiting *The Sunday Times* from publishing. Public policy on liability for personal injuries and the standards of the pharmaceutical industry were now being actively discussed, but deprived of the relevant information in *The Sunday Times'* draft article, this discussion was necessarily a limited one. There was a bill on dangerous drugs and disabled children, introduced in the Commons by an M.P. in his individual capacity, and there was the Royal Commission on Personal Injuries; both could benefit by knowing just what did happen in the thalidomide tragedy. There was, moreover, widespread public discussion of the thalidomide case—*The Economist* and other examples were given—and it was unfair that *The Sunday Times* should be singled out for suppression thirteen years after the unexamined withdrawal of the drug.

It was soon apparent from the interventions of the judges that the Court of Appeal was more sympathetic than the lower court had been. The attorney general, Sir Peter Rawlinson, found himself in difficulty when he suggested that the draft article could be considered distorted, and Lord Justice Scarman commented that the lower court had, for the purposes of argument, accepted the article as true: "It would be very odd if the truth muddied the purity of justice."

Throughout the lower court hearing, John Wilmers had been present to watch out for Distillers' interests. Now, at this point, he sought leave to speak, and he set about *The Sunday Times* and its editor with great vigour. There were many errors, he claimed. If *The Sunday Times* was going to say the article was true, Distillers might say it would spend the proposed compensation money in fighting a libel action. He attempted to go into the article point by point, but was warned off. "Don't trespass on our indulgence," Lord Denning told him. Later, as the vehement barrister ploughed on, Lord Justice Phillimore rebuked him again: "Incorrigible, Mr. Wilmers."

Sir Peter and Mr. Wilmers lost, three votes to none. The court found unanimously for *The Sunday Times*. It was persuaded by a number of arguments: it accepted the concept of the balance of interests; it thought the article was temperate—pressure, but legitimate pressure; it was influenced by the debate in the House of Commons; none of the actions had been set down for trial, and while the law of contempt must be enforced to prevent trial by newspaper, it applied only when litigation was actively in suit and when there was a real and substantial danger of prejudice.

The other two judges took up these themes, especially the last one of "dormancy." The discussion of public affairs, said Lord Justice Scarman, quoting an Australian judgement, could not be required to cease merely because it might cause some prejudice to a person who happened to be a litigant. They were dealing, said Lord Justice Phillimore, with something akin to shadow-boxing dressed up as litigation, and he redressed the balance of the arguments heard so often in the court about pressure being put on Distillers: "The company have been able to sit back and wait while pressure on the parents has mounted until it may force them to agree to the terms Distillers have offered. How is pressure on this corporation unfair? In my opinion these claims ought to have been settled years ago and on generous terms."

But *The Sunday Times'* success was short-lived, for the attorney general persisted, and won leave to appeal to the highest court in the land—the House of Lords. Very few law cases reach the Lords, but the procedure for hearing cases is well established.

All Britain's hereditary peers are entitled to speak in the full chamber of the House of Lords, along with newly created life peers, but legal cases are heard only by five eminent—and elderly—Law Lords. They sit in a separate room, without wigs and gowns and court ceremonial, and conduct a Socratic debate with counsel on the finer points of law. The thalidomide court was presided over by Lord Reid, revered, at eighty-two, for his quick wit and original mind. He sat with Lords Morris of Borth-Y-Gest, Diplock, Simon of Glaisdale, and Cross of Chelsea. In July 1973 they ruled unanimously that publication of the draft article could not take place pending the resolution of the legal claims against Distillers. The proposed article was in contempt of court, they said, because it prejudged the issues in the case.

There was a difference of emphasis among the Law Lords. Three of the five (Reid, Morris, and Cross) thought that it was legitimate publicly to influence litigants by fair if forceful comments—in other words that the September 24 article in *The Sunday Times* had been legitimate. But Diplock and Simon thought that this article too had been in contempt. Lord Diplock drew the line against *any* public criticism: Shylock and Antonio could be persuaded in private, he said, but "it would have been contempt of court to hold either Shylock or Antonio to public obloquy on the Rialto." Lord Simon was even more restrictive: even *private* persuasion of litigants was wrong, he argued.

Diplock and Simon refused to face the possibility of occasions where there might be greater public benefit from free speech than from preserving the legal cocoon intact. They reflected more luridly than the other judges the underlying fear of "trial by newspaper." Thus Diplock did not talk about public discussion or information, but about "abuse," "obloquy," "vilification," and "government by the media," and Simon talked not about publication but "execration" and chose to illustrate his criticism of free discussion by an example of somebody's being punched on the nose.

Eleven judges had now pronounced. Only by six judges to five was the original article launching *The Sunday Times'* "moral campaign" regarded as legitimate. Lord Reid, the presiding Law Lord, had some faint uneasiness about the implications of the final ban he imposed. The purpose of the law, he said, was not to *prevent* publication but to *postpone* it, and he added: "But if things drag indefinitely so that there is no early prospect either of a settlement or of a trial in court, then I think there will have to be an awakenment of the public interest in a unique situation."

The formal injunction was cast in the traditional and colourful language of the Lords:

> It is Ordered, by the Lords Spiritual and Temporal in the Court of Parliament of Her Majesty the Queen assembled, that the Cause be, and the same is hereby, remitted back to a Divisional Court of the Queen's Bench Division of Her Majesty's High Court of Justice with a Direction to grant an Injunction in the following terms: "That the Defendants, Times Newspapers Limited, by themselves, their servants, agents, or otherwise, be restrained from publishing, or causing or authorising or procuring to be published or printed, any article, or matter which prejudices the issues of negligence, breach of contract or breach of duty, or deals with the evidence relating to any of the said issues arising in any actions pending or imminent against Distillers Company (Bio-chemicals) Limited in respect of the development, distribution or use of the drug 'Thalidomide.' "

But if it was picturesque, it was also extremely prohibitive. It certainly prevented *The Sunday Times* from passing the banned article to an M.P.

so that he could reveal it in the House of Commons, for example, as Labour member Willie Hamilton offered, or to a newspaper outside the
jurisdiction of the court, say, one in the United States. There was a
strong criticism of the ban in the Commons, notably among Labour
members, led by Jack Ashley. Arthur Davidson thought the judgement
made investigative journalism more hazardous, but that the criticisms
should be directed not at the judge who had merely interpreted the law,
but at Parliament, "which had shown apathy on the whole subject of
Press freedom in contempt, Official Secrets and defamation." The peak
of political response was a remarkable speech from the leader of the opposition, Harold Wilson, followed up by a letter to *The Times*. If the law
is as the Lords authoritatively stated it, then Parliament, he said, had
not only the right but the duty to change it. "That task must begin
now."

Wilson's argument was that Parliament could not do its job of discussion and decision if the press was prevented from doing its work. A wise
ruling by the Speaker, followed up by a recommendation of a sub-com-
mittee on procedure, had enabled Parliament to modify its *sub judice*
rules and so discuss thalidomide—but now the House of Lords had effectively taken away that new freedom. Wilson said:

> The serious aspect of the House of Lords judicial decision in
> the context of the Parliamentary decision is this: Our debates
> and the ultimate outcome were inspired and informed by the
> original article in *The Sunday Times*. Without that article and
> the facts and arguments it adduced, Parliament would have
> been inhibited in a way none could attempt to justify so far as
> the merits of the thalidomide case are concerned. The gravity
> of the House of Lords decision in respect of a further, and still
> unpublished, article lies in the fact that, had that decision been
> operative a year ago, *The Sunday Times* article which was pub-
> lished together with supporting evidence could never have ap-
> peared.
>
> The result would have been that the Parliamentary debates,
> if they had taken place at all, would have been uninformed
> and lacking in decisive content, and the result which in fact
> flowed from those debates would never have occurred.
>
> The issue, therefore, is that this decision, if it is from now to
> condition public comment, will not only inhibit the freedom of
> press comment; it will equally inhibit Parliament in both its

legislative function and in its duty of holding the executive accountable to its authority.

There were few dissenting voices. *The Daily Telegraph* said there was no reason to be disturbed. Lord Ferrier, a Conservative peer, thought it wrong that there should be any criticism at all. It was "an outrage," he told the Lords, that the editor of *The Sunday Times* had been allowed to attack the judgement on BBC's "World at One."

A more intriguing perspective came from Lord Devlin, the former lord of appeal. He argued that the Lords' judgement was more useful to the press than the Court of Appeal judgement because it did not depend on the unique nature of the case. It *would* allow newspapers to campaign by fair and temperate moral pressure even when proceedings were pending. An editor would have to tread very warily indeed not to "prejudge" the case, of course, but in the inevitable conflict between fair trial and free speech the Lords' refinement was a concession to free speech, said Devlin.

Still, the weight of opinion, in editorials, speeches, and letters, was overwhelmingly critical of the ban. If the judges could not agree among themselves on the law they made by their judgements, said *The Observer*, the law was obviously in need of statutory reform.

The government had a ready answer to this call: in 1971 the Lord Chancellor had appointed a committee to examine the law on contempt of court, and the government said legislation must await its recommendations. The committee had been delayed by the death of one member and by the sickness of its chairman, Lord Justice Phillimore (the appeal court judge, who died shortly after giving his judgement in the thalidomide case). Now it would obviously have to delay itself long enough at least to take in the implications of the thalidomide case and the Lords' judgement; and it did indeed call for submissions from *The Sunday Times*.

The report, when it came, eighteen months later in December 1974, under the chairmanship of Lord Cameron, was all that the paper could have wished for. It was an emphatic and authoritative argument that the balance between the administration of justice and free speech had moved too far against the freedom of the press. The thalidomide case was cited as the leading example: "What lent *The Sunday Times* campaign so much strength was the fact that in the eyes of many people justice and the administration of the law in the thalidomide case were two

very different things. We think there is great force in the argument that
this is a legitimate matter for public comment."

The committee proposed a redefinition of the law of contempt of
court so as to liberate public discussion. "Persuasion of a litigant" should
not be in contempt of court unless it amounted to intimidation or un-
lawful threat. The test of contempt should not be prejudgement (which
it thought vague) or the creation of a serious risk of "prejudice," but
whether there was a risk that the course of justice would be seriously impeded or prejudiced—an argument that shifted the emphasis from the
degree of *risk* to the degree of *damage*. And the committee proposed a
clear and bold reduction in the period of time that the press can be
gagged. The thalidomide dispute had lain unscrutinized for thirteen
years because the *sub judice* period had run from the moment the first
writ was issued. The Phillimore report said civil proceedings should be
sub judice only from the moment a case was set down for trial, a matter of
months; and in criminal cases, beginning with the charge or service of
summons (instead of when these are imminent). If this had been the law
in 1972, nothing could have prevented the publication of the draft article or made the September 24 publication such an anxious and risky affair even after a decade of silence. Proceedings had not been set down for
trial; the moral persuasion was legitimate; and it was arguable whether
publication would seriously prejudice a trial before a judge without a
jury.

It was now two years since *The Sunday Times'* draft article had been
banned, but finally the way was open for reform. The delay had been
intolerable but there was at least the consolation that it had dramatized
the imbalance of the law between fair trial and free press. Nothing, it
seemed, stood in the way of relief for the press, since the Phillimore
committee recommended it and the leading political critics of gagging
orders were now in power and in the position to enact legislation. By
early 1975, Harold Wilson, who in 1973 had thought reform urgent, was
prime minister; Arthur Davidson was assisting the attorney general;
Peter Archer, who had shown considerable sympathy and deep interest
in personal injury cases, was solicitor general; and the Lord Chancellor
was Elwyn Jones, who had very ably defended London Weekend Television in the contempt case against it. Yet the expectation that this combination of circumstances and personalities would produce results proved
naïve.

Harold Wilson, who two years before had made the major debate possible, and then urged the need for reform of the laws of contempt, was in one of his bad down cycles in his relations with the press. Ever protective of his political secretary, Marcia Williams, he had been irritated by newspaper investigations that revealed her as having, through her brother, an interest in a land-speculation deal involving slag heaps in the north of England. In the Labour vocabulary, "land speculation" is next to "fascist beast." Wilson—who later retaliated at the slur on Mrs. Williams by making her a life peeress, so that she became Lady Falkender—was nimble enough to escape more than temporary embarrassment (it was, he declared, land reclamation and not speculation), but he was enraged when headlines were given up to a professional confidence trickster who forged Wilson's signature to give the impression that the prime minister himself had something to do with the deals. Wilson said now that he would bring in a reform of the law of contempt of court only if the press, in turn, would accept a new law to punish the invasion of privacy. Later, when the newspapers declared they would behave better over intrusion, Wilson appeared to recover his reforming zeal. But it was not enough to overcome the entrenched attitude of the civil service, and especially the lawyers in the government department responsible ultimately for the law in Britain—the Lord Chancellor's office. If the Lord Chancellor's department was in favour of anything, it was the *status quo.*

Two main hopes of relief remained. The first was that the thalidomide litigation would be settled. The second lay in the European Commission of Human Rights. Since 1953, Britain had been bound by the Convention for the Protection of Human Rights, which it had ratified but not passed into domestic law. Impatient of delays, *The Sunday Times* had decided late in 1973 to go to the commission, the body that polices the convention, with a complaint over thalidomide. A ruling in the paper's favour would accelerate an amendment in domestic law, so in January 1974, Harold Evans and his colleagues at *The Sunday Times* complained to the commission that they had been deprived of rights under Article 10, which guarantees everyone the right to free expression and to receive and impart information without interference by public authority. Something like 95 per cent of all complaints to the European Commission are dismissed at this stage as being groundless or outside its jurisdiction: all domestic remedies have to be exhausted first. The British government argued for rejection in a submission in September 1974 on the grounds that the House of Lords ban had been necessary for the maintenance of the authority and impartiality of the judiciary and for the protection and reputation of rights of litigants. In any case, it urged that the principles of the law of contempt applied by the House of Lords fell within the margin of appreciation permitted to the authorities, the Lords having fully considered all the relevant elements including the importance of free speech. Different laws in other member states—and the Phillimore report—were argued to be irrelevant.

The Sunday Times replied and the commission gave a preliminary decision in March 1975. The case was declared admissible. That was an important preliminary victory, but the decision did not prejudge whether there had been a breach of the convention. That now had to be argued in detail, and there was a hearing in Strasbourg December 11-12, 1975, with *The Sunday Times* facing British government lawyers. The proceedings were *in camera* and the commission simply announced afterwards that it would "pursue further its examination of the case, having regard to its dual task of establishing the facts of the case and being at the parties' disposal with a view to reaching a friendly settlement on the basis of human rights as defined by the Convention."

There was one sign that all this was having some effect. Word reached *The Sunday Times* that if it withdrew its European application, the attorney general might be inclined to go to court in Britain and argue that the thalidomide cases were now so close to a conclusion that the injunction should be lifted. *The Sunday Times* rejected this idea, because it would still leave the law of contempt as it was, as a general restriction; if the government would enact the recommendations of the Phillimore Committee, that would be a different matter.

In the event, the attorney general was himself dissatisfied with the reasons for the continued ban on *The Sunday Times* article, and in May 1976, he told the paper he would apply for a lifting of the injunction on the grounds that only a handful of the four hundred sixty thalidomide cases remained to be settled. On the interpretation of the earlier restrictive judgements, including that of the Lord Chief Justice, even the four cases extant would have required a continuance of the ban. But in a hearing before Lord Widgery that lasted only four minutes, the injunction was lifted. On June 27, 1976, *The Sunday Times* published a six-page report on thalidomide.

This long account—unchallenged by Distillers on publication or since—was not the draft article that had been banned. It could not be, and the law of contempt was only one of the handcuffs on the original piece. The other was the law of confidence, which had been ruled to forbid any use of Distillers' documents. *The Sunday Times* observed this ruling, and conceivably it came as a surprise to Distillers and others that the paper was able to publish anything at all. That it was able to do so was because of a major investigation begun by the team of journalists headed by Bruce Page—and what they accumulated was considerably superior to the draft article that had been the theoretical battleground all these years. The draft, though quoting documents disturbing to Distillers, had a weakness in that it accepted the fallacious idea that thalidomide's dangers might have been predicted from its chemical structure. It contained the extraordinary story of McBride's unheeded warnings, and to that extent advanced the logical case against Distillers, but being based largely on Distillers' own documents, it had not explored the wider question of what the standards of testing were in other drug companies at the time. In 1972, Page had, with Potter, begun studying the scientific literature at the time of thalidomide's original manufacture. As well as reading and interviewing scientists in Britain, he, Potter, and other colleagues went to the United States and Germany and revisited Australia, and in a few months they pieced together evidence that had eluded the parents' lawyers and the original *Sunday Times* inquiry. It was a better legal case than anyone anywhere had assembled.

The new evidence had to wait three years for publication, but it was the spearhead of the article of June 27, 1976, and clearly established that tests of drugs in pregnant animals were by no means uncommon in prethalidomide days. It was, of course, an incomplete article in the sense that precisely what went on in Distillers in the early 1960s could not be told. Dr. George Somers, the DCBL pharmacologist, had told his part frankly and honourably. What *The Sunday Times* learned from Distillers' documents it could not tell: how Distillers came to the decision to market the drug, what testing it did on animals, what clinical trials were held, how extravagant claims were made for the drug in advertising, the reactions to the reports received about side effects, the relations with medical journals, doctors, salesmen, and technicians. *The Sunday Times* was unable to report these facts, the core of the original draft article, because Mr. Justice Talbot in the Queen's Bench Division in July 1974 had ruled that the documents on these and other topics were protected by the law of confidentiality.

The case had come before him in March 1974, because *The Sunday Times* had told Distillers then that it was ending the tactical undertaking it had given during the contempt hearings not to use the Distillers documents. Distillers immediately sought a restraining injunction, arguing that the memoranda, letters, and reports were confidential and also their copyright. One strand in their case was that in the draft article, *The Sunday Times* had unfairly selected information from the reports to support criticism. *The Sunday Times'* response was that it was prepared to justify whatever it published in the end on penalty of the law of libel. (It would not, of course, with its knowledge at that time, have published the draft article as originally envisaged, because it did contain the erroneous aminopterin argument.) But the compelling argument for Distillers was less on the substance of the draft article than on the way the material in it had been obtained. The documents had been disclosed to the plaintiffs as part of the British legal process of discovery. This, said Distillers, was an improper use of discovery. The judge accepted the argument. "If discovery," he said, "were to result in documents becoming public, the process of discovery and with it the administration of justice would be in danger."

The Sunday Times' argument was that in this instance there was a higher public interest in learning how a disaster had been inflicted on innocent people. There was authority for this breach of confidence. A leading judgement in 1856 declared, "There is no confidence as to the disclosure of iniquity," and Lord Denning more recently had ruled that disclosure was justified not simply of crimes but of "any misconduct of such a nature that it ought in the public interest to be disclosed to others." Mr. Justice Ungoed Thomas held in 1973 that the public interest might justify disclosure of matters "medically dangerous to the public." *The Sunday Times* maintained that the thalidomide documents came into these categories. Mr. Justice Talbot took a different view. There was not even misdeed by Distillers, and even if there were, it was not enough to override confidentiality. "There is no crime or fraud or misdeed on the part of the plaintiffs and in my view negligence even if it could be proved, could not be within the same class so as to constitute an exception to the need to protect confidentiality."

The two strands of the thalidomide story had come together again in a knot: secrecy and the requirements of the courts. And there the story of the banned article and Distillers' documents would have ended but for a remarkable development in 1977 that may yet have galvanizing effects.

The European Commission of Human Rights found in favour of *The Sunday Times* in a report published on July 29, 1977. The finding, by eight votes to five, that the editor and thalidomide reporters had under Article 10 been deprived of free speech by the House of Lords was welcome enough. It placed the British government in the position of having to defend the laws of contempt of court before the European Court of seven judges from different nations, with the majority of the European Commission itself arguing against it.

But the European Commission's report did more than this: it included, as an appendix, the celebrated draft article that the House of Lords had banned. When the European Court ordered publication of the commission's report, it was thus placing in the public domain, with all its unique authority, information that British laws still maintained should be withheld from the public. The British government itself, during the European hearings, had supplied the commission with the draft article and protested at its disclosure. But could it be published in England? And could it, especially, be published by *The Sunday Times*, which was specifically enjoined against publication by Mr. Justice Talbot's injunction? These were pleasantly intriguing questions for *The Sunday Times.*

The news that the European Commission's report was now available to anybody who asked for a copy came through around noon on a Friday. During the afternoon, the paper told Distillers that it was going to use this event as grounds for a revision of Mr. Justice Talbot's injunction. The company said it could not consent to any revision, but it declined the invitation to be present at a special hearing that night in the home of Mr. Justice O'Connor, in Kensington. (The law courts had just closed for the vacation.)

The paper's lawyers—Brian Neill, Q.C., with James Evans and Antony Whitaker—put the case with some care. They did not seek a complete repudiation of the injunction, recognizing that it raised wider issues, and that the judge on emergency duty might be reluctant to overturn another judge's ruling on such a complex issue. They asked simply for a revision of the injunction so that it could not be held to apply to publication of the European Commission's report. This was granted, and on July 31, 1977, the remaining important elements of Phillip Knightley's original draft article were published. (Unhappily, and despite a midnight appeal by the editor to some professional workers, a labour dispute restricted printing, and a million readers were deprived of copies.)

It was four years and nine months since the original ban, and Mr.

Justice O'Connor had become the twenty-sixth jurist to pronounce on the article. The score card by then read: For publication: three Court of Appeal judges (Denning, Scarman, and Phillimore), one High Court judge (O'Connor), and eight European Commissioners; total, twelve. Against publication: three divisional court judges (Widgery, Brabin, and Melford Stevenson), five Law Lords (Reid, Morris, Diplock, Simon, and Cross), one High Court judge (Talbot), and five European Commissioners; total, fourteen.

The publication of the article marked the first time any light at all had been shed on what went on in Distillers during the manufacture and marketing of thalidomide; but more important than the incidental dent in the British law of confidentiality was the commission's reasoning in declaring that the British law of contempt in the thalidomide story violated rights to free speech. The commission recognized in its findings that there may be situations in which it is necessary to protect the authority of the judiciary, even though there may be no concrete danger to its impartiality. But it found that the authority of the judiciary was not directly put in question by the publication of the draft article at the time intended. This, it said, was because: the litigation was civil, the contents of the draft article need not necessarily be understood as passing legal judgement, and at the time the injunction was granted, the thalidomide proceedings were at a stage of settlement.

The commission said it had taken into account an additional element in the case—the role of the press in a democratic society and the duties and responsibilities of individual journalists:

> The facts underlying the thalidomide litigation with which *The Sunday Times* wanted to deal in the proposed article were not just the ordinary type of issues between private parties to civil litigation. The clarification of issues of negligence in connection with private activities which have led to a public disaster is also a question of public concern and the examination of responsibility in such a situation is, in itself, certainly a legitimate function of the Press in a democratic society. This has not even been denied by the respondent Government, who have emphasised that the main objection against the draft article was the time of its intended publication in relation to the state of proceedings in the thalidomide litigation.
>
> It is true that at the time of the intended publication of the draft article the thalidomide affair was mainly an issue of civil litigation between the parents of the thalidomide children and

Distillers. But this was so partly for the reason that a public investigation of the causes of the thalidomide tragedy which had repeatedly been demanded had never been carried out. In fact, it was finally refused by the competent Minister after the discharge of the injunction against *The Sunday Times* in summer 1976.

In so far as Parliament is concerned it impliedly renounced an investigation when resolving to await the outcome of the civil litigation before considering whether the thalidomide children required additional State assistance. As the matter was not being clarified by criminal proceedings nor by public investigation, it was entirely left to civil proceedings. These however need not necessarily bring to light all the relevant factors because they are in principle subject to the parties' disposition. In this respect it must be observed that already the 1968 thalidomide settlement which was meant to serve as a model for the current negotiations had excluded the issue of negligence by the withdrawal of the relevant allegations by the parents.

If the public interest to clarify matters of great importance cannot be satisfied by any kind of official investigation, it must, in a democratic society, at least be allowed to find its expression in another way. Only the most pressing grounds can be sufficient to justify that the authorities stop information on matters, the clarification of which would seem to lie in the public interest.

It was a ringing conclusion, and of course satisfying to *The Sunday Times,* despite the prospect of further argument before the European Court. But the laws of England remained the same in 1978 as they were in the decade of suppression from 1962 to 1972, and there is nowhere yet a real end to the thalidomide story and the ills it exemplifies.

Conclusion: It Could Happen Again

The issues raised by the thalidomide tragedy will reverberate for a long time—though some of the captains and kings have now departed the arena. Chemie Grünenthal and Richardson-Merrell continue to make drugs, but Distillers sold its pharmaceutical subsidiary, DCBL, in 1962 and Sir Alexander McDonald retired in 1976.

Dr. Phillips, who first aroused *The Sunday Times'* interest, died before the conclusion of the public battle with Distillers that he had wanted so much. George Somers, the Distillers pharmacologist who tried to make his superiors heed his fears about thalidomide, was deeply distressed by the tragedy, later retired from pharmacology, and now runs a pharmacy in Hull. E. G. Gross, the Distillers executive who brought the drug to Britain, has retired and lives in Australia.

The inventors—Wilhelm Kunz, Herbert Keller, and Heinrich Mueckter—are still active, as are those who prevented its claiming further victims. Dr. Mueckter lives in Aachen and retains his links with Grünenthal, where he acts as a part-time consultant. He is also a consultant on chemistry and therapeutics at the Aachen polytechnic teaching hospital. Professor Keller is chief medical superintendent and head of the institute of clinical chemistry and haematology at the canton hospital, St. Gallen, Switzerland. Dr. Kunz lives in the Bonn suburb of Villiprott and is employed by the Bad Godesberg pharmaceutical company Dolorgiet.

Of the dragon killers, Dr. Frances Kelsey, who was given the President's award for distinguished federal civilian service in 1962, is now, as director of the division of scientific investigations in the Food and Drug Administration, responsible for monitoring research done by clinical investigators. Dr. McBride remains a leading obstetrician in Australia. He became a Commander of the British Empire in 1969, France awarded him the gold medal from the Institut de la Vie for his work on thalidomide, and in 1977 he was given the Order of Australia.

But if distinction has been properly honoured, and the price of progress paid by eight thousand thalidomide families, the substance of progress in medicine and law has been more elusive.

People injured by drugs are still almost universally in the same position as the thalidomide families: they are at the mercy of antiquated legal systems that assume they have the money, knowledge, and mental fortitude to fight for compensation. Science has moved quicker than law. America (1962), Britain (1963), Sweden (1965), and Japan (1967) have made prominent national efforts to stiffen the scrutiny of new drugs, and the World Health Organization is pooling information from twenty-two member states on adverse effects. But drug monitoring is scientifically still at a relatively primitive stage. It has managed to give early warning that the contraceptive pill carries a risk of thrombosis to certain women in blood groups A, B, or AB—but the incidence of adverse reactions to most drugs in use today has never been recorded, and increased surveillance has failed to prevent death, blindness, and prolonged illness arising from treatment with new drugs. This concluding chapter therefore touches on some of the basic scientific and legal issues unresolved by the thalidomide tragedy. Could it all happen again? Yes, it could.

There is no excuse for the deceits and acts of greed documented in this book; the deceits, in particular, are a betrayal of man's intellect since it is the unexpected or "wrong" results of a scientific test—think of Fleming's bacterial culture inadvertently destroyed by the penicillin mould—that may lead to the great discoveries. But it is no part of the thesis of this book to portray drug companies as such as mendacious, profit-hungry organizations; the demand that the authorities should "get tough with the drug companies" is too crude a response to the complex, serious scientific and intellectual problems at the heart of honest pharmacology. The layman's reaction to a tragedy like thalidomide, naturally enough, is to say that drugs should not be let out unless they are "safe." But no effective drug, not even aspirin, is wholly free from risk or harm. If we were to insist on total safety and freedom from side effects, we would have to dismantle drug therapy altogether. Yet drugs and vaccines provide cheap health care and have transformed our lives in a generation, helping to halve the death rate from tuberculosis, peritonitis, dysentery, and syphilis; and wiping out polio in developed countries. So every very effective drug has a risk. The key question is whether the benefit is worth the danger. A drug that cured cancer but caused baldness would be regarded as a saviour of mankind, but a cure for baldness that had the remotest risk of cancer would be forsworn by the vainest of us and banned from the market. Unfortunately, the choices are not so simple as that; crucially, it is impossible to predict that side effects will not endanger human life. Animal experimentation may easily fail to predict accurately what will happen in man, and a single adverse result in animal tests is not necessarily decisive. What would one say of a new drug that proved fatal when administered to guinea pigs though not to other animals? Ban it? But that would have meant banning penicillin, which kills guinea pigs as surely as arsenic. Nor is clinical testing on *human* subjects, which may be possible for two to three thousand patients, conclusive. Such tests will demonstrate the obvious side effects. But the real final element of the risk equation is revealed only when the drug is administered to hundreds of thousands or even millions of men, women, and children, where it interacts with a multitude of variables—atypical genetic constitutions, climatic influences, different foods, other drugs, and so on. This knowledge is, in turn, only one of the variables in the therapeutic equation that the doctor contemplating drug therapy has to make. How ill is the patient? What would be the natural course of the disease without treatment? What are the other choices of treatment available? If they are drugs, what are their side effects, if any? What is the measure of expected benefit from such treatment? How does the incidence of "side effects" from the proposed drug therapy compare with the incidence of the same symptoms in the untreated population?

A doctor cannot be expected to make these judgements numerically or in that order, and the patient may have his own ideas about what side effects he is prepared to risk. There are many imponderables and one certainty: whatever the difficulties of a risk/benefit calculation for any given drug with any given patient, no sensible judgement is possible where basic information about drugs is lacking. This makes a drug-screening system of some kind indispensable to medicine and the public interest. The roles of the government, the drug industry, and the medical profession can vary. What is essential is that there should be, first, a drug-approval process that facilitates effective drugs reaching patients as quickly as possible compatible with safety; and, second, a drug-monitoring process that ensures speedy and accurate reporting of what released drugs do to patients. Some countries are attempting this optimization of benefit and risk. It is not easy. There are severe scientific and administrative problems. But before we examine the toilers in the foothills of this Everest, it has to be said that many of the world's governments have yet to acknowledge that there is any mountain to climb. Despite the thalidomide tragedy, there is hardly any recognition in many parts of the world of the responsibility of national health authorities to protect their citizens, who are vulnerable, in their millions, to skimped research, and unscrupulous selling to unsophisticated doctors and lay people. They live in societies—notably in Latin America, Asia, and Africa, but also in Europe—that have not begun to enforce the prethalidomide standard of the 1950s, and they must inevitably risk disaster.

This is because too many big drug companies have responded to relative freedom with irresponsibility. People are being killed and maimed because in underdeveloped countries the companies suppress information that they are compelled to make available in Britain and America. Chloramphenicol, for instance, is a powerful antibiotic that, used indiscriminately, can cause fatal aplastic anaemia. (It should be reserved for the toughest microbes, such as that which causes typhoid.) Milton Silverman, however, in his book *Drugging of the Americas* (University of California Press, 1976), has documented how Parke-Davis, Winthrop, McKesson, and Boehringer all distribute their brands of chloramphenicol in Latin America with recommendations for its use and without the warnings or contra-indications given with their same products in the United States. Winthrop, again, produces a steroid hormone called Winstrol which is listed in the United States as posing risks of stunting children's growth and interfering with their normal sexual development; few of these risks are disclosed in Mexico or Brazil, still fewer in Central America, and none in Colombia or Ecuador.

It may not be surprising that in such countries there are no sophisticated systems for controlling release of drugs and for monitoring adverse reactions. But even in Western Europe, there are extraordinary disparities in government concern. In Britain, Germany, Scandinavia, and Holland, it is possible to debate the merits of the different control systems. In France, Italy, Spain, and Belgium, it is hard—though the European Commission hopes to make progress—to talk about any system at all.

It is, for instance, ten years since the British Committee on Safety of

Medicines (CSM)* discovered that chloramphenicol was causing about one death a month, mostly among children who had been prescribed it, unnecessarily, for sore throats. The committee ruled that the drug should not be prescribed for minor conditions. Despite this, chloramphenicol has continued to be sold across the counter to anyone who asks for it in Italy and Spain. In Italy, it is available under some twenty labels and even used in plasters and skin powders; and in Italy, it should be added, it is notoriously easy for manufacturers to obtain clinical reports which minimize toxic side effects.

A more dramatic example of both the risks in the equation and the social-policy gap exploited by some manufacturers has emerged in Japan a full ten years after thalidomide. It is a disaster every bit as tragic as thalidomide, burgeoning on many of the same ills of secrecy and excessive salesmanship. In the late 1950s, Japanese doctors began to notice a new illness unlike anything they had ever noticed before. They called it Smon, which is short for sub-acute myelo-optic neuropathy. The symptoms are pain in the stomach and incontinence, followed by progressive paralysis of the legs and loss of sight. Its cause was finally tracked to a drug used to combat diarrhoea, known chemically as clioquinol and distributed for very many years under the trade name of Enterovioform and Mexaform by the Swiss-based company Ciba-Geigy, which vies for the position of fifth largest pharmaceutical company in the world. Some ten thousand Japanese have since claimed to be affected by blindness or paralysis caused by clioquinol. Some of these claims may be wrong, but there is no doubt that many thousands of people have been directly affected and no doubt either that the discovery of the connection between the disease and the drug was actually impeded by Ciba-Geigy. It repeatedly withheld information pointing to serious side effects, and it maintained throughout—on the basis of an erroneous experiment—that clioquinol acted only on the food passing through the bowel and was hardly absorbed into the body. So Japanese scientists spent twelve fruitless years looking for an infectious microorganism while clioquinol continued to be sold without restriction. When the evidence against the drug became decisive in 1970, thanks to research sponsored by the Japanese government in the wake of an epidemic of Smon in 1967–68, Ciba-Geigy still denied the danger. Then, in September, the Japanese Health Ministry banned the sale of the drug and

* At that time the Committee on Safety of Drugs (CSD).

Smon disappeared within months. Yet Ciba-Geigy and other companies continued aggressive marketing of the drug in the rest of the world. Ciba-Geigy maintained, in other markets, that Smon was a peculiar Japanese disease. A financial penalty has been paid by the company, as it was in the end by the thalidomide company. In 1977, it settled on about $200 million for compensation in Japan. But the human cost has been high, and the therapeutic benefit bought at such cost remains questionable. As far back as 1961, Dr. Irving Seigel of the FDA observed the potential toxicity of clioquinol and wrote in an internal memo that the claims for it were "false and misleading." Enterovioform-type drugs were therefore restricted in the United States not so much because risks were known but because benefits were not demonstrated. The sagacity of that particular decision is impressive, but it is less important than its philosophy and the machinery that allowed it to have effect. The FDA is the classic bureaucratic expression of a conservative drug-approval policy. Since it was one of the few agencies to prevent a full-scale thalidomide disaster, we must consider whether every country should have an FDA.

Stringent tests for safety were already a feature of FDA regulations when the thalidomide affair gave new direction and impetus to the congressional committee hearings on the industry then being conducted by Senator Estes Kefauver. Congress rapidly passed amendments to the Food, Drug and Cosmetic Act, of which the most notable was the anti-quackery amendment requiring drug companies to prove the efficacy of any new product. The FDA has certainly used its muscle. It has required every manufacturer wanting to market a drug to submit detailed, original safety and efficacy data. A manufacturer is not allowed to rely on data produced for the same drug entity by another manufacturer; the tests have to be repeated. After the elaborate animal tests, every drug must be demonstrated to be effective in well-controlled clinical trials. It must then justify its benefits by its risks in unrestricted use. A drug cannot win FDA approval solely on the grounds that its use would benefit limited groups of very sick patients.

This emphasis on prior screening is partly because the FDA has no express authority to require active monitoring of patients' experiences with a drug *after* it has been approved. The FDA is a tough customs barrier that has declared contraband a great deal of salesmanship smuggled in as science. Of that negative benefit there is not much doubt—but there is a wide spectrum of scepticism about FDA regulations. The agency is accused, with varying degrees of shrillness, of withholding life-enhancing drugs available to doctors in other countries but denied to Americans by FDA rejections or delays. Money, time and scientific resources, it is said, are wasted by the burdens imposed on the industry in meeting the FDA's elaborate pre-market requirements. This is the so-called "drug lag," a battleground between the pharmaceutical industry and the FDA that is heavily covered in smoke. The statistical argument is confused because the two sides use different terms. Much of what is categorized as "new" drug therapy is merely a technical or selling combination of a known chemical. Data provided by Paul de Haen, Inc., involving only new and important chemical entities, has enabled the FDA to demonstrate that some kind of drug lag exists in all five main drug-developing countries (Britain, France, the Federal Republic of Germany, Italy, Japan). In 1976, Americans had 15 "new" drugs compared with 39 in Germany, 38 in France, 23 in Italy, 21 in Britain and 14 in Japan. Seven of the American 15 (47%) had been previously marketed elsewhere, but drug lag in this form was more severe in Japan (86%), Germany (54%), Italy (57%) and France (53%). If figures like these can help to puncture the hyperbole with which attacks on the FDA are frequently mounted, two areas of disquiet must remain. One would expect the richest and most powerful country to remain a leader in drug therapy. Yet no drugs were introduced in the United States between 1963 and 1974 for treating high blood pressure, chest pain and heart disease, or chronic lung diseases, although several drugs for these had won acceptance in other countries. Italy's invention of rifamycin, safely effective against tuberculosis, took years to reach tuberculosis victims in the United States. Sodium valproate, effective against epilepsy in children, was similarly long-delayed. More research is needed to clarify just how much innovation like this is delayed by FDA regulation.

The second criticism of the American system does not need to wait for further findings. It is lamentably obvious that while the system is good at stopping or delaying new drugs, it hardly exists in monitoring the effects of old and new drugs once they are released to the public. It is possible to contend that the FDA has the balance wrong in that society would gain more if the agency could approve drugs more speedily while monitoring their effects more closely when in use. This is one of the conclusions of William M. Wardell and Louis Lasagna,* who have compared what has happened in Britain and America since thalidomide. Britain, with a prior-approval system operating on guidelines rather than enforceable regulations, has placed more emphasis on monitoring the effects of drugs once they are released. Wardell and Lasagna conclude that the United States has lost more than it has gained. Beneficial new drugs are introduced more quickly and in greater numbers in Britain, notably for angina, asthma, pyelonephritis and gastric ulcer. These losses to American health care have to be weighed against damage done by new drugs in Britain by the relatively more lax approval procedure. But Wardell and Lasagna argue that the United States has not fared all that well. The cost of Britain's policy in terms of damage through adverse reactions has, they say, been "small compared with existing levels of damage produced by older drugs." One can go further. The British post-marketing surveillance system has secured some notable successes. It was the first to spot that high-dose contraceptive pills pose the hazard of thrombosis in certain women. It also detected the chloramphenicol hazard, and three different drugs that cause serious jaundice. But if the British system has demonstrated the importance of post-market surveillance, it has by no means provided an easy blue-print. A serious weakness in the British monitoring system was exposed by the epidemic of asthma deaths in the 1960s, and more recently by the beta-blocker drug called practolol (trade name Eraldin). The beta-blockers offer considerable relief to sufferers from angina pectoris and hypertension, and a range of them was available to doctors in Britain and Europe early in the 1970s. Only one was available to American doctors, and practolol, with special benefit for asthma sufferers, was delayed because the FDA insisted in 1972 on long-term carcinogenic testing in animals; it suspected that a number of beta-blockers might produce tumours. The animal studies the FDA insisted on for 11 beta-blockers took until January 1978. Five of them were cleared for initiation of long-term clinical studies which suggest that for these five years countless American patients were needlessly deprived of a potential benefit. But 2 of the 11 beta-blockers

---

* In "Regulation and Drug Development," published by the American Enterprise Institute for Public Policy Research, Washington, D.C., 1975. Lasagna is professor and chairman of the Department of Pharmacology and Toxicology and Professor of Medicine at the University of Rochester. He came into the thalidomide story above, p. 21. Wardell is an assistant professor at Rochester.

were found to be clearly carcinogenic in animals and 2 produced a statistically significant increase in benign lesions and tumours. But, even more dramatically, by this time the beta-blocker practolol had been withdrawn from general use in Britain because it had been found to damage eyesight in some patients and induce the growth of a strangulating membrane in the bowels of others, some of whom died undergoing remedial surgery. Injuries extended to at least 1700 people, and the most serious—permanent or near-permanent blindness—is reported to have affected about one in 12,500 people who were prescribed the drug. This was a considerable failure for the British monitoring system. It depends on a voluntary arrangement by which doctors report any adverse side-effects on specially provided forms. The most common adverse side-effects of practolol were dry eyes and skin rash, and these were overlooked for nearly five years by doctors because they are common enough symptoms anyway. It was not until an eye specialist observed that a number of patients with dry eyes had been taking the drug that suspicions were raised.

This incident does not mean that improving drug-approval processes should take priority over drug monitoring. The crucial fact is that practolol was extensively tested on animals, but the drug's principal effects are such that animal tests do not reveal them. It is quite conceivable that if the British experience had not occurred in time, the American drug-approval system could have put practolol into circulation in the United States and produced a disaster as great as thalidomide. This is—to emphasize the point—because the United States has constructed no system aimed at testing the effects of old and new drugs in the circumstances of their actual use in the population. The United States' reporting rate is among the lowest of all twelve countries in the World Health Organization's international drug-monitoring programme. Feedback is almost non-existent. The practolol incident neither adds nor subtracts from the case for pre-market studies. It simply emphasizes the urgent necessity for much more sophisticated and effective post-marketing surveillance.

The logistical difficulties are real. Voluntary reporting by doctors and drug companies reveals only a fraction of the true incidence of drug reaction. In countries with some of the best reporting systems, the regulatory authorities hear about less than 10 per cent of the adverse reactions that occur. Dr. William H. W. Inman, of the Committee on Safety of Medicines, has identified the "seven deadly sins" of doctors who are supposed to report voluntarily: ignorance of drug effect, fear of involvement in litigation, complacent belief that if a drug has been marketed it must be safe, guilt from having caused harm to a patient, diffidence about reporting mere suspicions, lethargy, and ambition to collect and publish a personal series of cases. Dr. Inman* is one of a number of experts who has advocated schemes of "recorded release," which would require the recording or registration of all patients who receive a new drug and the submission of regular reports afterwards. So far, nothing has been achieved.

It must also be recognized that patients are at risk from doctors who give out drugs like popcorn. The professor of pharmacy at Queen's University, Belfast, has testified that between 10 and 20 per cent of patients in Britain suffer from a disease induced by doctors who prescribe multiple drugs without regular patient supervision. (The record in the British Isles appears to be held by a doctor in Hertfordshire who prescribed twelve items to one patient. They included a preparation for constipation; tablets for blood pressure and heart disease, potassium deficiency, allergy, and throat ailments; skin ointment; an expectorant; and medicines for rheumatism.) Patients must be enabled to protect themselves. They should certainly have fuller information in the form of warnings and correct indications for the use of drugs. Yet even this modest idea has been made to sound revolutionary, with the drug industry conjuring up pictures of thousands of hypochondriac patients filling the doctors' waiting rooms on the basis of symptoms imagined from the reading of the contra-indications. It is a persistent feature of the debate on drugs that it produces extreme reactions. Despite the inevitable imperfections of any drug monitoring, and the well-known tragedies, there are public people who would make a bonfire of regulations. In 1977, a hundred congressmen in the United States joined to sponsor a bill to eliminate the 1962 Efficacy Amendment produced by the thalidomide disaster. In Britain, the deputy secretary of the National Pharmaceutical Union, T. P. Astoll, has also argued for ending tests of efficacy. The American economist Milton Friedman, pursuing the theory of the market to an illogical conclusion, has even argued that the FDA itself should be abolished—and sought to justify the argument with figures that would not exist if the FDA were not there to supply them. It cannot be that all these public men are as reckless about public safety and as eager as they

* See discussion in *Drug Monitoring*, edited by F. H. Gross and W. H. W. Inman, Academic Press, London/New York/San Francisco, 1977.

seem to open the floodgates for the quack medicine that would follow "liberalization."

They are, perhaps, frustrated by the failure of science to find treatments for cancer and other killers; but there is no evidence that drug regulation is to blame for disappointment here. The President's Science Advisory Committee noted a world-wide slowing of new drug development which was "mainly as a result of limitations of scientific understanding of biological actions in disease processes." Those who argue for total freedom certainly risk a great deal for a theoretical benefit derived from the removal of control. There is no question but that disaster would be the result of some speedier treatments. Progress in medical and pharmaceutical science over the last forty years has produced drugs that are effective in minute quantities against diseases for which no remedy was formerly available. But it has also given us drugs notable for their great potential toxicity. Those who lead the assault on regulation—and those, too, who merely call for tightening pre-market approval—should be directing their intellects to devising post-marketing surveillance systems that are sensitive enough to detect rare and mild toxicity at an early stage of all drug intake.

Improvement in drug monitoring is more urgent than legal reform since it is better to prevent injury than to compensate it after it has occurred. But it is nonetheless shocking that there is hardly anything to show in legal reform anywhere for the travails that began so long ago when the thalidomide children were born. Money has been won for most of them at last, but everywhere except the United States it was won *in spite* of the legal and social system. The system had to be bent by force to accommodate the victims, and having been forced to do so, it has resumed its traditional shape. In most countries, nothing has changed to prevent the consequences of a thalidomide-type disaster being the same again. In all but one nation, government and law offer no more redress than they did in 1961. (The exception is West Germany, which in 1978 introduced a comprehensive insurance scheme to compensate all victims of adverse effects of drugs.)

In Britain, the most spectacular example of inertia, the compensation the children finally won was in a real sense an accident, dependent not on institutions but on a chance fusion of energies described in this book. The same system of legal censorship still prevails—indeed it has been extended—and society still accepts a primitive view of the duty of care. One leading drug manufacturer, ICI, has set an example, swiftly offering compensation over practolol without any legal compulsion. But the innocent victim has otherwise still to seek redress by proving negligence. That is costly, cumbersome, and virtually impossible for the individual not backed by a trade union or institution. It is frequently beyond the capacity, in complex cases, of the courts and lawyers. In Britain, as elsewhere, many people cannot afford to use the courts because of what one judge has described as the "dark shadow" of costs that extends over the whole of civil proceedings. Individuals risk having to pay huge sums not only if they lose but even, in some cases, if they win. The liability of both their own and their opponents' costs is unlimited.

In Britain, the legal system itself is the subject of a Royal Commission, and a Royal Commission on personal injury set up during the thalidomide campaign has advocated reforms. But legislation to affect personal-injury compensation, or the balance of power in litigation, or to provide for the acceptance of actuarial evidence, has still to surmount not merely the various vested interests but an institutional talent for inertia and a national habit of secrecy. As the law professor Harry Street has remarked, tomorrow's accident victims do not form a well-knit pressure group.

There are better ways of behaving. Society can choose a legal route or a social route to protect its citizens. The legal route is to introduce a strict liability for damage caused by a defect of a product, irrespective of faults or negligence on the producer's part. The Council of Europe and the EEC Commission have produced draft legislation for such strict liability. The argument for it is that manufacturers should not be allowed to take the profits of success and escape the responsibility for accidental failure. The American thalidomide experience suggests that a legal solution is possible in certain conditions. Publicity and incentive combined to make private litigation an effective remedy and enabled the thalidomide victims in the United States to receive better justice than anywhere else in the world. So it was also for the British and Japanese families who sued in California after the crash of the McDonnell-Douglas DC-10 outside Paris in 1975 in which 346 people died.

There are plainly three reasons for the American capacity to make litigation work. The first is the application of the law of strict liability, which eases the problem of proof (though it is still common to add negligence to the charges against the manufacturer). The second is that the contingency-fee system does a lot to redress the imbalance between the private citizen and public corporation. In Britain and other countries, many people cannot use the courts to seek redress because they cannot afford the legal costs—vast in a complicated negligence case requiring expert testimony. (In 1954 in Britain, something like 64 per cent of families with children were eligible for legal aid from the state; but by 1974, because of inflation, only 23 per cent were still eligible within these financial limits. Only the privileged rich and the privileged poor can sue.) In the United States, this problem is in certain cases met by the readiness of lawyers to work for nothing unless they win damages, in which case they may collect up to half of whatever damages or other settlements are awarded.

The third discernible advantage of the American system is that the citizenry—that is to say, any potential victim—lives in a society where the press is freer than it is anywhere else. The American press did not do much investigating of the thalidomide disaster, but the American lawyers involved in thalidomide cases all give credit to the newspapers for helping them to thrust their cases into the public mind—in precisely the way that was banned in Britain. It is an uncomfortable thought that the British law of contempt of court, which made the thalidomide families secret sufferers for so many years, would also have prevented the British press from doing, say, what *The Washington Post* did in the Watergate scandal: exposing wrongdoings and stimulating congressional inquiry. If America had been operating under British law then, once the five Watergate burglars had been charged, all press-reporting on the matter would have had to cease, and threat of being held in contempt of court would have prevented press comment or speculation through all the subsequent indictments and trials.

But if the American legal route to social justice is superior to the legal route in other countries, it is nonetheless flawed. The absence of post-marketing surveillance means, in the first place, that many people will not be able to trace their illnesses to drugs unless they are made aware that there is somebody to sue. They may be worse off in the United States than in many other countries because of the relative inaccessibility of good health care. Even if we assume that they can trace their misfortune to a manufacturer, they are then dependent on finding the right specialized legal advice; and it is not axiomatic, in a country where so few towns have competing newspapers, that the victim will always be assisted by a vigorous press. More fundamentally still, the legal route to social justice lacks equity. Death, injury and loss are commonplace in society, but compensation is something of a roulette game.

There has to be somebody or something to sue in the first place; the victims have to be in the robust mental condition required for litigation, and lucky chance can affect the size of awards. What is required is not millions of dollars for a minority of victims, but equal and adequate compensation for *all* victims. Compensation should be moved entirely out of the courts and out of adversary litigation. Public or private insurance is a better solution not only for drug prescription but for product liability in general. It can be objected that this removes an incentive for manufacturers to behave, but manufacturers may still be open to being sued by the insuring agency, whether public or private, and no diminution of liability for any criminal offence need follow. Various compensation schemes of this kind have been seen in New Zealand, Sweden, two states in Australia, and some states in the United States and Canada, but the most thorough-going is the New Zealand Accident Compensation Act of 1972, which radically abolishes nearly all actions for damages and sets up five compensation funds supplied by regular contributions from employers, holders of drivers' licences, and money appropriated by Parliament. The funds provide for medical treatment, compensation for loss of earnings, compensation for pain, and compensation to dependents if the victim dies.

The social policy for protecting the citizen seems superior, therefore, even to a litigation policy as effective as that practised in the United States. If there can be argument between those courses and debate between a conservative and liberal drug-approval system, there can surely be none at all for medicine that recklessly exposes the citizen to needless risk and then abandons a victim to a legal system that sacrifices him to an illusion of justice while preventing the press from crying "foul" until too late. The noxious fruit of the thalidomide story has been plain for all to see, but the same weeds still flourish. All the lessons have *not* been learned. Somewhere it could all be happening again right now.

Appendix: The Scientific Aspects
of Thalidomide

The scientific literature on thalidomide dates from 1956, when the papers from Chemie Grünenthal (Kunz, Keller, and Mueckter, 1956) and from the University Clinic in Cologne (Jung, 1956) appeared in the German journal *Arzneimittelforschung*. Hardly any scientific interest was shown in the compound until the first reports appeared linking thalidomide with teratogenicity (ability to cause deformations of the embryo or foetus), whereupon the number of papers on all aspects of the material suddenly burgeoned. Now the total number of citations is well over a thousand, ranging from highly technical studies on the teratology and the metabolism (fate within the body) of thalidomide to editorial comment in medical journals.

A comprehensive and detailed review of the literature is well outside the scope of this book. The purpose of the following notes is therefore to present thumbnail sketches of the more important aspects and properties now known about the substance, with particular regard to manifestations in the human.

References are provided in the bibliography for readers who wish to consult the original papers. Many of the early publications on thalidomide and malformations appear in a paper by Sievers (1964). Further titled references to papers on thalidomide published up to the end of 1965 are also listed in a review by Helm (1966); material appearing after that date is stored by MEDLARS, a computerized retrieval service.

Although emphasis is on citations of earlier literature, more recent writings have been quoted where an account is more detailed or more apposite. The relevance of thalidomide to the treatment of leprosy, where the continued use of the compound is not without controversy, and to cancer chemotherapy is also discussed. A paper by McBride

(1977) contains an important account of reports of the earliest cases of malformations together with the suspicions of the attending clinicians, as well as discussion of various other aspects of thalidomide.

1. The Pharmacology, Medical Use, and Acute Toxicity of Thalidomide

The first paper to describe the pharmacological and toxicological properties of thalidomide in animals was that of Kunz, Keller, and Mueckter (1956). Comparisons were made with substances known for their sedative or hypnotic properties; these included a barbiturate (phenobarbitone), ethinamate (ethynylcyclohexyl carbamate), the CIBA product glutethimide (also known as Doriden), an unsaturated tertiary alcohol, and sodium bromide. In mice, only sodium bromide had toxicity comparable with that of thalidomide, but the sleep-inducing dose was five times greater and took about fifteen times longer to act. The LD_{50} values by the oral route were in the range of 300–750 mg./kg., with the notable exception of thalidomide, which failed to cause any deaths up to a massive dose of 5,000 mg./kg. This was an important feature, because of the well-known suicide risk to patients deliberately taking an overdose of frequently used sleeping preparations, such as barbiturates. If Grünenthal's new patented sedative was not only virtually non-toxic but also effective, then the commercial advantage would be incalculable.

The paper also described how Keller, in conjunction with Dr. H. Wandschneider, had devised a special system of cages permitting a measure to be made of the total mobility of individual mice in groups of eight. In fact, the apparatus was a modified version of a device described by Straub some years before. The mouse is an awkward creature insofar as barbiturate anaesthesia is preceded by peculiar tremors of the body; a similar excitation phase is also induced by glutethimide. These untoward effects showed up clearly in the apparatus, and contrasted sharply with the behaviour of thalidomide, where no comparable action was seen. Indeed, combined application of thalidomide with another barbiturate was claimed to abolish excitatory activity. No side effects were reported in rats, mice, guinea pigs, or rabbits in response to substantial dosages (100–500 mg./kg. daily) given subcutaneously for thirty days. Blood counts showed no changes; urine production was normal; sites of injection showed no inflammation; and body weights, a useful index of toxicity, remained in the normal range. In cats, the electro-encephalo-graph recorded typical sedative action, while similar doses (100 mg./kg. or more) had no effect on the heart or on respiration rates in either cats or dogs. Many of these findings were confirmed by Somers (1960), who showed in addition that thalidomide extended the hexobarbitone-in-duced sleeping time of mice. Thalidomide also dampened the increased temperature response of the guinea pig to a pyrogenic bacterial prepara-tion, and potentiated the effects of several pain-killing substances. The authors claimed that their observations established thalidomide as a sed-ative of a new type.

Meanwhile, doctors in Germany and in Switzerland had been given the material to try out on human patients. Clinical testing was started by Jung at the beginning of 1955, a bare eight months after the applica-tion for the pharmaceutical patent had been lodged. More than 300 pa-tients suffering from various conditions received thalidomide; in 1956, Jung published an impressive testimonial to the virtues of the com-pound, appearing as a clinical corollary to Grünenthal's laboratory in-vestigations (Kunz, Keller, and Mueckter, 1956). Jung asserted that the major application of the substance was in the control of sleep disorders, and claimed excellent results with a nightly dose of 100 mg. Thalido-mide was also valuable in the treatment of patients who had expressed dissatisfaction with barbiturates; the use of the new compound in con-junction with these drugs assured success. With daily doses of 25, 50, or 100 mg., Jung reported that liver function remained unaltered even in patients suffering from enlarged livers. Blood counts showed no changes after four to six weeks, as in animals; the pattern of variation in blood-sugar levels was unaltered; steroid metabolism was unaffected; but sub-stantial doses (up to 1,000 mg. daily) effected useful reductions in the basal metabolic rate of patients with hyperthyroid activity. Thalido-mide restored a normal pattern of sleep to patients undergoing treat-ment for tuberculosis of the lung; relieved shortness of breath in asthmatics; dampened the inclination of a small number of youths to-wards masturbation; enabled the morphia dose for a cancer patient in severe pain to be halved; and, in conjunction with cholic acid, formed the basis of successful treatment of patients with gall bladder disorders.

There were, however, some disappointments. In patients with hyper-tension, the substance lowered the blood pressure only at dose levels so excessive as to cause fatigue and giddiness, and produced no beneficial effects with regard to gastric disorders. Jung did observe drowsiness,

restlessness, shivering, and constipation in a few cases—symptoms that
soon disappeared on lowering the dose or withdrawing the material;
women appeared to be more susceptible than men. Only 1 patient out of
300—a woman—was unable to tolerate the compound.

In Düsseldorf, Esser and Heinzler (1956) reported success with thalidomide as a sedative for excited patients, and asserted the value of the
substance both as a sleeping pill and in the management of thyrotoxi-
cosis (excessive thyroid activity). The only unwanted side effect noticed
by these authors was constipation in bed-ridden patients. Stärk (1956),
working in a tuberculosis sanatorium in Basle, used thalidomide as a
sedative by day in the control of asthma, and also as a sleeping pill. In
England, Burley, Dennison, and Harrison (1959) reported that thalidomide (100 or 200 mg.) compared well with a barbiturate (200 mg.) as a
means of inducing sleep in 83 hospital in-patients. In one group of 49
patients, two-thirds claimed 100 mg. to be sufficient to produce an opti-
mum night's sleep, but most of the remainder needed 200 mg. Elderly
patients tolerated the drug well, and those with chronic respiratory
disease obtained sleep with no associated respiratory depression. The
substance was not completely without side effects: 5 complained of
"hangover," consisting largely of dizziness, which cleared up within
ninety minutes of waking; 3 other patients developed skin rashes, which
cleared up promptly on withdrawal of the material.

None of these authors, in any of their papers, made any reference of
any kind to the effects of thalidomide on the foetus, either in the human
or in the experimental animal.

At this point, two statements (Ryder, 1975) should be quoted,
namely:

> It should never be forgotten that thalidomide was extensively
> tested upon animals and its dangers were not discovered. . . .

and

> In the first place it should be understood that thalidomide *was*
> tested on animals—and as rigorously as any product was, at
> the time of its production.

The first statement was completely unjustifiable; regarding the second,
the author added a quotation from Paget (1970):

> It is commonly remarked, in fact, that the toxicity tests that
> had been carefully carried out on thalidomide without excep-

tion had demonstrated it to be an almost uniquely safe compound.

The meaning originally intended is restored by the qualifying sentence that follows in Paget but was omitted by Ryder:

> What was required in this instance, and I think it true to say in many other instances, was not a further proliferation of tests but rather an awareness in those concerned that situations might exist in which hazards might arise that were not covered by the extensive tests they had performed.

Not all the findings were confirmed. In 1960, Lasagna published the results of a controlled trial in medical and surgical in-patients where thalidomide, at doses of 100 or 200 mg., was replaced by a placebo. The mean duration of sleep was not significantly different in patients receiving the placebo and those given 100 mg. of the substance; on the other hand, the higher dose was significantly better in inducing and maintaining sleep. Lasagna concluded that thalidomide was a "potent hypnotic" at 200 mg., but was ineffective at 100 mg., the dose that other clinicians had claimed to be optimal in most cases. Side reactions occurred in only 1 out of 41 patients who had taken placebos; in contrast, some 16 per cent of patients taking thalidomide reported untoward effects the next day, both at 100 and at 200 mg. These effects consisted mostly of drowsiness and dizziness, but one patient who had taken 200 mg. woke up during the night and complained of nausea, which persisted into the morning. Sheskin, Sagher, *et al.* (1968) found that leprosy patients appear to be more susceptible to side reactions, which include constipation, dryness of mucosal surfaces, and oedema (see section 6, pp. 274ff.).

Long after the teratogenic potential of thalidomide had been appreciated and the compound had been withdrawn from medical use, various properties of the two optical isomers of the substance were described by Fabro, Smith, and Williams (1967). Optical isomerism, an attribute shown by a number of carbon compounds, occurs when at least one of the carbon atoms in the molecule is linked to four atoms or groups of atoms, all four of which are chemically different from each other. Such a carbon atom is termed asymmetric. Under these conditions, the molecule can exist in two different spatial forms, depending on the internal arrangements of the atoms or groups around the asymmetric carbon atom. These two forms, the (+) or D form and the (−) or L form, are known as optical isomers, and can be distinguished from each other by their ability, in solution, of rotating the plane of polarized light in either of two directions. This property is termed optical activity, and disappears when equal amounts of the two isomers are mixed. A mixture of equal parts by weight of the isomers is known as the optically inactive ($\pm$) form, or racemate.

Many substances of biological origin exhibit optical activity; very often biological systems show a high degree of specificity towards one form and not the other. That the pharmacological properties of a drug can be dramatically altered when one optically active isomer is used in place of the other or of the racemate is not therefore surprising.

Thalidomide, as prepared on a commercial scale, seems to have been composed chiefly of the racemate, depending on the temperature of the synthesis and the length of time for which the reaction was allowed to proceed. The ability of the two isomers to extend the hexobarbitone-induced sleeping time in mice was no different from that of the racemate. On the other hand, the optically active forms proved much more toxic to mice than the racemate, with LD_{50} values of 400 mg./kg. and 700 mg./kg. for the (+) and (−) isomers respectively by the oral route. In contrast, no fatalities were seen with the optically inactive form at 10,-000 mg./kg. (Fabro, Smith, and Williams, 1967).

2. Side Reactions of Thalidomide Affecting the Central Nervous System

Suspicions that side reactions more serious than dizziness could develop in response to thalidomide medication appeared in the English scientific literature (Florence, 1960) some years after the German clinical experiences had been described. That earlier reports had not by that time appeared in German journals, despite the longer and wider availability of the substance in Germany, may testify to the effectiveness of Grünenthal's suppression of unfavourable findings. Florence reported symptoms of neuritis developing in a minority of patients who had taken 100 mg. of thalidomide nightly for eighteen to twenty-four months. Marked tingling sensations were noticed first in the feet and then in the hands. Coldness of the extremities and marked pallor of toes and fingers were seen on exposure to even moderately cold conditions. Sometimes slight loss of movement occurred, and cramps were experienced in the leg muscles at night. A more detailed report of further cases appeared

(Fullerton and Kremer, 1961); other, similar descriptions followed. The basic disorder was recognized as an inflammation of peripheral nerves; interference with the electrical characteristics of nervous conduction, numbness and loss of sensory feeling, wasting of muscles, and limb weakness were added to the list. The onset of symptoms was described as haphazard, and differences in individual responses were very marked. The incidence of the effects does not appear to be known, but a Distillers' estimate of 0.5 per cent in patients taking thalidomide for two months or more was cited by Fullerton and O'Sullivan (1968).

Follow-up studies of affected patients (Hafström, 1967; Fullerton and O'Sullivan, 1968; Gibbels, et al., 1973) indicated that adverse effects sometimes tended to disappear when the compound was withdrawn, but improvement was generally slow and in some cases did not begin until three years after administration was stopped (Fullerton and O'Sullivan, 1968). The chances of recovery appeared to be lower in older patients. In general, muscular strength was first to return, but loss of sensory feeling tended to persist.

3. The Metabolism of Thalidomide

As soon as the teratogenic nature of thalidomide was established, the metabolism of the substance became a focus of biochemical research. A number of detailed studies appeared soon after (see, for example, Keberle, Faigle, et al., 1965; Keberle, Loustalot, et al., 1965; Smith et al., 1965; Williams, Schumacher, et al., 1965; for early review, see Williams, 1968).

The thalidomide molecule is so constructed that hydrolysis, the process of reaction with water, may take place at one or more of a total of four sites. The spontaneous hydrolysis of the substance has been examined by Schumacher, Smith, and Williams (1965). Thalidomide reacts with water in a multiplicity of ways, depending on the order in which the four vulnerable sites are involved, to yield a diversity of intermediates; the final products of complete hydrolysis are always phthalic acid, glutamic acid, and ammonia.

Very similar changes occur within the body. The chief metabolic fate of thalidomide in most organs of the rabbit and rat is straightforward hydrolysis, although the rate of breakdown is much faster in rabbit liver. Comparison of values for the half-life of the substance (the time taken for half of a given amount to decompose) in rats, in rabbits, and in aqueous solution at comparable alkalinity suggests that breakdown is largely spontaneous and, except perhaps in the liver, is not mediated by tissues of the body (Schumacher, Blake, and Gillette, 1968). Some limited attack on other parts of the molecule does, however, occur; small amounts of derivatives of 3-hydroxy- and 4-hydroxy-phthalic acids have been found in rabbit urine (Schumacher, Smith, and Williams, 1965).

The biochemical events underlying the teratogenic action of thalidomide are still obscure, despite numerous careful and painstaking investigations. It has been established that thalidomide is able to traverse the placental membrane and enter the embryo (Keberle, Faigle, *et al.*, 1965), and that numerous products of hydrolysis lack the powerful teratogenic property of the parent compound (see, for example, Fabro, Schumacher, Smith, Stagg, and Williams, 1965; Keberle, Faigle, *et al.*, 1965; Keberle, Loustalot, *et al.*, 1965; see also section 4, pp. 263ff.). The abilities of some of these products to penetrate the placental membrane and reach the embryo during the sensitive stages of pregnancy have also been examined. Jurand (1966) tentatively concluded on the basis of his studies with the electron microscope that the primary destructive action was manifested against mitochondria within the cells that constitute the arterial wall in axial limb buds. Mitochondria are cellular structures that oxidize fatty acids and intermediary products of carbohydrate metabolism to produce chemical energy. Mitochondrial dysfunction is being increasingly regarded as a primary event in cellular injury and death.

Schumacher, Terapane, *et al.* (1972) examined certain chemical and biological properties of EM_{12} (2-[2,6-dioxopiperidon-2-yl]-phthalimidine), an analogue of thalidomide that differs by the replacement of a carbonyl by a methylene group in the phthalimide residue. The introduction of this minor structural modification had two principal consequences.

$$EM_{12}$$

First, the half-life of the new compound in water under slightly alkaline conditions (pH 7.4) and at 37°C. was 37 hours, while that of thalidomide under the same conditions was only 2.4 hours. Second, when given to pregnant rabbits at 50 mg./kg. from the eighth to the eleventh day of pregnancy, the proportion of dead or resorbed foetuses was 20 per cent, as opposed to 12 per cent with the same dose of thalidomide, and 92 per cent of the survivors were malformed (18 per cent with thalidomide). The enhanced teratogenicity of the derivative may of course be due to alterations in chemical properties arising from the modification in structure, but the dramatic increase of stability of the molecule may be a more important factor.

Aspects of the chemistry and metabolism of thalidomide and related compounds have been discussed in a detailed and comprehensive review (Jönsson, 1972).

4. The Mechanism of Teratogenic Action

Despite the interest and attention that has been focused on the way or ways in which thalidomide brings about deformities of the embryo, the precise mechanism of action still appears elusive. Two main explanations have been advanced. First, McCredie (1973) reported that the limbs of children with thalidomide malformations show changes analogous to those which can occur in the adult as a consequence of pathological alterations to peripheral nerves. The finding has been extended to a general concept of injury to the neural crest, an embryonic structure from which parts of the central nervous system (the cerebrospinal ganglia) are derived during the foetal stage. On this basis, the suggestion has been advanced that the ultimate expression of damage to the neural crest may be seen in the range of malformations induced by the compound. The hypothesis owes much to the careful work of McBride since 1973 (see McBride, 1977, for a brief review), but has encountered a certain degree of opposition; Wolpert (1976), for example, has raised some points of criticism.

A more plausible explanation is that of Poswillo (1973). It had been noted by Jurand (1966) that thalidomide caused a thinning of the arterial wall in the axial limb buds of the chick embryo. The validity of this study is not open to doubt, since Jurand was careful to use chalk powder in the controls. This thinning sometimes led to a ballooning-out of the weakened wall; tiny gaps in the blood vessels were occasionally visible by means of the extremely high magnification obtained with the electron microscope. Poswillo reported the occurrence of localized areas of bleeding (haematomas, or blebs) in the embryos of macaque monkeys in response to thalidomide administration to pregnant females. These blebs arose as a result of the failure of certain embryonic blood vessels to join together during development. Data from Poswillo (1973 and personal communication) have been cited by Wolpert (1976) in support of the concept that the haemorrhagic blebs produce deformities by simple mechanical interference with the proper processes of development. Discussing the findings with regard to deformities of the ear and face, Poswillo (1975) wrote:

> The haphazard nature of an expanding haematoma or haemorrhagic bleb accounts satisfactorily for the variations in extent and degree of damage found in association with these [thalidomide-induced] anomalies both in animal and man. The obstructive and destructive effects of the extravascular blood clot result in sequential processes of focal tissue death, repair and redifferentiation.

The question of the chemical identity of the actual teratogen has been discussed in part in the previous section. Studies have also been described in which the teratogenic potential of substances chemically related to thalidomide (other than intermediate products of hydrolysis) have been examined (for example, Fabro, Schumacher, Smith, and Williams, 1964; Wuest, Sigg, and Fratta, 1964; Wuest, Fratta, and Sigg, 1966; Stockinger and Koch, 1969; Köhler and Ockenfels, 1970; Ockenfels and Köhler, 1970; Schumacher, Terapane, et al., 1972; see Williams, 1968, and Jönsson, 1972, for reviews). Of these, N-methyl thalidomide was found to be an active teratogen in the rabbit (Wuest, Sigg, and Fratta, 1964).

The integrity of the phthalimide moiety of the molecule appears to be an essential feature in the teratogenic process; not only does replacement of the benzene ring by a 1,4-endomethylene-cyclohexane substituent abolish the capacity of the molecule to deform in the rabbit foetus (Stockinger and Koch, 1969), but also a hydrolysis product, phthaloyl-DL-glutamic acid, caused resorptions and malformations in the mouse (Köhler and Ockenfels). Further work established a surprising difference in behaviour of the two optical isomers; the D-form was totally inactive, but the response to the L-form was similar to that of the racemate (Ockenfels and Köhler). In sharp contrast, both the L- and the D-forms of thalidomide itself caused malformations in the rabbit foetus (Fabro, Smith, and Williams, 1967). The enhanced teratogenicity of the thalidomide derivative EM_{12} has already been mentioned in connection with the increased stability of the molecule (see Section 3; Schumacher, Terapane, *et al.*).

5. Thalidomide as a Teratogen

A. IN MAN

The earliest description of a thalidomide-induced congenital deformity was probably that of Weidenbach (1959), although the origins of the malformations remained a mystery for a further eighteen months. Wiedemann (1961) reported that deformities of rare and unusual kinds were suddenly becoming comparatively common in human offspring; in addition to his own cases, he referred to others in a number of cities in northwestern Germany. The chief defect was the rare deformity phocomelia (gross foreshortening or absence of long bones in the limbs); many of the affected children died soon after birth. Wiedemann regarded the outbreak as serious, but he too could find no cause. The connection with thalidomide was put forward independently by McBride (1961) and Lenz (1961, 1962).

Doses of thalidomide taken by pregnant women were generally 25 or 100 mg. daily, corresponding to levels of 0.5 mg./kg. and 2 mg./kg. respectively in a subject weighing 50 kg. (110 lbs.) When these amounts are compared with the relatively huge levels administered to animals in relation to effects on the offspring (see section 5C, pp. 270ff.), it becomes apparent that man as a species is exceptionally sensitive to the deformative powers of the material. This is well illustrated in a case described by McBride (1977) in which irregular pupils, palsy, and malformation of the external ear occurred in a child whose mother had taken only 50 mg. of thalidomide in early pregnancy.

The types of malformation seen in response to thalidomide range widely with regard to both the identity of the organs affected and the extent of damage. Reviews have appeared by Swinyard (1969), Smithells (1973), and McBride (1977). Pliess (1962) described a number of malformations in 14 cases of early death. Severely affected babies often failed to survive. Smithells cited a mortality rate of 45 per cent in a group of 29 children who were either stillborn or who died soon after delivery. The causes, where identified, included lesions of heart, kidneys, or digestive tract. On the other hand, most of the visually apparent defects can be classified into three groups, depending on the particular phase of pregnancy during which thalidomide was taken:

Defects of the ears and eyes (sensitive period, twentieth to twenty-fifth day of development). The external ear (pinna) is small and deformed, or even absent. Malformations of the middle and inner ears can also occur, and may be of such severity that hearing is impaired or non-existent. Facial palsy may be seen, sometimes associated with defects of the pinna. Abnormalities of the eye range from paralysis of the ocular muscles, clefts of the iris or certain other parts of the eye, and fissure of the eyelid to smallness or even complete absence of the eyeball.

Defects of the upper limbs (sensitive period, twenty-sixth to thirtieth day of development). The thumb may be small or absent, and the index finger may be missing. Further defects of the hands (webbing or abnormal numbers of fingers) can also occur (McBride, 1961). The radius (a long bone of the arm) may be shortened, with a normal ulna (long bone paired with the radius), or may be absent. Alternatively, both radius and ulna may be shortened; ulna and humerus (the long bone connected to the shoulder) may be shortened; fusion of radius and ulna or, less commonly, of humerus and ulna, may be seen; or, in extreme cases, all long bones may be missing.

Defects of the lower limbs (sensitive period, thirty-first to thirty-fifth day of development). The hip may be congenitally dislocated, or the feet may be deformed. The number of toes may be normal, or increased to seven or eight. Malformations of the tibia and fibula (long bones of the leg) may be seen, especially shortening. The femur (first long bone) may be shortened, the lower part of the leg being relatively normal. Last, the pelvis and foot may be separated by only a rudimentary bone. Minor defects of the leg are uncommon.

None of these malformations is mutually exclusive of any of the others, and as mentioned above, the extent of the malformations can be very variable. In addition, although bilateral defects may appear superficially to be identical, close examination almost invariably reveals features of asymmetry.

This list is by no means exhaustive; children sometimes presented visceral defects of varying severity, such as closure of the duodenum or anus, but these abnormalities tended not to be found in the absence of at least some of those described in the three groups above. Smithells (1973) expressed the opinion, on the basis of examining 125 affected children from 1968 onwards, that "the relative infrequency of visceral lesions in survivors with severe defects of all limbs suggests that most children in this group with internal defects died young."

The question of a causative link between thalidomide intake by pregnant women and malformations in babies prompted Chemie Grünenthal to publish a detailed consideration in *Arzneimittelforschung*. This massive fifty-page review by Grünenthal's Sievers (1964) was introduced by Professor Hans Grebe. "It is surely time," Grebe wrote, "that the pendulum that has swung so much for and also against the connection between medication and malformation should now return to the middle, in full and unbiased objective research, free from polemics."

Sievers had been extremely thorough, and reviewed the pre-Wiedemann literature on human malformations with much skill. He also considered the geographical and temporal aspects of the outbreak of malformations suspected to be due to thalidomide; family histories of birth-defects; smoking habits of the mothers; social positions of both parents; sleeping patterns and medications taken in earlier pregnancies; and incidences of stillbirths and malformations in a number of towns and cities in West Germany. The English summary of the paper is given below:

> In regard to the cause of serious hypoplastic and aplastic malformations of the extremities observed during the period 1960–1962 and the possible influence thereon of thalidomide, published data and the author's personal findings (analysis of incidence of malformations in various towns in Germany, etc.) permit the following summarised conclusions:
>
> a) the aetiology of the typical malformations of the extremities ("dysmelia" syndrome) must still be regarded as obscure;
>
> b) the causes of the much increased incidence of phocomelia and amelia—and associated congenital malformations—is likewise obscure;
>
> c) from all relevant published data, no definite conclusion can be reached as to whether thalidomide has a deleterious influence on blastogenesis or embryogenesis of the human foetus, whether it otherwise exerts any influence on a previously damaged embryo, or whether it has any influence at all on the embryo or on the pregnant woman. For each of these three possibilities, arguments for and against exist;
>
> d) if it be assumed that thalidomide does have a deleterious effect on the human embryo, this potential risk must be estimated at approximately 5%. That is a somewhat higher per-

centage than might be expected as hereditary taint in the whole population, and in 12% of the families of children with serious congenital malformations of the extremities a hereditary factor can be found;

e) the assumption that thalidomide is the solely responsible cause of the serious "typical" malformations of the extremities cannot be maintained from the author's point of view. [A similar attitude was still maintained by Grünenthal at the end of 1965 (Helm, 1966; see section 5C, pp. 270ff., for details).]

Despite its fullness, its objectivity, and its freedom from polemics, Sievers's work suffered from a serious omission. At no point was any attempt made to correlate, either positively or otherwise, the local occurrence of the malformations with the distribution and sales of thalidomide in the various towns and countries mentioned. Data giving the incidence of birth defects in a total of forty towns and cities in West Germany were presented in tabulated form for the three years 1960, 1961, and 1962. The averages come out at 1.2 per cent (1960), 1.4 per cent (1961), and 1.2 per cent (1962). The second highest incidence of all was 2.8 per cent, recorded in Stolberg in 1961.

Stolberg is the town in which the firm of Grünenthal was based.

B. IN PRIMATES OTHER THAN MAN

Early reports by McBride (1961) and Lenz (1961, 1962) implicating thalidomide as a possible cause of the unusual spate of human malformations seen over the previous few years provoked considerable interest within the scientific community. A trickle of papers in which the effects of the substance were investigated in the embryos of a wide variety of species began to appear in 1962. Soon the trickle became a flood; by the end of 1965, the count stood at approximately one hundred.

It is vital to understand from the outset that in any group of pregnant animals treated with thalidomide during the period of embryotoxic sensitivity not all the offspring are likely to be affected. In addition, there is often a direct, although by no means strictly proportional, relationship between the amount of substance given and the frequency and severity of the resulting malformations. Many of the experimental animals studied normally yield multiple births; other teratogens in addition to thalidomide produce a range of effects varying in both incidence and magnitude within any one litter. For example, as in humans, twins in the marmoset manifest different degrees of deformity in response to thalidomide (Poswillo, Hamilton, and Sopher, 1972). A similar situation was reported in certain non-primate species. For example, malformed puppies were born of thalidomide-treated bitches along with normal litter-mates (Weidman, Young, and Zollman, 1963). In the mouse, "within the same litter from a treated mother, some embryos had no malformations while the malformed ones exhibited considerable variation in nature and severity of a particular defect" (diPaolo, Gatzek, and Pickren, 1964).

Of the substantial amount of research carried out into the teratogenic activity of thalidomide, investigations in monkeys probably constitute the area most relevant to the human condition. Despite the desirability of obtaining data from animal models that resemble the human condition most closely, work with primates is not easy for such reasons as relatively high cost and difficulty in procuring experimental material. As a result, studies with primates form a minority of the investigations into thalidomide-induced malformations. This is unfortunate, for the limited amount of work that has been done shows not only that man's exceptional sensitivity to thalidomide is shared by other species of primates, but also that the responses to the compound are fundamentally very similar.

One early study was that of Lucey and Behrman (1963), who administered thalidomide to a total of 44 female rhesus monkeys immediately after mating. The creatures were divided into two groups: 20 animals received 50 mg. and 24 received 200 mg. of thalidomide daily for thirty-three to forty-five days. The weights of the animals ranged from 5 to 13 kg., which meant that the ranges of dosage were 4–10 mg./kg. and 16–40 mg./kg. for the two groups. These dosages were higher than the upper levels given for purposes of sedation in the human (2 mg./kg. and 4 mg./kg., corresponding to 100 mg. and 200 mg. in a subject weighing 50 kg., or 110 lb.), but were not beyond what would be regarded as fully accounted for by species differences. No pregnancies, no abortions, and no live births were seen in any of the thalidomide-treated monkeys, whereas 11 live births and one abortion were seen in 57 females in a control group. The authors concluded that thalidomide had killed the embryos prior to implantation; no further toxic effects were seen. In contrast, thalidomide at 5 mg./kg. had no apparent effect on conception in the baboon, but the same dose given within the first thirty days of pregnancy caused a wide range of embryotoxic effects. These included spontaneous abortion, apparent death of the foetus within the mother, resorption, retarded growth, and shortening of the long bones of the limbs. A high proportion of the treated animals (83 per cent) were affected (Hendricks, *et al.,* 1966).

Delahunt and Lassen (1964) treated a total of 7 macaques with thalidomide at 10 mg./kg. between the thirty-second and forty-second days of pregnancy. Only 1 of the offspring was normal; 2 animals produced teratomata (tumours containing misplaced teeth, hair, or other material in the wrong place), while the remaining foetuses were grossly malformed. Malformations included the typical absence or shortening of limbs seen in the human (phocomelia), increases in the volume of spinal fluid within the skull (hydrocephaly), facial tumours of blood capillaries, underdevelopment of small bones of the hands and feet, and absence of the pinna or the entire ear. Further work (Delahunt, Kiss, *et al.,* 1965) led to the conclusion that: "Thalidomide administered to pregnant monkeys, after implantation but before limb bud formation, produced congenital malformations in this species strikingly similar to those in man." Similar conclusions were reached by Wilson and Gavan (1967). A short review of the situation was written by Lenz (1967).

More recently, administration of thalidomide to the common cotton-eared marmoset in pregnancy has been shown to produce reduction deformities of the limbs (Poswillo, Hamilton, and Sopher, 1972), diminution or absence of ears, and defects of the jaws typically seen in the human (Poswillo, 1972; Hamilton and Poswillo, 1972). The usefulness of the marmoset as an experimental model lies in the close parallel between the anatomical and temporal aspects of embryonic development in this species and in the human in the early phase of gestation from implantation onwards (Poswillo, Hamilton, and Sopher, 1972).

C. IN NON-PRIMATE SPECIES

Most of the investigations into the teratological effects of thalidomide have been carried out in creatures other than primates, chiefly mammals. The amount of work now recorded is very substantial indeed, and only a very brief selection of papers is cited below. Not only does the range of species employed show very considerable variation with regard to their individual sensitivities to the compound, but also the malformations seen in creatures other than primates are rarely similar to those found in the human. This limitation has sharply restricted the relevance of many animal models to the problem of teratogenesis in man. It should also be understood that the foetus is susceptible to the effects of a teratogen only at certain times during embryonic development. As in man, these phases correspond to the production of malformations in specific parts of the body. A further complication not fully appreciated in a few early investigations is the extreme insolubility of thalidomide in water. Attempts to prepare aqueous solutions by treatment with alkali followed by neutralization with acid resulted in extensive destruction of the compound through hydrolysis; false negative results were sometimes reported for this reason. Grünenthal itself may have been partly responsible for this error, since the British Patent specification (1957) states, "The substance [thalidomide] is also soluble in strong lyes [alkalis], the solutions obtained having a yellowish colour."

The first animal in which malformations "remarkably similar to those seen in humans" were described in the offspring was the New Zealand white rabbit (Somers, 1962). In the first experiment described, 4 does were given substantial amounts of thalidomide (150 mg./kg. orally) daily from the eighth to the sixteenth day of pregnancy; a total of 18 births were recorded, as opposed to 29 normal offspring from 4 untreated controls. Five animals from the test does were stillborn, and 13 were malformed: the front legs were foreshortened owing to reductions in the paired long bones, and the hind legs were twisted. Similar results were obtained by Giroud, Tuchmann-Duplessis, and Mercier-Parot (1962a). In addition, the animals sometimes showed a peculiar lateral curvature of the body. Staples and Holtkamp (1963) found that the incidence of malformations in pregnant rabbits under a regimen similar to that of Somers (1962) increased with rising dosage above 25 mg./kg. daily. Shortening or absence of the long bones in all the limbs was not seen, but skeletal abnormalities included complete or partial absence of the radius or tibia (paired long bones of the forelimb and hindlimb respectively). Total absence or malformation of the first digit and alteration of ossification sites in the sternum or tail were also reported. In addition, other such malformations of the digits as webbing, permanent swelling, lengthening, or an increase in number were observed by Fratta, Sigg, and Maiorana (1965). Further deformities, especially of the head, were described by Schumacher, Blake, Gurian, and Gillette (1968).

The effects of thalidomide were also studied in the rat, which, however, reacts atypically and displays some degree of insensitivity in response to the compound. Differences in diet and in the particular strain studied may account in part for discrepancies between the reported results. As Warkany wrote: "It was . . . unusual that the rat embryo, so extensively used in previous teratological experiments, proved very resistant to thalidomide." Indeed, Fratta, Sigg, and Maiorana were unable to show any effect on the rat foetus at daily doses of 150 mg./kg. orally, unless the rats (Long-Evans and Dunning-Fischer strains) had been placed on a diet deficient in certain vitamins. Similar negative results were reported in the Sprague-Dawley rat (Staples and Holtkamp).

The primary response to thalidomide in pregnant rats of a sensitive strain such as the Wistar is to resorb a proportion of the embryos in the uterus rather than to give birth to malformed young (see, for example, Christie, 1962). Giroud, Tuchmann-Duplessis, and Mercier-Parot (1962b) reported similar results in the Wistar, August, and Long-Evans strains. Normally the number of offspring in a single litter is around 10. Obbink and Dalderup (1963) showed that the average litter size decreased as the daily dose of the material was increased up to 400 mg./kg.; a significant proportion of resorptions was seen at the lowest dose level tried (25 mg./kg.). Examination of the skeletons revealed no serious deformities other than abnormality of the fifth ossification centres of the sternum. Increasing doses of thalidomide led to a higher incidence and greater severity of this abnormality, but the authors reported that the long bones of the limbs were all present, and were of normal size. In this particular study, no evidence of embryonic stunting of growth was seen in the animals at birth.

The mouse is similar to sensitive strains of rats in responding to thalidomide by resorption of a proportion of the foetuses (Woollam, 1962; Giroud, Tuchmann-Duplessis, and Mercier-Parot, 1962a, b; diPaolo, Gatzek, and Pickren; Fratta, Sigg, and Maiorana). In some of the strains tested, the offspring also showed various malformations. For example, a wide range of malformations could be observed in strain A mice, including misshapen rib cages, bending of the spine, certain long bones of the forelimb (ulna and radius) or hindleg (tibia or tibia and fibula), or even absence of the lower part of the spine and the lower extremities (diPaolo, 1963). Malformations of the soft tissues were reported in three other strains of mice (Giroud, Tuchmann-Duplessis, and Mercier-Parot, 1962a, b). On the other hand, mice of the CF_1 and ICR strains responded only by resorption, and produced no deformed offspring (Fratta, Sigg, and Maiorana). Pregnant mice dosed with thalidomide experienced difficulty in giving birth; the offspring were stunted in growth, and tended to die within the first month (Woollam, 1962).

Other mammalian species proved still more refractory to the effects of thalidomide. In the dog, frank malformations were not seen, but the first toes and the tips of the tails were necrotic in a proportion of the offspring. Puppies tended to die within two days of birth (Weidman, Young, and Zollman, 1963). Hamsters appeared insensitive to oral doses of 150 mg./kg. daily from the third to the twelfth day of pregnancy (Fratta, Sigg, and Maiorana), although a diet incorporating as much as 0.6 per cent thalidomide did result in 6 per cent of grossly malformed offspring. The malformities included split cranium, abnormal positioning of the fore- and hindlimbs, twisted paws, twisting and kinking of the tail, and cleft palate. Evidence for serious stunting of embryonic growth was found in some litters (Homburger *et al.*, 1965).

At one time it appeared that the fertilized hen's egg might provide a convenient and useful model for testing teratogenic effects, and a number of reports appeared in 1962 and 1963 describing malformations in response to thalidomide. However, the extreme insolubility of the substance in water proved an unexpected complication. Williamson, Blattner, and Lutz (1963) showed that when finely powdered thalidomide was introduced into the amniotic cavity, the compound persisted for several days in an undissolved state. These authors also found that when eggs were treated in exactly the same fashion with four other materials, also finely ground, defects of a very similar kind were produced. The four substances were sand, powdered glass, colloidal alumina, and colloidal clay; all are even less soluble in water than thalidomide. Moreover, the variety of malformations produced by these means "in no way resembled the thalidomide-induced defects of the human." The administration of thalidomide to laying hens affected neither the incidence of gross malformations in the resulting chicks, nor egg production (Shorb *et al.*, 1963). On the other hand, increases were noted in the proportion of infertile eggs, in the number of fertile eggs failing to develop, and in the incidence of embryonic death during development.

Despite the various problems of variations in species sensitivity, the elicitation of atypical responses, and the misleading experimental model of the hen's egg, the literature that had accumulated by the end of 1965 left no doubt whatsoever that thalidomide possessed embryotoxicity and teratogenicity to a rare and unusually severe degree. Yet Helm (1966), after reviewing precisely this literature in a paper published from the pathology division of Chemie Grünenthal, concluded:

1. The teratogenic activity of L-(N-phthalidomido)-glutari-
mide (thalidomide) is a very complicated problem, since the
mechanism of the action of thalidomide in the foetus has not
been elucidated despite very important investigations in this
field.

2. Teratogenic tests are very difficult, extensive research
work will be necessary to obtain clear results.

3. The various animal species responding differently to the
same teratogenic substance, it is rather difficult now, as ever, to
apply in humans the experimental findings.

6. Thalidomide in the Treatment of Leprosy

Leprosy is a chronic infectious disease caused by the organism *Mycobacterium leprae*. In nature, man appears to be the only victim susceptible
to the condition, which has been known since biblical times. The peripheral nervous system is primarily affected; organs secondarily involved
include the skin, mucosal regions of the mouth and upper respiratory
tract, eyes, muscles, bones, testes, and the reticulo-endothelial system,
the body's defence system against infection.

The malady, always regarded as serious, is now largely confined to
tropical areas. Of the social aspects of the condition, Bryceson and
Pfaltzgraff (1973) wrote:

> There is no other disease so associated with stigma and fear.
> This seems to be related to the fact that leprosy is deforming
> and disabling but seldom kills, so that those it has crippled live
> on getting steadily worse and yet for all to see. . . . Leprosy
> has commonly been considered to be a punishment from God.
> The attitude of society towards those suffering from leprosy
> has given rise to many unfortunate incidents of insult, rejection
> and even murder of patients, and in many societies this still
> continues. . . . The patients themselves . . . respond in vari-
> ous ways. . . . Occasionally they take their own lives as their
> only release from suffering.

The clinical picture shown by the disease, which is very variable, is
largely determined by the response of the host to the organism. Development is slow, partly because of the sluggish growth of *M. leprae,* and also
because lower temperatures than blood heat are more favourable for

bacterial multiplication. Leprosy manifests itself essentially in two basic forms, tuberculoid and lepromatous; a third condition, borderline leprosy, is also known, in which features of both forms are represented. In the tuberculoid form, where host immunity is well developed, the disease tends to be restricted to the large peripheral nerves and to skin lesions. Affected nerves become thickened and damaged; when motor nerves (i.e., those that relay messages from the brain to the sites of action) are involved, weakness and wasting of muscles occur. Anaesthesia develops in parts of the body served by affected sensory nerves; sensations to touch and to a pinprick are initially lost, but total anaesthesia of the limbs and even of part of the trunk may ultimately result. The lepromatous condition sets in if the patient has a low resistance. Nervous tissue is again affected, but in contrast with the tuberculoid form, bacterial growth becomes widespread, affecting especially the skin, the eyes, and the testes, in addition to other parts of the body. Spontaneous recovery is not unknown, but is much commoner in the tuberculoid than in the lepromatous condition.

The advent of sulphone therapy in the early forties revolutionized the treatment of leprosy. The most widely used drug is dapsone (*bis*-(4 aminophenyl)-sulphone), which is effective in rendering lepromatous patients non-infectious within six months. However, relapses may occur, and some authorities maintain that treatment should be continued for life. Degenerative changes already induced in the body cannot be reversed by the drug. Recently, dapsone-resistant strains of the bacterium have begun to emerge; the importance of uninterrupted treatment cannot be overstressed. Sulphonamides, certain derivatives of thiourea, clofazimine, and a few antibiotics can also be effective therapeutically.

Unfortunately, dapsone is not without side effects, which were more serious in the early days of treatment before it was realized that the drug was effective in smaller dosage than had at first been used. The most important of these side effects is the so-called lepra reaction, which is characterized chiefly by the appearance of painful red nodules. Fever and general malaise are also often present; painful and tender nerve swelling may also be seen, with further swelling of hands, face, or feet. Lesions of the skin may alter rapidly, becoming more prominent, shiny, and warm, sometimes with breakdown and ulceration. Anaemia and allergic rashes constitute further possible side effects.

Prompt and temporary reduction in drug dosage is usually effective in coping with the condition. Wide differences occur between estimates of the proportion of treated cases in which the reaction occurs, which may reflect racial factors; thus Crawford (1969) cited 3 per cent in leprosy sufferers generally in Nigeria, while Swift (1973) gave a figure of up to 50 per cent in lepromatous patients in the United States. Lepra reaction, which tends to affect lepromatous sufferers more than those with the tuberculoid condition, is not a specific side effect of dapsone, but may erupt in response to any successful form of leprosy treatment. Injury, surgical operation, physical stress, protective immunization, pregnancy, and childbirth may also cause the reaction to develop.

The use of thalidomide dates from late 1964, when Sheskin (1965), impressed by the claim made for the pain-killing and hypnotic properties of the substance, employed it in the treatment of severe lepra reaction. Sheskin had hoped at least for some relief from pain and sleeplessness, but much to his surprise, he found that the reaction itself was attenuated. The finding has been confirmed in double-blind trials (Sheskin and Convit, 1969; Waters, 1971; Iyer *et al.*, 1971). However, the advisability of using a substance with established capacity to induce neuropathic effects in order to deal with a side reaction arising out of the successful treatment of a disease of the nervous system appears open to doubt. Alternative means of dealing with the lepra reaction are available; these include organic antimony compounds, steroids, or clofazimine, a drug which can be used against leprosy on its own. Unfortunately, these also have their drawbacks; for example, antimony compounds do not always work, and clofazimine can cause disfiguring skin discolorations that take a long time to clear.

Still, success in coping with the lepra reaction and apparent improvement in some non-reactional lesions suggested trials in which thalidomide was given as the sole treatment for leprosy (Sheskin, Sagher, Dorfman, and von Schrader-Beielstein, 1968). Von Schrader-Beielstein, a Grünenthal employee, entered the firm in 1957. The trials were not successful. Of 24 patients who were given thalidomide at 400 mg. daily for between 3 and 19 months, 5 improved, 8 remained unchanged, while the others deteriorated. Bacteriological assessment showed no change in 20 patients, while 4 became worse. The authors also reported a high incidence of side effects; two-thirds of the patients complained of constipation and dryness of mucosal surfaces, while oedema was observed in one-third.

For the present, the state of thalidomide usage in leprosy remains unresolved. In many parts of the world, the substance is supposed to have status only as a research tool, but at the Bergen Leprosy Congress (1973) it appeared that its use is widespread, and includes certain developing countries. Jopling (1971), Waters, and Bryceson and Pfaltzgraff are adamant that the compound should never be given to women of child-bearing age. The existence of such a substantial group of leprosy patients who should not be treated with thalidomide provides a further spur for investigating safer ways of treating lepra reaction. In addition, Jopling listed numerous other side effects associated with the thalidomide treatment of this condition.

The possible complication of irreversible peripheral neuritis developing in certain cases in response to thalidomide treatment in the lepra reaction still remains, although Sheskin (1975) reported no evidence of sensory neuropathy. Further, Waters claimed not only that thalidomide had a beneficial effect on lepra neuritis, but also that the neuritis returned when the compound was withdrawn. However, Iyer *et al.* concluded: "The early detection and differential diagnosis of drug-induced neuritis has its specific difficulties in leprosy patients because of the neuritis caused by *Mycobacterium leprae.*"

These authors also cited the further drawbacks of the teratogenic and leucopaenia-inducing properties of thalidomide before concluding that thalidomide therapy is attended by high risks. The case for retaining the substance in the treatment of lepra reaction will not be easy to prove.

7. Thalidomide in Cancer

The direct role of thalidomide in cancer treatment is even more tenuous than in leprosy. In the early paper describing the general effects of the substance, Kunz, Keller, and Mueckter (1956) of Chemie Grünenthal were unable to influence the growth of the Ehrlich carcinoma, a transplantable tumour of the mouse. However, substances that exert damaging effects on cancers are very often active in creating deformities of the foetus. When the teratogenic properties of thalidomide became generally known, various investigators turned their attention to the possibility of influencing cancerous growths adversely. But the material was found almost without exception to be ineffective against a range of established cancers. Nonetheless Mueckter and Moré (1966) subsequently made the surprising claim that carcinostatic effects were obtained with large doses of thalidomide in growths induced by the carcinogen dimethylbenzanthracene in the rat. Moreover, it was also alleged that the sedatives phenobarbitone and chlorpromazine (Largactil) actually stimulated the rate of increase in area of the same tumours. Substituted derivatives of thalidomide have been patented by Chemie Grünenthal for use in conjunction with hormone therapy in the treatment of certain human tumours (South African patent 69 06, 824; 1970). However, other work (Miura, Southam, and Wuest, 1970) has shown that when methylcholanthrene, a skin carcinogen, was applied to the skins of mice, the simultaneous administration of thalidomide in comparatively large amounts led to the development of greater numbers of papillomas (incipient skin cancers). Certainly the treatment of cancer with thalidomide has produced no startling breakthroughs; on the contrary, the usefulness of the substance itself is nothing if not highly questionable.

Yet one tenuous link persists between the molecule and successful cancer chemotherapy. Over twelve years ago, Creighton, at the Imperial Cancer Research Fund, in London, was preparing analogues of thalidomide as potential anti-tumour agents. He was also aware of the association between the anti-tumour action of certain substances and their chelating ability, an association spotlighted earlier by Furst (1963). Chelating ability is a measure of the capacity of a compound to bind certain derivatives of various metals in soluble forms in which the metals become almost unreactive. Unfortunately, these compounds, known as chelating agents, may bear several charges in solution, a property that makes the penetration of cancer cells virtually impossible. Creighton began to seek ways of masking the molecule by removing the charges; the modified compound would then have a much better chance of entering the cancer cells. If the masking process was achieved by an internal reaction involving the elimination of water, then, once the substance had entered the cell, there would be a strong possibility that reaction with water might strip off the mask and regenerate the original chelating agent.

In thalidomide, the two negative charges on the glutamic acid residue have been removed by condensing the acidic carboxyl groups with ammonia. The same trick was to serve a logical purpose. Creighton was working with a powerful chelator known as EDTA (ethylene diamine tetra-acetic acid). One modification proved unsuccessful; while considering another, he realized that drastic reaction with foramide could lead to ring closure, producing a *bis*-dioxopiperazine structure in which the charged groups were reacted to give a neutral substance, as in thalidomide. The compound that he isolated was designated ICRF 154. Complete hydrolysis with water will regenerate the original chelating agent together with ammonia, a mildly toxic substance of physiological occurrence, which normally presents the body with no special problems. In accordance with standard practice, Creighton went on to prepare a number of related substances.

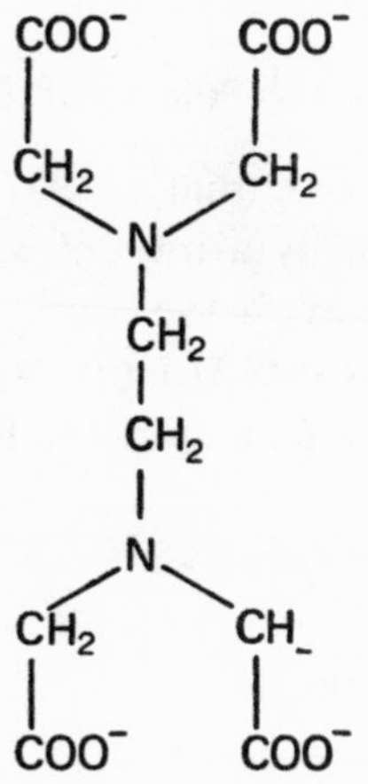

EDTA
(charged form)

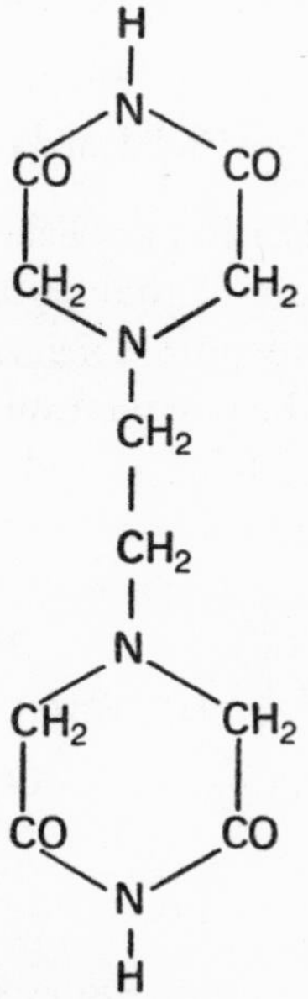

ICRF 154

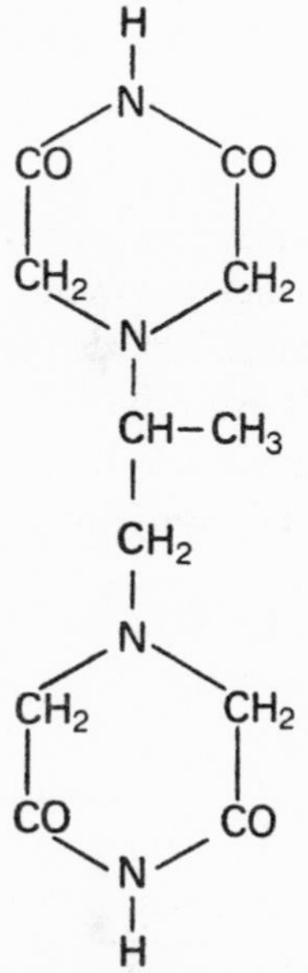

ICRF 159

In this new group of compounds, ICRF 154 and the derivative ICRF 159 achieved some measure of success when tested against experimental tumour systems in mice (Creighton, Hellman, and Whitecross, 1969). Gratifyingly, ICRF 159 was also shown to be abnormally potent against the Lewis tumour, a peculiar cancer in which secondary deposits form spontaneously in the lung. Prompt treatment of affected mice prevents the spread of cancer to the lung almost completely (Hellman and Burrage, 1969). By 1976, ICRF 159 had already undergone clinical trials. In May 1977, Creighton wrote: "Razoxin is the ICI brand name for razoxane, the official name given to ICRF 159 in the U.K. It was put on the market by ICI on March 1, 1977, but initially its use is restricted to soft tissue sarcomas in combination with X-rays." The story evidently has further to go. Beneficial results obtained by treating the skin lesions of psoriasis with razoxane have been reported recently (Atherton, Wells, and Hellman, 1976). To quote the authors: "We believe . . . that razoxane may become a useful addition to present treatments for this distressing and disabling disease. . . . Since razoxane is not specifically available for clinical trials in psoriasis at present, plans for . . . further studies are being discussed with the manufacturers and with the Committee on Safety of Medicines."

8. A Chemical Assessment of the Thalidomide Patent (British Patent 768,821)

The British patent specification published by Grünenthal in 1957 describes the synthesis not only of thalidomide itself by a total of seven routes, but also of four N-substituted derivatives, namely the ethyl (patent example 1; $R = C_2H_5$), the phenyl (example 5; $R = C_6H_5$), the benzyl (examples 7, 8, 9; $R = C_6H_5CH_2$), and the allyl (example 14; $R = C_3H_5$)compounds.

N-SUBSTITUTED DERIVATIVE OF THALIDOMIDE

That at least one of the synthetic routes for the preparation of thalidomide itself can indeed yield the required product is not in doubt, but certain aspects of the syntheses of the derivatives automatically strike the organic chemist with suspicion. In example 14, the volatile weakly-basic compound allylamine (boiling point 56° C) was heated with a neutral anhydride to 175° C under conditions in which no precautions were given to prevent loss of allylamine through evaporation. The situation in example 1 is not entirely dissimilar, although in this instance the anhydride was replaced by a dibasic acid; reaction with the volatile base ethylamine (boiling point 17° C) to give an intermediate salt which could break down at elevated temperature to give N-ethyl thalidomide as the final reaction product is, at least in theory, feasible. Although the synthesis of N-phenyl thalidomide (example 5) appears valid, preparation of the chemically similar derivative N-benzyl thalidomide (example 7) gave a product with an ill-defined and unexpectedly low melting point (104°-108° C), a strong indication that the material was impure. Elsewhere substances were either obtained with poorly defined melting points (examples 8 and 14), again suggesting that the products were not pure, or, more commonly, no melting points were stated at all. Melting points of derivatives tend in general to be higher than the melting point of the parent compound, but the melting points of those cited in the patent are lower than that of thalidomide itself.

Accordingly, Yarsley Research Laboratories Ltd, of Stoke Poges, Buckinghamshire, a division of the Fulmer Research Institute, were approached with a request to attempt the synthesis of each of the four thalidomide derivatives by the means described in the British patent (1957). Only in the case of example 7 (N-benzyl thalidomide) was the desired substance obtained, and then as a secondary product in low yield. The true melting point of N-benzyl thalidomide is 179° C (Berlin and Sla-30vin, 1970), contrasting with the material obtained by Grünenthal (melting point 104°-108° C).

The full report of the Yarsley Research Laboratories is set out below:

PREPARATION OF THALIDOMIDE DERIVATIVES:
A RE-STUDY OF BRITISH PATENT 768,821 GRANTED TO
CHEMIE GRÜNENTHAL GmbH.

---

1. INTRODUCTION

Fulmer Research Institute was asked by Dr. R. Jones, a consultant to *The Sunday Times* of London, to attempt Examples 1, 5, 7, and 14 of British Patent 768,821, granted to Grünenthal GmbH. This was to prove or disprove the claims made in these examples.

2. RESULTS AND DISCUSSION

The four reactions to be attempted involved either N-phthalylglutamic acid (I) or its anhydride (II). These materials were made by published methods (Nefkins, Tesser, and Nivard, 1960; U.S. Patent, 1960):

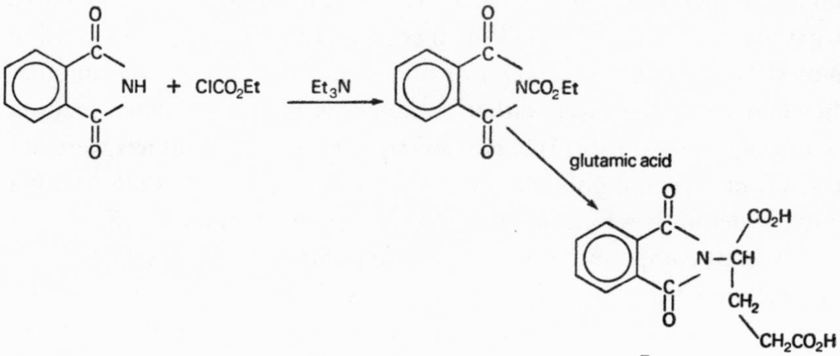

I

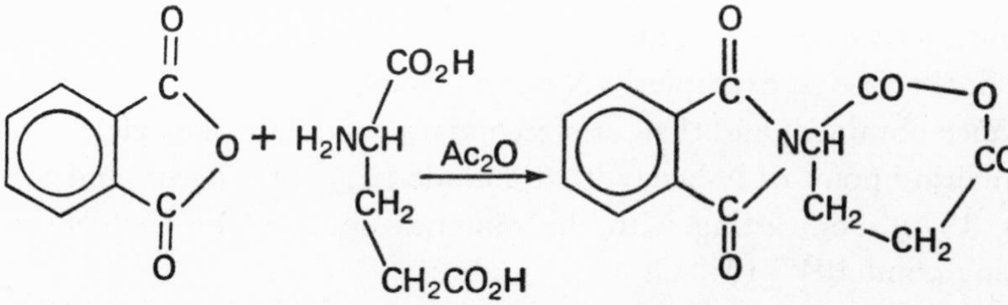

II

The four reactions in question were then attempted with the following results:

Example 1

N-phthalylglutamic acid and a 33% solution of ethylamine (the weights used being the same as those described in the patent) were heated to 170° C and left at this temperature for 20 minutes. The solution precipitated a white crystalline solid on cooling overnight. The melting point of this solid (154° C) was much lower than that described in the patent (209° C). Indeed, an IR spectrum and C, H, N analysis suggested the solid to be N,N'-diethylphthalamide (III).

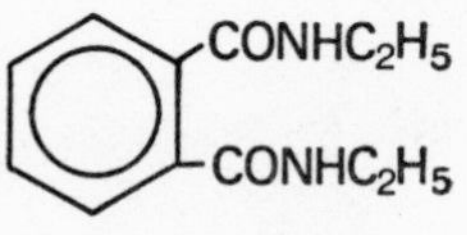

III

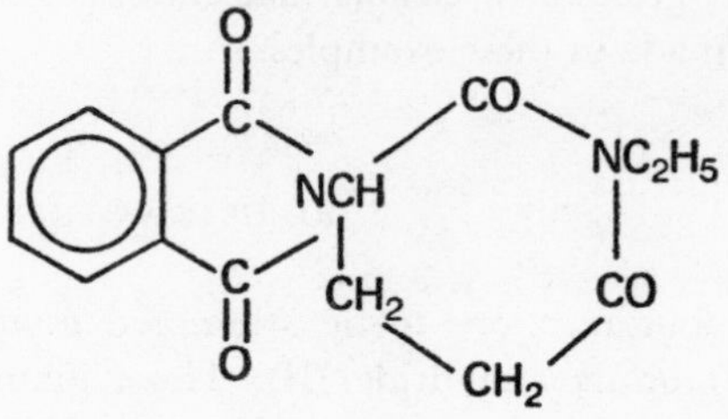

IV

No 1-ethyl-3-phthalimido-2,6-dioxopiperidine (IV) was isolated.

Example 5

This example was repeated using a similar technique to that described in the patent save that the reaction was carried out for 30 mins. Recrystallisation of the dark coloured reaction product gave N-phenyl-phthalimide (V) as the main fraction. No 1-phenyl-3-phthalimido-2,6-dioxopiperidine (VI) was identified.

V   VI

Example 7

The reaction was carried out in a similar manner to that described in the patent save that a reaction time of 30 mins. was used. The first fraction of crystals proved to be N-benzylphthalimide (VII) while on continued standing, a white powder separated. The infra-red spectrum and the C, H, N analysis suggested that this powder was the required material; however, the recorded melting point (176° C) was much higher than that quoted in the patent (104–108° C).

The reaction was carried out with heating for 20 mins. (15 mins. in the patent) when some N-phthalylglutamic acid anhydride remained unreacted. Again N-benzylphthalimide was the major product together with a small amount of the required material.

Example 14

The reaction was carried out in a similar manner to that described in the patent. After heating for 15 mins., some N-phthalylglutamic acid anhydride remained unreacted. However, the mixture was crystallised from aqueous alcohol (the N-phthalylglutamic acid anhydride was insoluble). The only solid to crystallise was N-allylphthalimide.

The reaction was repeated with heating for 30 mins. (until the N-phthalylglutamic acid anhydride dissolved); N-allylphthalimide was the only solid to crystallise.

The claims made in the patent were not reproducible, so more evidence on the subject was sought. A thorough literature search yielded no further publications on the subject (this in itself being unusual), save for one paper (Berlin and Slavin, 1970) describing the preparation of 1-benzyl-3-phthalimido-2,6-dioxopiperidine (VIII).

VII   VIII

The method of synthesis adopted was almost identical to Example 8 in the patent. In this case, N-phthalylglutamic acid anhydride and benzylamine were heated together in xylene under reflux. The required product (VIII) was isolated in a 14.5% yield (cf. the patent which stated a yield of 80%) while the major by-product was N-benzylphthalimide (VII). The melting point of the required compound (VIII) was given as 179–180° C which is much higher than that quoted in the patent (104–108° C). The melting point is in agreement with the product isolated by ourselves and thought to be compound VIII.

The melting points quoted in examples 7, 8, and 9 in the patent are identical (104–108° C) which in itself is unusual in that the product isolated in each is obviously a mixture (probably of N-benzylphthalimide and the required product) and yet different methods of synthesis were adopted, i.e. varying proportions of compounds would be expected from each preparation which would give a different melting point. The fact that the melting point is over so wide a temperature range certainly confirms a mixture exists; this obvious fact seemed to have been overlooked by the authors of the patent. The information unearthed concerning the benzyl derivative certainly shows that the claims 7, 8 and 9 are unfounded. Extending this, our work shows that the other claims (i.e. 1, 5 and 14) are also unfounded. Certainly more information could have been given in the Examples cited with regard to product crystallisation in that in all cases, the usual statement was "the product was recrystallised from 95% alcohol by fractionation." No analytical or instrumental data was cited to substantiate the claims which, again, was unfortunate.

[In a subsequent letter, Yarsley Laboratories made the following statement: "The key Russian paper mentioned in the Report arrived after typing. . . . Basically, Berlin and Slavin (1970) attempted to prepare benzylthalidomide by Method 8 in the Patent (British Patent 768,821, 1957) and noted errors; they prepared the compound by an alternative route to verify that the melting point quoted in the patent (104–108° C) was incorrect.]

3. EXPERIMENTAL

3.1. *Preparation of N-Phthalylglutamic Acid*

3.1.1. *Preparation of N-Carboxyethoxyphthalimide*

Phthalimide (145 g: 1.01 mole) was dissolved in dimethylformamide (500 ml) and triethylamine (102 g; 1.01 mole); the solution was cooled to 5° C. Ethylchloroformate (100 ml; 113.5 g; 1.04 mole) was added dropwise over 1 hr. The cooling bath was removed, and stirring was continued for a further 30 mins. The reaction product was poured into water (3.1); the precipitated solid was filtered off, washed well with water, and crystallised from ethanol.

Yield 151.4 g (72.0%); m.pt. = 82° C (lit = 80° C).

3.1.2. *Preparation of N-Phthalylglutamic Acid*

Glutamic acid (29.4 g; 0.2 mole), sodium carbonate decahydrate (57.5 g; 0.2 mole) and N-carboxyethoxyphthalimide (45 g; 0.21 mole) were stirred in water (300 ml) at room temperature for 6 hrs. until the N-carboxyethoxyphthalimide had dissolved. The reaction mixture was filtered, and acidified with 12 N-hydrochloric acid. The oil which separated crystallised on standing overnight.

Yield 38.4 g (69.3%); m.pt. = 157° C (lit = 160° C).

3.2. *Preparation of N-Phthalylglutamic Acid Anhydride*

Glutamic acid (250 g; 1.70 mole) and phthalic anhydride (250 g; 1.69 mole) were melted together at 165° C and left at this temperature for 1½ hrs. The reaction mixture was cooled to 108° C, and acetic anhydride (300 ml) was added. After maintaining the temperature at 100° C for 15 mins. the mixture was allowed to cool to 50° C (the product began to crystallise) before pouring into xylene (900 ml) and storing in the freezer at −20° C overnight. The product was filtered off, washed with diethylether, and crystallised from ethyl acetate.

Yield = 253.9 g (57.6%); m.pt. = 195° C (lit = 195° C).

Found: C, 60.08%; H, 3.65%; N, 5.68%. $C_{13}H_9NO_5$ requires: C, 60.2%; H, 3.48%; N, 5.40%.

3.3. *Reaction between Ethylamine Solution and N-Phthalylglutamic Acid (Example I)*

N-Phthalylglutamic acid (13.9 g; 0.050 mole) was mixed with 33% aqueous ethylamine solution (33 g; 0.24 mole), slowly heated to 170° C, and maintained at this temperature for 20 mins. On cooling overnight, colourless crystals (4.10 g; m.pt. = 154° C), thought to be N,N-diethylphthalamide, precipitated.

On prolonged standing, a waxy solid (2.55 g; m.pt. 105–115° C) separated. This presumably was very impure N,N'-diethylphthalamide.

3.4. *Reaction between Sym-diphenylurea and N-Phthalylglutamic Acid Anhydride* (*Example 5*)

N-Phthalylglutamic acid anhydride (13 g; 0.050 mole) and *sym*-diphenylurea (21.2 g; 0.1 mole) were melted together at 180° C and maintained at this temperature until gas evolution had ceased (30 mins.). The dark mixture was cooled, extracted with diethylether (to remove aniline which is produced), and crystallised from 95% ethanol. A pale yellow crystalline solid separated (yield = 7.72 g; m.pt. = 213° C); identified as N-phenylphthalimide, m.pt. = 210° C).

No other solids separated from the mother liquors.

3.5. *Reaction between Benzylamine and N-Phthalylglutamic Acid Anhydride* (*Example 7*)

3.5.1. *Reaction Time 20 mins.*

Benzylamine (6.0 g; 0.056 mole) and N-phthalylglutamic acid anhydride (13 g; 0.050 mole) were heated together for 20 mins. at 180° C; after this time, some of the anhydride still remained undissolved. However, the mixture was cooled, heated with 95% ethanol, filtered, and left to crystallise. The first fraction (yield 2.8 g) had a m.pt. = 115° C (identified as N-benzylphthalimide, m.pt. = 115° C).

On standing, a second solid separated (yield = 0.73 g; m.pt. = 174° C), thought to be 1-benzyl-3-phthalimido-2,6-dioxopiperidine (lit m.pt. = 179–180° C).

Found: C, 68.48%; H, 5.17%; N, 8.46%. $C_{20}H_{16}N_2O_4$ requires C, 69.0%, H, 4.60%, N, 8.05%.

3.5.2. *Reaction Time 30 mins.*

The reaction was repeated using benzylamine (3.0 g; 0.028 mole) and N-phthalylglutamic acid anhydride (6.5 g; 0.025 mole), with heating to 180° C for 30 mins. (until all the solid anhydride had melted). Recrystallisation from 95% ethanol gave two fractions:

Fraction 1 : yield = 2.32 g; m.pt. = 114° C (N-benzylphthalimide).
Fraction 2 : yield = 0.30 g; m.pt. = 176° C (N-benzyl thalidomide).

3.6. *Reaction between Allylamine and N-Phthalylglutamic Acid Anhydride* (*Example 14*)

3.6.1. *Reaction Time 15 mins.*

Allylamine (5.7 g; 0.1 mole) and N-phthalylglutamic acid anhydride (13 g; 0.050 mole) were heated at 180° C for 15 mins. After this time some solid anhydride was left unreacted. The reaction mixture was heated with 95% ethanol, filtered, and left to crystallise. A solid separated (yield = 1.73 g) of m.pt. = 70° C (identified as N-allylphthalimide; m.pt. = 71° C). No other solids were isolated.

3.6.2. *Reaction Time 30 mins.*

The reaction was repeated using similar quantities of allylamine and N-phthalylglutamic acid anhydride, heating at 180° C for 30 mins. Work-up gave N-allylphthalimide only (yield = 3.72 g; m.pt. = 71° C).

Bibliography

Ashford, N. A.; Butler, S. E.; and Zolt, E. M. 1977. *Drug Regulation and Innovation in the Pharmaceutical Industry.* Cambridge, Mass.: Center of Policy, Massachusetts Institute of Technology.

Atherton, D. J.; Wells, R. S.; and Hellman, K. 1976. Razoxane (ICRF 159) in psoriasis. *Lancet* 2: 1296.

Berlin, A. Y., and Slavin, M. N. 1970. Derivatives of 3-amino-2, 6-piperidine-dione. *Chem. Abstr.* 72: 32208. (*Khim. Geterotsikl. Soedin 1969,* 652–54).

British Patent 768,821. 1957. Novel products of the amino-piperidine-2,6-dione series.

Bryceson, A., and Pfaltzgraff, R. E. 1973. *Leprosy for Students of Medicine.* Edinburgh: Churchill Livingstone.

Burley, D. M.; Dennison, T. C.; and Harrison, W. 1959. Clinical experience with a new sedative drug. *Practitioner* 183: 57–61.

Christie, G. A. 1962. Thalidomide and congenital abnormalities. *Lancet* 2: 249.

Crawford, C. L. 1969. The effect of out-patient dapsone in an area of endemic leprosy. *Leprosy Rev.* 40: 159–163.

Creighton, A. M.; Hellman, K.; and Whitecross, S. 1969. Antitumour activity in a series of *bis*-diketopiperazines. *Nature* 222: 384–85.

Delahunt, C. S., and Lassen, L. J. 1964. Thalidomide syndrome in monkeys. *Science* 146: 1300 and 1305.

———; Kiss, N.; Feldman, E.; and Oakes, M. 1965. Some comparative pharmacological studies in man and the monkey with thalidomide. *Toxicol. Appl. Pharmacol.* 7: 481–82.

diPaolo, J. A. 1963. Congenital malformation in strain A mice: its experimental production by thalidomide. *J. Amer. Med. Assoc.* 183: 139–41.

———; Gatzek, H.; and Pickren, J. 1964. Malformations induced in the mouse by thalidomide. *Anat. Record* 149: 149–53.

Esser, H., and Heinzler, F. 1956. Klinische Erfahrungen mit einem neuen Sedativum und Hypnotikum. *Therapie der Gegenwart* 95: 374–76.

Fabro, S.; Schumacher, H.; Smith, R. L.; and Williams, R. T. 1964. Teratogenic activity of thalidomide and related compounds. *Life Sciences* 3: 987–92.

————; Schumacher, H.; Smith, R. L.; Stagg, R. B. L.; and Williams, R. T. 1965. The metabolism of thalidomide: some biological effects of thalidomide and its metabolites. *Brit. J. Pharmacol.* 25: 352–62.

————; Smith, R. L.; and Williams, R. T. 1967. Toxicity and teratogenicity of optical isomers of thalidomide. *Nature* 215: 296.

Florence, A. L. 1960. Is thalidomide to blame? *Brit. Med. J.* 2: 1954.

Fratta, I. D.; Sigg, E. B.; and Maiorana, K. 1965. Teratogenic effects of thalidomide in rabbits, rats, hamsters and mice. *Toxicol. Appl. Pharmacol.* 7: 268–86.

Fullerton, P. M., and Kremer, M. 1961. Neuropathy after intake of thalidomide (Distaval). *Brit. Med. J.* 2: 855–58.

————, and O'Sullivan, D. J. 1968. Thalidomide neuropathy: a clinical, electrophysiological, and histological follow-up study. *J. Neurol. Neurosurg. Psychiat.* 31: 543–51.

Furst, A. 1963. *Chemistry of Chelation in Cancer.* Springfield, Ill.: Thomas.

Gibbels, E.; Scheid, W.; Wieck, H. H.; and Kinzel, W. 1973. Die Thalidomid-Polyneuropathie im Spätstudium: eine klinische Dokumentation. *Fortschr. Neurol. Psychiatr.* 41: 378–417.

Giroud, A.; Tuchmann-Duplessis, H.; and Mercier-Parot, L. 1962a. Observations sur les répercussions tératogènes de la thalidomide chez la souris et le lapin. *Comptes rendus Soc. biol.* 156: 765–68.

————; Tuchmann-Duplessis, H.; and Mercier-Parot, L. 1962b. Thalidomide and congenital abnormalities. *Lancet* 2: 298–99.

Gross, F. H., and Inman, W. H. W. 1977. *Drug Monitoring.* London and New York: Academic Press.

Hafström, T. 1967. Polyneuropathy after neurosedyn (thalidomide) and its prognosis. *Acta Neurol. Scand.* 43: supp. no. 32, 1–41.

Hamilton, W. J., and Poswillo, D. E. 1972. Limb reduction anomalies induced in the marmoset by thalidomide. *Proc. Anat. Soc.,* in *J. Anat.* 111: 505–506.

Hellman, K., and Burrage, K. 1969. Control of malignant metastases by ICRF 159. *Nature* 224: 273–75.

Helm, F. 1966. Tierexperimentelle Untersuchungen und Dysmeliesyndrom. *Arzneimittelforschung* 16: 1232–44.

Hendrick, A. G.; Axelrod, L. R.; and Clayborn, L. D. 1966. "Thalidomide" syndrome in baboons. *Nature* 210: 958–59.

Homburger, F.; Chaube, S.; Eppenberger, M.: Bogdonoff, P. D.; and Nixon, C. W. 1965. Susceptibility of certain inbred strains of hamsters to teratogenic effects of thalidomide. *Toxicol. Appl. Pharmacol.* 7: 686–93.

Iyer, G. S.; Languillon, J.; Ramanujam, K.; Tarabini-Castellani, G.; de las Aguas, J. T.; Bechelli, L. M.; Uemura, K.; Martínez Domínguez, V.; and

Sundaresan, T. 1971. WHO coordinated short-term double-blind trial with thalidomide in the treatment of acute lepra reactions in male lepromatous patients. *W. H. O. Bulletin* 45: 719–32.

Jönsson, N. A. 1972. Chemical structure and teratogenic properties III: a review of available data on structure-activity relationships and mechanism of action of thalidomide analogues. *Acta Pharm. Suecia* 9: 521–42.

Jopling, W. H. 1971. *Handbook of Leprosy.* London: William Heinemann.

Jung, H. 1956. Klinische Erfahrungen mit einem neuen Sedativum. *Arzneimittelforschung* 6: 430–32.

Jurand, A. 1966. Early changes in limb buds of chick embryos after thalidomide treatment. *J. Embryol. Exp. Morphol.* 16: 289–300.

Keberle, H.; Faigle, J. W.; Fritz, H.; Knüsel, F.; Loustalot, P.; and Schmid, K. 1965. Theories on the mechanism of action of thalidomide. In *Symposium on Embryopathic Activity of Drugs,* ed. J. M. Robson, F. M. Sullivan, and R. L. Smith, pp. 210–26. London: J. & A. Churchill.

———; Loustalot, P.; Maller, R. K.; Faigle, J. W.; and Schmid, K. 1965. Biochemical effects of drugs on the mammalian conceptus. *Ann. N. Y. Acad. Sci.* 123: 252–62.

Köhler, F., and Ockenfels, H. 1970. Teratogene Wirkung der N-Phthalyl-DL-glutaminsaüre nach intraperitonealer Applikation bei der Maus. *Experientia* 26: 1157–58.

Kunz, W.; Keller, H.; and Mueckter, H. 1956. N-Phthalyl-glutaminsaüre-imid. *Arzneimittelforschung* 6: 426–30.

Lasagna, L. 1960. Thalidomide—a new nonbarbiturate sleep-inducing drug. *J. Chron. Dis.* 11: 627–31.

Lenz, W. 1961. Kindliche Missbildungen nach Medikament-Einnahme während der Gravidität? *Deutsche medizinische Wochenschrift* 86: 2555–56.

———. 1962. Thalidomide and congenital abnormalities. *Lancet* 1: 45.

———. 1967. Die sensible Phase der Thalidomid-Embryopathie bei Affe und Mensch. *Deutsche medizinische Wochenschrift* 92: 2186–87.

Lucey, J. F., and Behrman, R. E. 1963. Thalidomide: effect on pregnancy in the rhesus monkey. *Science* 139: 1295–96.

Mason, D. 1976. *Thalidomide: My Fight.* London: George Allen & Unwin.

McBride, W. G. 1961. Thalidomide and congenital abnormalities. *Lancet* 2: 1358.

———. 1977. Thalidomide embryopathy. *Teratology* 16: 79–82.

McCredie, J. 1973. Thalidomide and congenital Charcot's joints. *Lancet* 2: 1058–61.

Miura, M.; Southam, C. M.; and Wuest, H. 1970. Potentiating effect of thalidomide on methylcholanthrene oncogenesis in mice. *Experientia* 26: 305–306.

Mueckter, H., and Moré, E. 1966. Thalidomid und Tumor. *Arzneimittelforschung* 16: 129–34.

Nefkens, G. H. L.; Tesser, G. I.; and Nivard, R. J. F. 1960. A simple preparation of phthaloyl amino acids via a mild phthaloylation. *Rec. Trav. Chim.* 79: 688–98.

Obbink, H. J. K., and Dalderup, L. M. 1963. Effects of thalidomide on the rat foetus. *Experientia* 19: 645–46.

Ockenfels, H., and Köhler, F. 1970. Das L-Isomere als teratogenes Prinzip der N-Phthalyl-DL-glutaminsaüre. *Experientia* 26: 1236–37.

Paget, G. E. 1970. In *Methods of Toxicology*, ed. G. E. Paget, p. 4. Oxford and Edinburgh: Blackwell Scientific.

Pliess, G. 1962. Thalidomide and congenital abnormalities. *Lancet* 1: 1128–29.

Poswillo, D. E. 1972. The marmoset as a model for teratological research. *Proc. Anat. Soc.,* in *J. Anat.* 111: 505.

———. 1973. The pathogenesis of the first and second branchial arch syndrome. *Oral Surg., Med. & Path.* 35: 302–28.

———. 1975. Haemorrhage in development of the face. *Birth Defects* 11: 61–81.

———; Hamilton, W. J.; and Sopher, D. 1972. The marmoset as an animal model for teratological research. *Nature* 239: 460–62.

Ryder, R. D. 1975. *Victims of Science*, pp. 42, 155. London: Davis-Poynter.

Schumacher, H.; Smith, R. L.; and Williams, R. T. 1965. The metabolism of thalidomide: the spontaneous hydrolysis of thalidomide in solution. *Brit. J. Pharmacol.* 25: 324–27.

———; Smith, R. L.; and Williams, R. T. 1965. The metabolism of thalidomide: the fate of thalidomide and some of its hydrolysis products in various species. *Brit. J. Pharmacol.* 25: 338–51.

———; Blake, D. A.; Gurian, J. M.; and Gillette, J. R. 1968. A comparison of the teratogenic activity of thalidomide in rabbits and rats. *J. Pharmacol. Exp. Therap.* 160: 189–200.

———; Blake, D. A.; and Gillette, J. R. 1968. Disposition of thalidomide in rabbits and rats. *J. Pharmacol. Exp. Therap.* 160: 201–11.

———; Terapane, J.; Jordan, R. L.; and Wilson, J. G. 1972. The teratogenic activity of a thalidomide analogue, EM_{12}, in rabbits, rats and monkeys. *Teratology* 5: 233–40.

Sheskin, J. 1965. Thalidomide in the treatment of lepra reactions. *Clin. Pharmacol. Therap.* 6: 303–06.

———. 1975. Therapeutische Erfahrungen über den Einfluss des Thalidomids bei der Lepra-Reaktion. *Der Hautarzt* 26: 1–5.

———; Sagher, F.; Dorfman, M.; and von Schrader-Beielstein, H. W. 1968. Unsatisfactory results with thalidomide as a specific treatment for leprosy. *Israeli J. Med. Sci.* 4: 901–904.

————, and Convit, J. 1969. Results of a double blind study of the influence of thalidomide on the lepra reaction. *Int. J. Leprosy* 37: 135–46.

Shorb, M. S.; Smith, C.; Vasaitis, V.; Lund, P. G.; and Pollard, W. 1963. Effect of thalidomide treatment of hens on embryonic development and fertility. *Proc. Soc. Exp. Biol. Med.* 113: 619–22.

Sievers, G. 1964. Klinisch-statistische Studien zu aktuellen Missbildungsproblemen. *Arzneimittelforschung* 14: 605–55.

Sjöström, H., and Nilsson, R. 1973. *Thalidomide and the Power of the Drug Companies.* New York: Basic Books.

Smith, R. L.; Fabro, S.; Schumacher, H.; and Williams, R. T. 1965. Studies on the relationship between the chemical structure and embryotoxic activity of thalidomide and related compounds. In *Symposium on Embryopathic Activity of Drugs*, ed. J. M. Robson, F. M. Sullivan, and R. L. Smith, pp. 194–209. London: J. & A. Churchill.

Smithells, R. W. 1973. Defects and disabilities of thalidomide children. *Brit. Med. J.* 1: 269–72.

Somers, G. F. 1960. Pharmacological properties of thalidomide (α-phthalimido glutarimide), a new sedative hypnotic drug. *Brit. J. Pharmacol.* 15: 111–16.

————. 1962. Thalidomide and congenital abnormalities. *Lancet* 1: 912–13.

Stärk, G. 1956. Klinische Erfahrungen mit dem Sedativum K17 in der Lungenheilstätte und der allgemeinen Praxis. *Praxis* 45: 966–68.

Staples, R. E., and Holtkamp, D. E. 1963. Effects of parenteral thalidomide treatment on gestation and foetal development. *Exp. Mol. Pathol. Suppl.* 2: 81–106.

Stockinger, L., and Koch, H. 1969. Teratologische Untersuchung einer neuen, dem Thalidomid Strukturell nahestehenden sedativ-hypnotisch wirksamen Verbindung (K-2004). *Arzneimittelforschung* 19: 167–69.

Swift, T. F. 1973. Thalidomide in erythema nodosum leprosum. *Lancet* 2: 966.

Swinyard, C. A. 1969. *Limb Development and Deformity: Problems of Evaluation and Rehabilitation.* Thomas: Springfield, Ill.

Teff, H., and Munro, C. 1976. *Thalidomide: The Legal Aftermath.* London: Saxon House.

United States Patent 2,951,090. 1960. Preparation of DL-glutamine. Washington, D.C.: Government Printing Office.

Wallace, M., and Robson, M. 1975. *On Giant's Shoulders: The Terry Wiles Story.* London: Times Books.

Warkany, J. 1965. Development of experimental mammalian teratology. In *Teratology: Principles and Techniques*, ed. J. G. Wilson and J. Warkany, pp. 1–11. Chicago and London: University of Chicago Press.

Waters, M. F. R. 1971. An internally-controlled double blind trial of thalidomide in severe erythema nodosum leprosum. *Leprosy Rev.* 42: 26–42.

————; Rees, R. J. W.; and Sutherland, I. 1967. Chemotherapeutic trials in leprosy. 5. A study of methods used in clinical trials in lepromatous leprosy. *Int. J. Leprosy* 35: 311–35.

Weidenbach, A. 1959. Totale Phokomelie. *Zentralblatt für Gynäk.* 81: 2048–52.

Weidman, W. H.; Young, H. H.; and Zollman, P. E. 1963. The effect of thalidomide on the unborn puppy. *Proc. Staff Meetings Mayo Clinic* 38: 518–22.

Wiedemann, H.-R. 1961. Hinweis auf eine derzeitige Häufung hypo- und aplastischer Fehlbildungen der Gliedmassen. *Medizinische Welt* 37: 1863–66.

Williams, R. T. 1968. Thalidomide: a study of biochemical teratology. *Archs. Envir. Hlth.* 16: 493–502.

————; Schumacher, H.; Fabro, S.; and Smith, R. L. 1965. The chemistry and metabolism of thalidomide. In *Symposium on Embryopathic Activity of Drugs,* ed. J. M. Robson, F. M. Sullivan, and R. L. Smith, pp. 167–82. London: J. & A. Churchill.

Williamson, A. P.; Blattner, R. J.; and Lutz, H. R. 1963. Abnormalities in chick embryos following thalidomide and other insoluble compounds in the amniotic cavity. *Proc. Soc. Exp. Biol. Med.* 112: 1022–25.

Wilson, J. G., and Gavan, J. A. 1967. Congenital malformations in nonhuman primates; spontaneous and experimentally produced. *Anat. Record* 158: 99–110.

Wolpert, L. 1976. Mechanisms of limb development and malformation. *Brit. Med. Bull.* 32: 65–70.

Woollam, D. H. M. 1962. Thalidomide in the mouse. *Brit. Med. J.* 2: 920.

Wuest, H. M.; Sigg, E. B.; and Fratta, I. 1964. Pharmacological properties and teratogenic action of 2-[hexahydro-phthalimido] glutarimide and 2-phthalimido-N-methylglutarimide. *Life Sciences* 3: 721–24.

————; Fratta, I.; and Sigg, E. B. 1966. Teratological studies in the thalidomide field. *Life Sciences* 5: 393–96.

Index